Design of Industrial Ventilation Systems

Design of Industrial Ventilation Systems

Fifth Edition

How to Design, Build or Buy Industrial Ventilation Systems that Will Perform Adequately and Economically. Covers Local and General Exhaust Ventilation, Hood and Piping Design, Makeup Air Supply, Energy Conservation, Isolation, Low Pressure Pneumatic Conveying, and Selection of Collectors and Exhaust Fans

By John L. Alden, Management Consultant
and John M. Kane, Industrial Consultant

Industrial Press Inc.
200 Madison Avenue
New York, New York 10157

Library of Congress Cataloging in Publication Data

Alden, John Leslie, 1892–
Design of industrial ventilation systems.

Previously published as: Design of industrial exhaust systems.
Includes bibliographical references and index.
1. Exhaust systems--Design and construction.
2. Ventilation. I. Kane, John M., 1908– . II. Title.
TJ960.A6 1981 697.9′2 81-19194
ISBN 0-8311-1138-0 AACR2

THIRD PRINTING

FIFTH EDITION

DESIGN OF INDUSTRIAL VENTILATION SYSTEMS

Contents

List of Tables viii

Prefaces to 1st, 4th, and 5th Editions ix

1 Flow of Fluids 1

Standard Air—Compressibility—Contaminant Impact on Density—Static, Velocity, and Impact Pressures—Units of Pressure, Velocity, and Volume—Static Pressure: A Measure of Resistance—Measurement of Pressures—Relation of Velocity Pressure to Velocity—Bernoulli's Theorem—Nature of Fluid Flow—Critical Velocity—Reynolds' Dimensional Analysis—Reynolds Number—Critical Reynolds Number—Flow Always Turbulent in Exhaust Piping—Pipe Friction in Laminar and Turbulent States—Velocity Distribution—Flow of Mixtures

2 Exhaust Hoods 15

Hood Types—Contaminants—General Rules for Design of Hoods—Dispersion of Dusts—Local Air Movements and Counteracting Velocities—Effectiveness of Suction Openings—Typical Hood Contours—Relation of Face Area to Velocity—Summary of Hood Face Characteristics—Effect of Hood Structure in Rear of Face—Flanged Hood Faces—Influence of Adjacent Planes—Hoods for Hand Tools—Hoods for the Capture of Coarse Particles—Hoods for Woodworking Machinery—Saw Hoods—Shaper Hoods—Planer Hoods—Sander Hoods—Complete Enclosure—Booth or Tunnel—Side Hood—Downdraft Hood—Overhead or Canopy Hood—Air Flow Distribution within Hoods or Enclosures—Hoods for Material Handling—Hoods for Bench Operations—Hoods for Melting-Furnaces—Hoods for Surface Treatment Operations—Hoods for Bulk Loading

3 Local Exhaust Systems—Exhaust Volume Determinations 55

Capture Velocity—Indraft Velocity: Booths and Enclosures—Field Determination of Exhaust Volumes—Usual Exhaust Volumes for Typical Operations—Grinding, Polishing; etc.—Open Surface Tanks—Spray Booths

4 Air Flow through Hoods 74

Air Volume Entering Hood—Coefficient of Entry—Typical Orifices and Nozzles—Static Pressures at a Suction Opening—Effect of Suppressed Contraction—Entry Coefficients of Hoods—Synthetic Entry Coefficients—Entry Coefficients of Typical Hoods—Typical Flow Calculations—Flow Calculations: Economical Hood Design

5 Pipe Resistance **89**

Conveying Velocity—Special Considerations—Friction Loss in Round Pipes—Friction Loss in Rectangular Pipes—Friction Loss of Mixtures—"Velocity Head Rule" for Pipe Friction—Friction Loss in Hose—Losses in Elbows—Influence of Aspect Ratio—Influence of Angle of Turn—Influence of Approach Velocity—Compound Elbows—Venturi Elbows—Enlargements—Losses in Abrupt Enlargements—Losses in Tapers—Losses in Contractions—Losses in Tees—Losses in Breechings—Vacuum Booster—Losses in Transformers—Weather Protection

6 Piping Design **110**

Outline of Piping Design Procedure—Necessity for Systematic Calculation—Data Sheets—Blast Gates and Floor Sweeps—Calculation of Typical Exhaust Systems—Design of a Woodworking System—Balancing the System—Influence of Density Changes—Design of System for Process Material—The System Characteristic Curve—Reduction of Fire and Explosion Hazard—Make-up Air—Checking Design of Purchased Systems

7 Collectors **127**

The Collector as an Air Pollution Control Tool—The Collector as a Product Salvage Device—Preferred Characteristics of Air Cleaning Plants—Cleaning Efficiency—Location of Collector and Cleaned-air Discharge—Size Properties and Settling Rates of Dusts—Mechanics of Separation—Utilization of Collection Mechanisms—Types of Particulate Collectors—Characteristics of Particulate Collectors—Gravity Chambers—Miscellaneous Traps—Hood Traps—Cyclones—Vortical Flow through Cyclone—Factors Affecting Separation—Separation Coefficient of Cyclones—Angular Travel During Separation—Field of Application of Large Diameter Cyclone—Pressure Drop through Cyclones—Low-Loss Cyclones—High Efficiency Cyclones—Intermediate Diameter Cyclones—Small Diameter Cyclones—Cyclone Air Outlets—Factors Affecting Separation Efficiency—Dust Bins—Axial Flow Separators—Inertial Separators—Wet Particulate Collectors—Chemical Additives—Fabric Collectors—Principle of Operation—Pressure-Drop Relationships—Fabric Selection—Dust-Cake Removal—Maintenance—Electrostatic Precipitators—Plate Type—Tube Type—Unit Collectors—Air Filters—Control of Gaseous Emissions—Dilution—Absorption—Adsorption—Incineration

8 Low Pressure Conveyors **182**

Conveying Velocities—Air Volume per Pound of Conveyed Solids—Suction versus Pressure Systems—Unloading and Feeding Devices—Venturi Tube Theory—Typical All-Pressure Conveying System—Tandem Fans—Double Fans—Belt-Driven Fans—Economical Pipe Sizes—Relay Systems—Special Considerations for Conveying and Relay Systems

9 Centrifugal Exhaust Fans **196**

Analysis of System Pressures—Fan Rating Pressures—Inlet and Outlet Connections—Power Consumption—Effect of Air Density on Power Consumption—Performance Curves of Centrifugal Exhausters—Effect of Speed on Fan Characteristics—Effect of Size on Fan Performance—Effect of Direction of Rotation—Fan Types—Material Handling Fans—Wheel Types—Fans for Gaseous Materials—Special Fans—Fan Drives—Noise and Vibration—Ejector Systems—Dust-separating Fans

10 Axial-flow Fans **213**

Propeller Fans—Tubeaxial Fans—Vaneaxial Fans—Direction of Flow—Representative Installations—Fan Characteristics—Sound Level—Axial Flow versus Centrifugal Fans

11 Structural Details and System Planning **222**

Tapers—Elbows—Tees—Equalizers—Blast Gates—Ball and Telescope or Slip Joints—Cleanouts—Back Pressure Dampers—Switches—Pipe Supports—System Size—Overhead, Floor-level, and Under-floor Piping—System Arrangement—Typical Construction Specifications for Local Exhaust Systems

12 General Exhaust Ventilation and Air Supply **236**

General Ventilation—Area Ventilation—Curtain Walls—Air Supply

13 Monitoring Industrial Ventilation Systems **246**

Monitoring Schedule—Field Measurements—Location of Test Points—Pitot and Impact Tube Traverses—Preferred Location of Pitot Tube Traverse—Static-Pressure Holes in Pipe Walls—Estimating the Volume Rate of Flow—Flow Direction Finder—Test to Check Design Assumptions—Locating and Diagnosing Trouble

14 Isolation **260**

Isolation of the Process—Isolation of the Worker—Enclosing the Workspace—Increasing the Distance between Worker and Process—Combined Ventilation Techniques

15 Energy Conservation **266**

Heat Loss—Fuel Conservation—Heat Recovery

Index **277**

List of Tables

Table		Page
1-1	Critical Velocities for Air, R=3000	9
1-2	Density and Viscosity Factors	11
3-1	Indraft Velocities	56
3-2	Ventilation Traverse of 18 × 16 ft Spray Booth (Values in fpm)	57
3-3	Usual Exhaust Volumes and Conveying Velocities for Dust-Producing Equipment	62-65
3-4	Usual Branch Sizes and Exhaust Volumes	66-69
3-5	Ventilation Rates for Open-Surface Tanks	70
4-1	Comparison Between Synthetic and Actual Entry Coefficients	86
5-1	Conveying Velocities for Dust Collecting	90
5-2	Effect of Angle of Bend on Elbow Resistance	99
5-3	Resistance of Weather Caps	109
6-1a	Computations for Pattern Shop Exhaust System	117
6-1b	Computations for Pattern Shop Exhaust System	118
6-2	Density Factors for Change in Temperature and Elevation	121
6-3	Computations for Spray Dryer Exhaust System	124
7-1	Approximate Settling Rate of Spheres (sp gr 1.0) in Still Air at 70F	131
7-2	Approximate Median Size of Airborne Dusts	132
7-3	Micron Dimensions of Standard Sieves	133
7-4	Approximate Minimum-particle Size for which Various Collector Types are Suitable	135
7-5	Collector Types used in Industry	136-137
7-6	Dimensions of Helical-Top Cyclones	150
7-7	Wet Collector Performance	160
7-8	Characteristic of Collector Fabrics	170
8-1	Velocities for Low-Pressure Pneumatic Conveying	184
8-2	Influence of Pipe Size on Cost of Pneumatic Conveying System	193
11-1	Recommended Thickness of Sheet Metal	224
11-2	Rivet or Spot Weld Spacing for Circumferential Seams	224
12-1	Estimates of Energy Metabolism (M) of Various Types of Activity	237
12-2	Heat Gain from Lighting, Machinery, and Process	237
12-3	Acceptable Air Motion at the Worker	243
12-4	Spot Cooling Air Volumes (Supply Air Temperature = 80F)	243
13-1	Flow Estimated by Several Methods	255
15-1	Degree Days per Year	268

Preface

To the Fifth Edition

Previous editions of this volume were devoted to the subject of local exhaust systems. While such systems provide the major control device for acceptable air quality at the work station, the scope of this edition has been expanded to cover the interrelated areas of general exhaust ventilation and makeup air supply. The need for energy conservation and for the physical isolation of the workspace from major contaminant generation zones have also been recognized and coverage has been included. The change in title reflects this broadened scope.

Traditional English units of measurement have been retained in this edition because fan performance tables and other reference tables still use this system. Where the end result is to be expressed in metric terms, it is simpler to use English units for the computation and to convert the result rather than to use metric units throughout.

To the Fourth Edition

In view of the growing national concern about atmospheric pollution, the present revision of this book is not only timely, but in order that it best reflect the influence of good exhaust system design on the problem, John M. Kane, a leading consultant in contaminant control, has been persuaded to accept the responsibility of coauthorship. His experience in this field dates from 1933 and includes important work as supervising engineer, division manager, vice president and director of foreign operations of a prominent firm manufacturing dust- and fume-control equipment. He is a member of the American Society of Heating, Refrigerating, and Air Conditioning Engineers; the American Foundry Society; and the American Industrial Hygiene Association. He has also been a member of and adviser to various public bodies concerned with industrial hygiene and air pollution and has written many authoritative papers on these subjects.

The background of John L. Alden includes research and development work on fans and dust collectors; experience as a system contractor; and as a user—of varied types—in manufacturing operations. He has had a hand in drafting both state and industry exhaust codes and has also published papers on exhaust matters. Both authors are licensed professional engineers, their qualifications are complementary, and the influence of each will be seen throughout the revised volume.

Those familiar with earlier editions will observe much new material throughout this new edition of the book. The chapters on hoods, flow-through hoods, piping, piping design, dust collecors, and fans have been expanded substantially. Updated and completely new data are presented in graphic and tabular form. It is hoped that this fourth edition will prove even more practical and useful than have its predecessors.

To the First Edition

This book makes no attempt to cover the broad fields of health hazards, industrial dusts or the pathological phases of industrial hygiene. Able investigators have extended the horizon of these subjects immensely in recent years. Industry, therefore, is well informed of the need for exhaust sanitation. It is not well informed as to how best to satisfy that need. The purpose of this book is to tell the engineer how to design and build or how to buy an exhaust system that will adequately and economically perform the functions prescribed by the industrial hygiene expert or by law.

Although exhaust ventilation has been practiced for more than 90 years and has been recognized by statute for more than 60 years, the literature is astonishingly scanty. There seem to have been two major contributing factors. First, the field has been relatively small and inconspicuous and has not attracted the attention of colleges and other independent investigators. The second, and perhaps predominant, factor has been that many of those within the industry have treated their accumulated data as precious trade secrets to be divulged neither to competitors nor to customers. The author aims to dispel most of the mystery surrounding exhaust work and to express many of the trade secrets in straightforward engineering terms. He is fully conscious of the shortcomings of this book but believes that sufficient data have been presented to permit the design of adequate and low-cost systems or to appraise competitive designs and the claims of rival contractors. It is hoped that the reader will be encouraged to measure, record and publish engineering facts concerning exhaust systems to the end that our collection of basic data will become more complete and more reliable.

The subject of exhaust ventilation embraces the theory of air flow, the application of this theory to practical design, the selection of commercial fans and dust collectors, the construction of the physical plant and the testing of the completed system. There is no lack of published material on the subject of fluid flow. Unfortunately, the information is widely scattered and much of it is to be found in papers not easily accessible to the busy engineer. Moreover, many confusing contradictions are encountered, requiring intensive study to reconcile conflicting statements and conclusions. The author has selected and abridged the most authentic data for the theoretical portions of the book.

Acknowledgments are due to C. H. B. Hotchkiss, Editor, HEATING & VENTILATING, who guided portions of the material through serial publication, and to E. J. Crane, Western Electric Co., Inc., for his advice and criticism of the earlier chapters.

CHAPTER 1

Flow of Fluids

The design or selection of an industrial ventilation system component is dictated principally by the laws of fluid flow; the fluid being air or a mixture of air and contaminants which are either in the solid or gaseous state. Knowledge of these laws is a necessary fundamental for design engineers, and a thorough understanding of basic theory is essential to successful solution of the unconventional problem or to the refinement of design that distinguishes professional workmanship.

This chapter reviews briefly the fundamentals of fluid flow that have significant application to air movement within industrial ventilation systems.

Standard Air

In the following pages standard air will be taken as being air whose density is 0.075 lb per cu ft. This is substantially equivalent to dry air at a barometric pressure of 29.92 in. of mercury and a dry bulb temperature of 70 F. It is consistent with the engineering and industrial standards in current use. In the discussion of fluid flow throughout this book the fluid is standard air unless specifically stated otherwise.

Compressibility

Air, of course, is compressible. Nevertheless, during the study of flow phenomena it will be considered as incompressible. The development of the laws of flow is simplified thereby without loss of validity for the majority of ventilation systems. Furthermore, the assumption of incompressibility introduces no important errors into the practical expressions for friction losses, power, air volume, and other design factors.

Atmospheric pressure at sea level, translated into inches of water, equals 407.5 inches and the pressures in exhaust systems are usually less than 12 inches above or below atmospheric. However, there are some applications in which the system pressures may equal or exceed 40 to 50 inches. In these instances the fluid must be treated as compressible and subject to pressure correction.

Contaminant Impact on Density

The presence of dust and other conveyed solids is ignored in the development of the fluid laws. Their presence may be neglected in the practical design of dust collecting systems wherein the ratio of solids to air is low. In such systems the concentration of solids seldom exceeds 10 grains (0.00143 pounds) per cubic foot of air, or about 2% by weight. The treatment of high concentrations of suspended material is discussed in Chapters 5 and 8.

Where contaminant is in a gaseous or vapor state, the change in density of the mixture is even less significant in exhaust ventilation systems. Density can, however, be noticeably affected by addition of water vapor from cooling of high-temperature process gases or from processes where the molecular weight of a process gas substantially differs from that of air.

Static, Velocity, and Impact Pressures

A unit mass of fluid flowing through a pipe is acted upon, simultaneously, by two distinct pressures; one, known as "static" pressure, is the force tending to compress or expand the fluid. The other, "velocity" pressure, is that pressure which was required to accelerate the flowing mass from rest to its existing velocity. Conversely, it may be defined as the pressure opposing flow necessary to bring the flowing mass to rest. Velocity pressure acts only in the direction of flow. Static pressure, on the other hand, acts equally in all directions, tending not only to compress or expand the fluid but to burst or collapse the pipe as well. A third pressure, known as "impact," "total," or "dynamic" pressure (or "head"), is the algebraic sum of the static and velocity pressures (velocity pressure always being a positive value) acting simultaneously at a given point in a piping system. Because it contains a velocity component, total pressure, also, is measured in the direction of flow.

Units of Pressure, Velocity, and Volume

The customary unit of pressure in exhaust work is the inch of water displaced in a "U"-shaped tube or manometer. Fan performance tables, resistance charts, and other data are expressed in this unit, abbreviated: in. wg. One inch of water equals 69.3 ft of standard air. Pressures too high to be measured conveniently with a water filled "U"-tube are measured by a mercury manometer. One inch of mercury is equivalent to 13.6 in. of water. Velocities are usually expressed in feet per minute and volume rates of flow in cubic feet per minute; abbreviated: fpm and cfm, respectively.

Static Pressure—A Measure of Resistance

The pressure used in overcoming resistance to flow is the static pressure. Hence, static pressure is sometimes called "frictional" or "resistance"

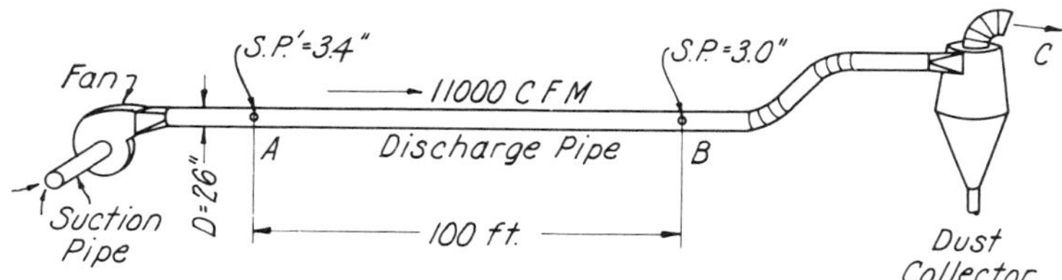

Fig. 1-1 Diagram illustrating drop in static pressure due to friction.

pressure. The measure of fluid friction in a pipe is the drop in static pressure from one cross-sectional plane to a similar downstream plane of equal area. Thus, in Fig. 1-1, 0.4 in. of water of static pressure is employed to force 11,000 cfm through 100 ft of 26-in. pipe from *A* to *B*. The static pressure at *A*, 3.4 in. of water, is the sum of all resistances between *A* and the atmosphere at *C*. Similarly, the 3-in. static pressure at *B* is the sum of all piping friction, collector pressure loss, and other resistances between *B* and the atmosphere.

Measurement of Pressures

Static pressure is measured at right angles to the direction of flow in order to avoid the influence of the fluid velocity. The small hole through the pipe wall in Fig. 1-2, connected to a manometer, is a typical device for measuring

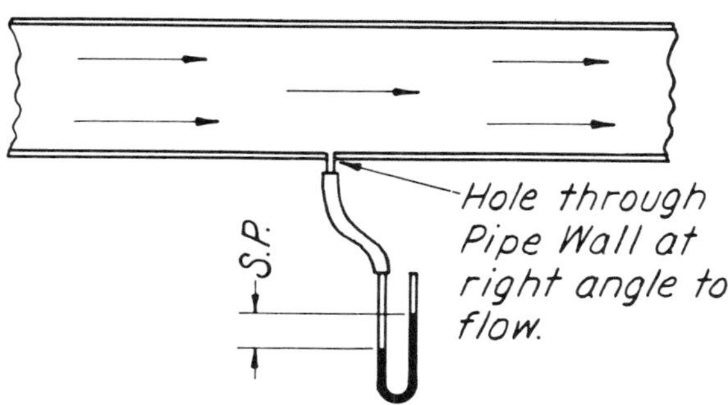

Fig. 1-2. Typical device for measuring static pressure.

static pressure. Velocity pressure is more difficult to measure because it cannot be separated from the static pressure which always accompanies it. The only exception is a measurement made at the open end of a pipe discharging to the atmosphere in which case the static pressure is zero. To obtain the velocity pressure in a pipe it is necessary to measure the total pressure and the static pressure occurring simultaneously; the difference constitutes the velocity pressure.

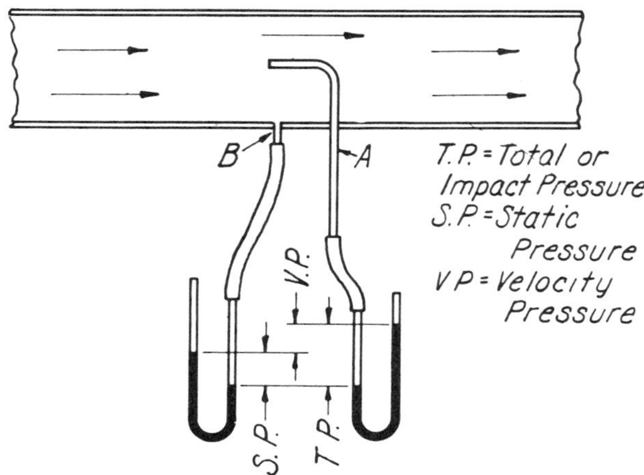

Fig. 1-3. Typical arrangement for measuring static and impact pressures.

In Fig. 1-3, an impact tube, *A*, is shown pointing directly upstream in a pipe under pressure. The manometer to which it is connected registers not only the velocity pressure acting axially of the pipe but also the superimposed static pressure. A separate measurement of static pressure is made as at *B*. Subtracting, algebraically, the static from the impact pressure leaves the velocity pressure. Where the pipe is under negative pressure both manometers will indicate negative values. The difference of these values, the velocity pressure, will be positive. Because velocity pressures are always positive (representing a potential for conversion back to a postive pressure value), the static pressure reading in this case will be larger than the total pressure reading by the amount of the velocity pressure. The conventional Pitot tube with its self-contained impact and static openings can be connected to a single manometer in such manner as to indicate the velocity pressure directly.

Relation of Velocity Pressure to Velocity

When the velocity, pressure, and density are expressed as fpm, in. wg, and pounds per cubic foot, the equation relating velocity to velocity pressure is

$$V = 1096 \sqrt{\frac{\mathrm{VP}}{w}}$$

and demonstrates that for a given VP the velocity will vary as the square root of the density (w). See Chapter 6 for additional discussion on the influence of densities differing from that of standard air.

For standard air with $w = 0.075$

$$V = 4005\sqrt{\text{VP}}$$

This expression has wide application in ventilation system design and makes mental conversion easy. For example, 1 in. wg= 4000 fpm; ¼ in. wg = 2000 fpm; 1/16 in. wg = 1000 fpm.

Bernoulli's Theorem

The pressures associated with a given volume of fluid are directly proportional to the energy content of that fluid. The velocity pressure is a measure of the kinetic energy or energy of motion. The static pressure is a measure of the potential energy. The total pressure, comprising the algebraic sum of the static and velocity pressures, is, therefore, a measure of the total energy of the fluid volume. Since potential and kinetic energies are mutually convertible, static pressure may be transformed into velocity pressure and vice versa. This is the foundation of Bernoulli's theorem which states that, neglecting losses, the impact pressure at any point in a pipe is equal to the impact pressure at any other point. Thus, regardless of the varying proportion of static and velocity pressures, their algebraic sum (total pressure) is constant throughout the length of the pipe if energy is neither gained nor lost.

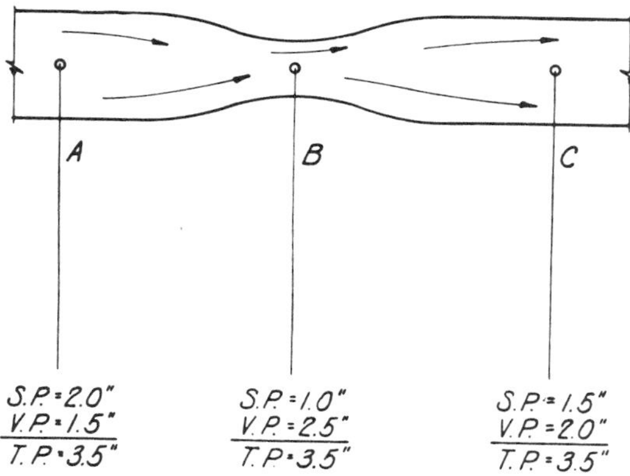

Fig. 1-4. Diagram illustrating that the total pressure is steady at all cross sections.

Let Fig. 1-4 represent a pipe with a constriction which causes the velocity at B to be greater than that at A, so that the velocity pressure has increased from 1.5 inches of water at A to 2.5 in. at B. The static pressure at A is 2.0 in., making the total pressure at that point 3.5 in. of water. From Bernoulli's theorem, the total pressures at B and C must also be 3.5 in. The static pressures at B and C then become 1.0 and 1.5 in. of water, respectively.

Bernoulli's theorem is of considerable practical importance to the designer of exhaust systems. While theoretically perfect conversions of velocity to static pressure never occur, the conversion in impact tubes, metering nozzles and a few other structures is so nearly perfect that this theorem applies almost without correction. Considerable departure from perfect conversion takes place in tapers, transformers, traps, and other commercial fittings in which appreciable velocity changes occur. In such instances, the degree of departure from Bernoulli's theorem is the measure of the static pressure losses. During acceleration of the stream within a system the loss will be less than that during deceleration. See Fig. 5-16.

Nature of Fluid Flow

When a fluid flows through a pipe at very low velocities, the particles follow predictable paths free from eddies or swirls. The flow then is said to be "streamline," "viscous," or "laminar." As the velocity increases, the character of flow changes; eddies form; and the paths of the fluid filaments are sinuous and swirling. This type of flow is known as "turbulent" flow and is usually that encountered in exhaust systems. Each type of flow has its own laws of resistance to motion. These laws apply to all fluids, including water, air, and oil, regardless of the individual characteristics of the fluid.

It must be understood that the turbulent state of flow is one of minute whirls, sinuosities, and vortices. The turbulence is microscopic rather than macroscopic. It has been observed, for example, that sinuous motion of fluid laminae exists as close as 0.000025 in. from the wall of a smooth pipe during the turbulent state. It is not a turbulence caused by poor design or workmanship of the piping system. It is an inescapable condition always existing when the velocity exceeds certain critical values even though the pipe be drawn glass tubing of the utmost smoothness.

A brief description of the color band experiments of Osborne Reynolds[1] will help to visualize the characteristics of laminar and turbulent flow. These were conducted for the purpose of locating the zone of transition from one type to the other. The apparatus is illustrated schematically in Fig. 1-5. For convenience, the fluid used was water although the principles illustrated apply equally well to other fluids.

The apparatus consisted of a glass tank into the side of which was sealed a glass exit tube with a well-rounded inlet. A valve in the exit tube regulated the rate of flow. A small tube entering the inlet zone introduced a thin filament of aniline dye into the flowing stream.

[1] "Water—Direct and Sinuous Flow," by Osborne Reynolds, *Philosophical Transactions of the Royal Society*, Vol. 176 (1883), 935-984.

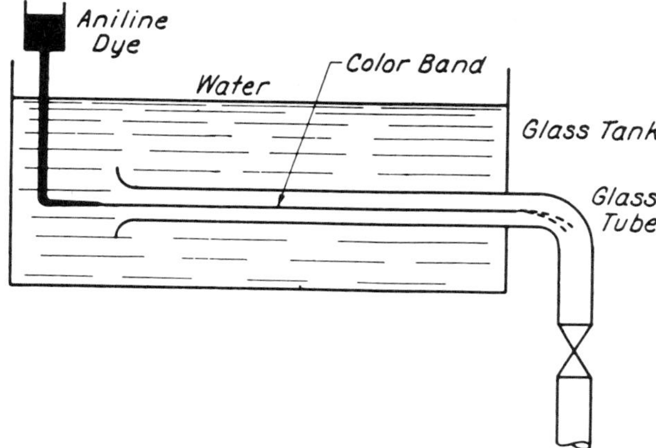

Fig. 1-5. Reynolds color band apparatus.

At low water velocities the colored filament extended the full length of the tube and was sharply defined as though motionless in the slowly moving stream. As the velocity increased, the filament attenuated until a speed was reached at which eddies began to form at the outlet end. Further increase in velocity caused the eddies progressively to approach the inlet until finally the entire stream was in violent motion.

Critical Velocity

The velocity at which eddies begin to form, as determined by the color band experiment, is called the "higher" critical velocity. The "lower" critical velocity is that at which eddies die out when the velocity of turbulent flow is reduced slowly. Between these boundary speeds lies an unstable zone in which the flow may be either laminar or turbulent. The existence of two distinct values of the critical velocity indicates a pronounced tendency for the existing state of flow to persist even after passing the critical speed. The lower critical velocity is the more definite of the two and is usually taken as the true critical velocity.

A second zone in which flow phenomena undergo a change is the region close to the velocity of sound in the fluid. For air, this is about 1100 ft per sec which is far beyond the highest velocities found in exhaust systems. This region is of principal concern to the ballistics and aerospace engineer, since in this zone the drag coefficient of aerodynamic shapes increases to about three times the values existing at lower speeds.

Reynolds' Dimensional Analysis

It is important that the designer of piping systems be able to predict the friction losses of fluid flow with reasonable accuracy. In the past, many empirical formulas have been fitted to experimental data, each fitted to a specific fluid and to a limited range of pipe sizes. These have proved useful when the conditions confronting the designer have been consistent with those on which the formulas were based. No common basis for comparison of flow data existed until Reynolds, in 1883, made use of the Principle of Dynamic Similarity originated by Newton. Reynolds' work was lost sight of until 1914 when Stanton and Pannell[2] employed his methods in analyzing the data resulting from their elaborate experiments on a variety of fluids. They showed that Reynolds' method of dimensional analysis was both theoretically and practically correct and that a single formula, dimensionally homogeneous, applies to all fluids. Their conclusions are fully verified by later research and by analyses of past data by Kemler and by Pigott.[3]

Reynolds Number

Briefly stated, dynamic similarity is attained in two or more conditions of flow through smooth pipes if a dimensionless quantity called the "Reynolds Number" is the same in both cases. This fact enables flow data to be compared on the basis of the Reynolds number which takes into account the essential physical properties of the fluid, the diameter of the tube and the fluid speed.

The factors affecting pressure loss due to friction in a pipe are pipe diameter and length, fluid density and viscosity, and the velocity of flow. The friction loss of head may be expressed as:

$$\Delta p = w\Delta h = \frac{flwv^2}{2gd}$$

where:

Δp = pressure drop, lb per sq ft,
Δh = pressure drop, ft head of fluid,
w = density of fluid, lb per cu ft,
f = friction factor, dimensionless, function of Reynolds number, $R = vdw/\mu$,
l = length of pipe, ft,
v = velocity of fluid, ft per sec,
g = acceleration of gravity, 32.17 ft per sec^2,
d = diameter of pipe, ft,
R = Reynolds number, dimensionless,
μ = absolute viscosity of fluid, lb per (sec) (ft).

[2] "Similarity of Motion in Relation to the Surface Friction of Fluids," by T. E. Stanton and J. R. Pannell, *Philosophical Transactions of the Royal Society of London*, Vol. A-214 (1914), 199-244.

[3] "The Flow of Fluids in Closed Conduits," by R. J. S. Pigott, *Mechanical Engineering*, Vol. 55, No. 8 (Aug. 1933), 497-501, 515.

That is known as the "dimensional" formula. The friction factor, f, in this equation must be dimensionless if the principle of dimensional homogeneity is to be satisfied. Reynolds showed that f must be a function of $vdw/\mu = R$, the Reynolds number.

The Reynolds number has been a useful tool not only to researchers in the field of fluid flow but to practicing engineers as well. It has reduced much empirical data to a rational basis. Moreover, it has been the means of reconciling conflicting friction formulas since it has been shown that seemingly unrelated values for oil, water, air, gas, tar, and similar substances, fall on a common curve when plotted against the Reynolds number.

Critical Reynolds Number

It has been found that laminar flow is stable against all disturbances at $R = 1160$ or below. The upper limit of the unstable zone is close to $R = 3000$. Above $R = 3000$ the flow is always turbulent; below 1160 always laminar, and between, it may be either.

Flow Always Turbulent in Exhaust Piping

The most frequent range of Reynolds numbers in industrial ventilation systems is from 100,000 to 1,000,000. An exceptionally low value would be $R = 30{,}000$, which corresponds to 2-in.-diameter pipe at 200 fpm. It is evident that only turbulent flow will be present in any duct system. The brief table of critical velocities for various pipe sizes, Table 1-1, shows that laminar flow is impossible under operating exhaust system conditions. However, laminar flow will occur within fabric dust arresters, some types of air filters and heat exchangers.

Table 1-1. Critical Velocities for Air, R = 3000

Pipe Diameter, in.	Critical Velocity, fpm
3	120
6	60
12	30
24	15
36	10

Pipe Friction in Laminar and Turbulent States

It had long been observed that the frictional resistance obeyed two apparently different laws in the laminar and the turbulent states, varying as the second power for turbulent flow and as the first power for laminar flow. More recently it has been established that the dimensional formula is valid for both states of flow. In the laminar flow region $f = 64/R$ and the dimensional formula becomes:

$$\Delta p = \frac{32\mu l v}{g d^2}.$$

This is Poiseuille's law for the resistance of viscous flow. It has little or no application to exhaust work but is mentioned as further evidence of the validity of the dimensional formula.

The friction factor, f, for turbulent flow through dead-smooth pipes, such as glass, is plotted against the Reynolds number in Fig. 1-6. The effect of

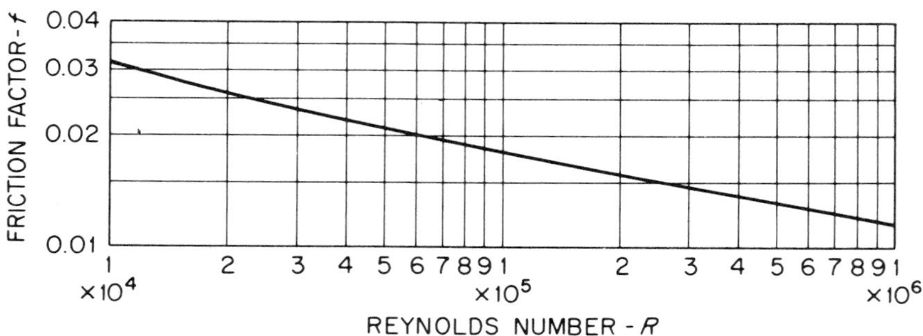

Fig. 1-6. Friction factor versus Reynolds number.

roughness and other irregularities is to increase the value of f by an amount which must be determined by experiment. The alignment chart, Fig. 1-7, permits quick graphical calculations of R for standard air. If the temperature, humidity, and pressure conditions are greatly different from those defining standard air, it may pay to compute a special value of R for the expected conditions. The principal influence of these variables is on the density. Viscosity is only moderately affected by the temperature, and practically not at all by the humidity and pressure. Hence, R can be adjusted upward or downward in proportion to the change in density. In nearly all cases, however, values for standard air are entirely satisfactory as a basis for the Reynolds number and friction factor.

With laminar flow the influence of viscosity is significant with the friction factor increasing as the first power of viscosity. One of the few situations where laminar flow is encountered in local exhaust systems is within the fabric type of particulate collector operating at elevated temperatures. Usual flow rates through the small apertures in the dust cake adhering to the fabric produce laminar flow, resulting in a relatively constant friction factor. As indicated in Table 1-2, the increase in viscosity at elevated temperatures about offsets the decrease in density.

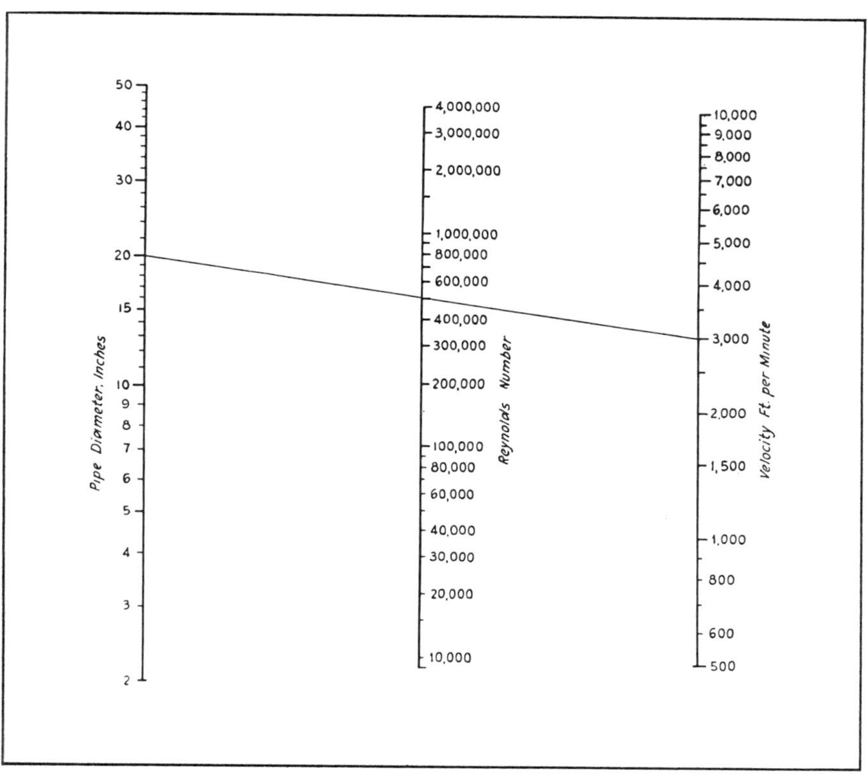

Fig. 1-7. Chart for calculation of Reynolds number.

Table 1-2. Density and Viscosity Factors

Temperature, F	Viscosity Factor	Density Factor
0	0.90	1.15
70	1.00	1.00
100	1.04	0.95
200	1.17	0.80
300	1.31	0.70
400	1.42	0.62
500	1.54	0.55
600	1.64	0.50
700	1.72	0.46
800	1.80	0.42
900	1.88	0.39

A convenient friction chart for standard air, flowing through galvanized steel pipes, of the usual exhaust system sizes and construction appears in Chapter 5. It is based on extensive laboratory tests and has been confirmed by field measurements.

Velocity Distribution

The rate of flow of air through a pipe is greatest near the axis, and least near the wall. Even in turbulent flow, the boundary layer next to the wall is practically at rest for a distance at least equal to molecular thickness. Figure 1-8 represents a longitudinal section through the axis of a long, straight,

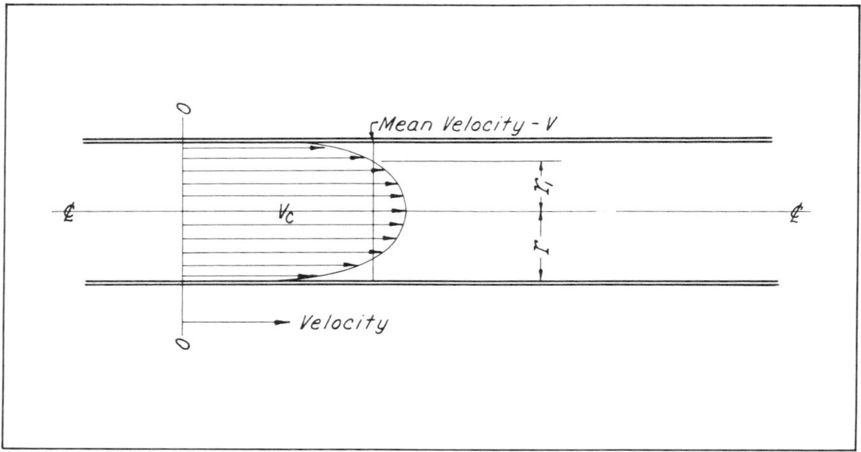

Fig. 1-8. Velocity distribution in straight pipe.

cylindrical pipe. The velocities at various radial distances from the axis are represented in magnitude by the length of the arrows indicating the direction of flow. For streamline flow, a curve drawn through the tips of the arrows is parabolic in shape. When the flow is turbulent, the velocity profile is substantially parabolic, from the axis to a point about 8/10 of the radius outward from the centerline. From there to the pipe wall the shape of the profile varies with the Reynolds number.

Occasionally, it is necessary to obtain the mean velocity from a single Pitot tube measurement on the centerline of the pipe. If the approach to the Pitot station is long and straight, normal velocity distribution similar to that in Fig. 1-8, will prevail. The ratio of the mean velocity to the centerline velocity has been plotted against the Reynolds number in Fig. 1-9. This curve is useful if upstream disturbances have not upset the velocity distribution. It will be observed the $V/V_c = 0.5$ and is constant at all Reynolds numbers

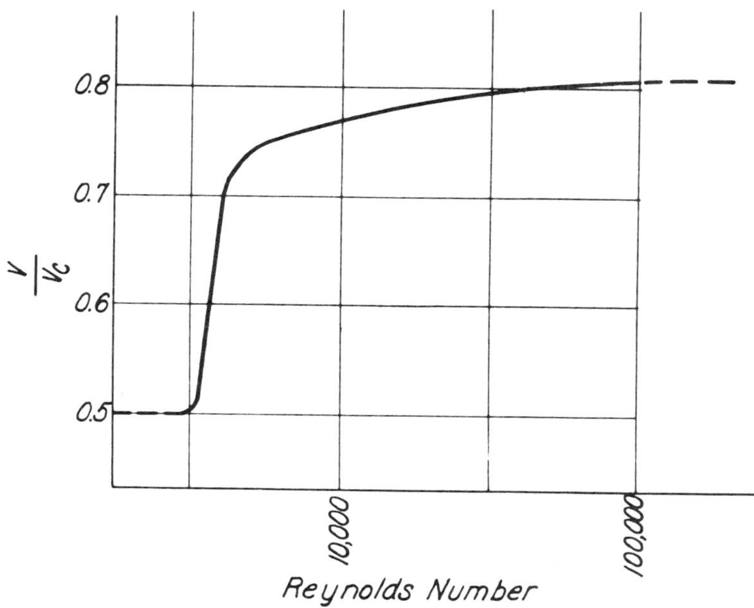

Fig. 1-9. Ratio of mean velocity to centerline velocity.

below the critical. This is the theoretical value in the region of laminar flow. At high Reynolds numbers the curve flattens and appears to attain a constant level of about 0.82 above $R = 100{,}000$.

It is possible to find, experimentally, a point in the cross section of a pipe where a single Pitot tube reading will be that of the mean velocity. If the velocity profile is symmetrical and otherwise normal, a Pitot tube located between 7/10 and 8/10 of the radius outward from the pipe axis will give mean velocity pressure readings. In Fig. **1-8**, r_1 is such a location since it represents the radial distance to the intersection of the velocity profile and the line of mean velocity. r_1/r, like V/V_c, depends upon the Reynolds number although the relationship is not so well established. If the mean velocity must be found from a single reading, it is better to take that reading at the centerline of the pipe and apply Fig. 1-9 than to attempt to locate the exact point on the velocity curve where the line of mean velocity crosses.

Stanton and Pannell used straight runs of pipe from 90 to 140 diameters long in approaching the plane at which data for Fig. 1-9 were taken. It is probable that the curve is not valid for approaches shorter than 40 to 50 diameters of straight pipe. Long runs of straight pipe of these proportions are rare in exhaust systems. Hence, the velocity pattern seldom approaches the symmetry of Fig. 1-8. In such instances, *a single centerline reading is apt to be grossly misleading.* Once flow rate has been determined, a single reading will be sufficient to calculate changes in flow rate for a fixed system if reading is taken in the same location.

Flow of Mixtures

A homogeneous fluid has been assumed in the preceding discussions. In practice, the fluid flowing in an exhaust system is a mixture of air and suspended particulate or diffused gaseous or vapor contaminants. In most instances the contaminant is a small fraction of the weight of the carrier air stream. Therefore, the density of the mixture so closely approaches that of air that friction loss would not be significantly altered.

The weight and volume of dust per cubic foot of air is very small in ordinary dust control systems. In dry grinding, for example, it is rare that less than 10,000 cu ft of air is handled per pound of mixed abrasive and metallic dust. The dust thus comprises not more than 1/8 of 1% by weight of the mixture. By volume, the dust does not exceed 1/20,000 of 1%. Intermittent tool grinding often produces a concentration of less than 1 lb of dust per 100,000 cu ft or less than 1 lb of solids per 7,500 lbs of air.

There are, however, conditions where changes in density will require use of other than the density of standard air. For example:

1. The conveying of solids in low-pressure pneumatic conveying systems. See Chapter 8.
2. The saturation of elevated temperature air with water vapor by wet scrubbers causing a considerable reduction in density of the mixture.
3. Changes in the molecular weight of the carrier fluid such as the carbon dioxide quantities released during the calcining of limestone.

CHAPTER 2

Exhaust Hoods

The hood is the orifice through which contaminated air enters an exhaust system. Its importance in the system cannot be overestimated. Proper design of exhaust hoods is necessary if a local exhaust system is to effectively control atmospheric contamination at its source, with a minimum of air flow and power consumption. The theory of capture velocity depends on the creation of air flow past the source of contaminant, sufficient to remove the highly contaminated air around the source, or issuing from that source, and to draw the contaminated air into an exhaust hood. If the hood is proportioned poorly, nothing done later in the system can compensate for this initial inadequacy. The penalties for indifferent hood design are excessive size and first cost of the system; high energy costs; and, probably, unsatisfactory or inconsistent control.

The more completely the source of contamination is enclosed, the more positive the control, and the lower both the exhaust volume and cost of the exhaust system. It is also important that supervisory operating personnel be reasonably familiar with the limitations of local exhaust hoods in order that they may understand and accept installations where unfortunate, but unavoidable interference with customary operating, material handling, and maintenance procedures occur.

Hood Types

The general classes of exhaust hoods are: (1) local hoods; (2) side, downdraft, overhead hoods; and (3) booths or enclosures.

Many examples of local exhaust hoods are shown in the technical press [1,2] and in manufacturers' and contractors' literature.

Local hoods are relatively small structures, enclosing or located close to

[1] J. M. Kane, "Scrapbook of Exhaust Hood Design" (Portable grinding; Stand grinding and buffing; Cast-iron machining; Swing-frame grinders; Foundry shakeouts; Oil mist; Flour dust in bakeries; Melting furnaces; Pottery manufacturing; Mixing; Toxic materials; Woodworking.), *Heating and Ventilating*, July 1950-June 1951.

[2] Industrial Conference of Governmental Industrial Hygienists, *Industrial Ventilation Manual*.

the point of contaminant release. Capture occurs before dispersion can take place to the adjacent areas of the operation. Typical uses are: exhaust of abrasive grinding wheels, woodworking machinery, electric-arc welding, conveyor transfer points, downdraft grilles, work benches, stone cutting and finishing, portable grinding and sanding, tool room and cast iron machining.

The second group, generally, are larger concepts of the local exhaust that rely on larger exhaust volumes to prevent contaminant escape beyond the control zone. Typical examples are bench type of operations, exhaust of plating tanks, foundry shakeouts, conveyor transfer points, melting furnaces, and metal pouring.

Booths or enclosures are the most effective hood designs because the contaminant generation is isolated from the workspace and an inward flow of air through access or inspection openings can be developed to prevent escapement from such hood structures. As pressures from more stringent air quality standards and for noise reduction increase, methods will be found to adapt such hood approaches to many more industrial operations. Typical uses include spray finishing, bucket elevators, vibrating and rotary screens, foundry shakeouts, abrasive cleaning, mixers, and storage bins.

General Rules for Design of Hoods

The following principles of contaminant control at the source will meet most requirements; they are amplified in succeeding paragraphs.

1. Reduce the cause of dispersion as far as possible by modification of the process, machine or material before designing hoods.
2. Place the hood as close as possible to the source of contamination, preferably enclosing it.
3. Locate and shape the hood so that the contaminant released from the source is either directed into the mouth of the pipe or in the case of dust particles, are caused to ricochet into it by impact with hood sides or shields.
4. Cause air to flow past the dust source and into the hood with a velocity at the point of dust origin greater than the velocity of escape of the particles.
5. So locate the hood that the operator is never between the dust source and the hood.

Hoods for refuse removal purposes require careful positioning and relatively high face-velocities if coarse particles are to be captured. Moreover, the velocity between the point of entrainment and the branch pipe must be sufficient to prevent fallout. In contrast, fumes, mists, vapors, and airborne dust particles may be captured and conveyed to the exhaust pipe at much lower velocities, without fallout.

Contaminants

Dusts, smokes, fumes, mists, vapors, or gases are released from a broad spectrum of industrial processes and operations. The methods of control through local exhaust ventilation are the same whether the purpose is nuisance abatement, reduction of health hazard, prevention of product contamination, or elimination of fire and explosion hazard.

The particles of dust and fumes of hygienic importance are extremely small—5 microns[3] and smaller. Fortunately, these are the particles most readily entrained by local exhaust ventilation regardless of the purpose for which the system is installed.

Usual definitions for these contaminants are:

Dust: Small, solid particles created by the breaking-up of larger particles by processes such as crushing, grinding, drilling, explosions, etc. Dust particles already in existence in a mixture of materials may escape into the air through such operations as shoveling, conveying, screening, sweeping, etc.

Particles range largely from 0.25-micron to coarse particles retained on a 60- or 100-mesh screen. The nuisance-size range, where fallout occurs rapidly, is, basically, above 20 to 30 microns. Airborne dusts that stay in suspension for a considerable time will normally be under 20 microns with the majority, by count, in the 0.25- to 5.0-micron range; by weight, in the 10- to 20-micron zone.

Fume: Small, solid particles formed by the condensation of vapors of solid materials. Sizes range from 1 micron to the upper limits of Brownian movement with substantial numbers by particle count, in the 0.01- to 0.1-micron range. Many fumes have a high agglomerating ability and quickly develop agglomerates in the dust-size range.

Smoke: An air suspension (aerosol) of particles, usually, but not necessarily solid, often originating in a solid nucleus formed from combustion or sublimation. Particle size-ranges are under 0.5 micron and are often carbonaceous products of incomplete combustion having a high staining ability and will often agglomerate to form "soot."

Mist: Small droplets of materials that are ordinarily liquid at normal temperature and pressure. Particle sizes range in the area of airborne dusts and are generated in a number of different ways such as: spraying, electroplating, and condensation during cooling. The fog-like products of plating are often combinations of mist and vapor.

Vapor: The gaseous form of substances which are normally in the solid or

[3] 1 micron = 1/1000 millimeter = 0.00003937 in. = 1/25000 in.

liquid state and which can be changed to the vapor state either by decreasing the pressure or increasing the temperature. Vapors diffuse.

These products of evaporation are found often in industry, e.g., steam from hot water, solvents for cleaning, and thinners for paints and glues.

Gas: A formless fluid that tends to occupy an entire space uniformly within a certain time frame and at ordinary temperatures and pressures.

Dispersion of Dusts

The manner and degree of dispersion of dust is a function of particle size. Large particles thrown from a wheel or cutter may be distributed over a wide area by virtue of their kinetic energies and without assistance from air currents. Small particles, on the other hand, are dependent entirely upon air currents for their dispersion. The mass of a tiny particle is so small and the kinetic energy so little that it is incapable of sustained flight. It loses velocity rapidly and cannot be projected far from the point of generation.[4]

Fine dusts in suspension drift with the general air currents. Their dispersion depends almost entirely upon drift. Fine dusts, therefore, must be controlled by controlling the flow of the entraining air. Coarse particles, on the contrary, are but little affected by local currents of mild intensity. Their dispersion by dynamic projection requires that the hood be placed, target-like, so that the particles are thrown directly into the pipe mouth, or impinge on a hood wall to deflect the trajectory.

The particles of smokes, fumes, or mists cannot be projected far through still air. Their kinetic energies are small, yet their surface areas, which tend to resist movement, are relatively large. They lose velocity rapidly and tend to drift in suspension. The problem of entrapment, therefore, is that of controlling the movement of the entraining air. This may be accomplished by general ventilation, by local exhaust hoods, or by a combination of the two. The same media may be used to control objectionable vapors. A further method of vapor control, although generally less reliable, is that of dilution through the mixture with uncontaminated air.

Contaminated air can be exhausted upward, horizontally, or downward. The choice of direction is regulated by the nature of the contaminant, the manner of its generation, the location of the workman with respect to the zone of generation and the facilities with which he works. More often than not, the form and location of the exhaust hood and the volume of air to be exhausted are dictated by the size and shape of the work pieces, the baskets, racks, or other containers, and the material-handling means such as: hoists, monorails, etc.; the control objective is to keep ambient air as clean as possible.

[4] A 10-micron abrasive particle thrown from a wheel at 10,000 fpm can fly about 1 in. in still air. At the same speed a particle 1/16 in. in diameter may be thrown 100 ft.

Local Air Movements and Counteracting Velocities

Some evaluation of stray air-currents is necessary before effective counteracting velocities can be determined. Convection currents from radiators, ovens, and furnaces seldom exceed 25 to 75 fpm. Cross drafts from open doors, windows and "man cooling" floor fans can be substantially higher, often in the 300–1,000 fpm range. During the heating season similar disruptive air currents exist especially where plant is under negative pressure caused by substantial exhaust volumes without makeup air supply systems.

Direct window drafts can be reduced by closing windows or by installing screens, baffles, or deflectors. Flywheels, large pulleys and even abrasive wheels frequently cause disturbance over considerable area. Excessive machine vibration, particularly of large flat panel surfaces, often keeps in suspension dust which would otherwise settle. The first puff of dust-bearing air displaced from bags and barrels during gravity filling has been observed to escape at velocities as high as 250 fpm. If dust control currents are to be effective over an exposed dusty source, the very minimum tolerable velocity toward the hood is 75 to 100 fpm. Even when aided by baffles or a partial enclosure, higher velocities often are required, even up to 500 fpm and higher. The smaller the hood, the higher the indraft for comparable control because of the rapidly diminishing air-flow patterns in front of it. Large hoods requiring large exhaust volumes obtain a "defense-in-depth" effect from the mass of air moving within the room toward the hood—a beneficial type of room air movement. To determine the minimum control velocity it is necessary to make some estimate of the escape velocities either from experience or by means of the exploring hood described in Chapter 3.

All suction openings tend to draw air equally from all directions and would do so, in fact, if the suction source were a point in space. With a point source of suction, the locus of all points of equal inward velocity would be a sphere. This sphere could be called a contour surface and the trace of the sphere on an intersecting plane, a contour line. The latter would be a circle, of course. In practice, a point source of suction is an impossibility and we have instead a hood and branch pipe of finite dimensions. The presence of these distorts the flow lines and the velocity contour surfaces so that the latter are no longer spheres but are bulged transversely of the hood axis. Figure 2-1 shows a comparison between the circular velocity contour lines produced by a point source of suction, *p*, and the flattened, oval contours produced by the finite hood. The inward velocities at all points on the circular contours *a* and *a'* are identical with those on the oval contours, *b* and *b'*.

The region in the vicinity of the hood mouth may be explored with a small impact tube by which both the velocity and direction of flow may be found. These may be plotted as in Fig. 2-2, part a, which shows the velocity contours and flow directional lines lying in a longitudinal centerline plane of

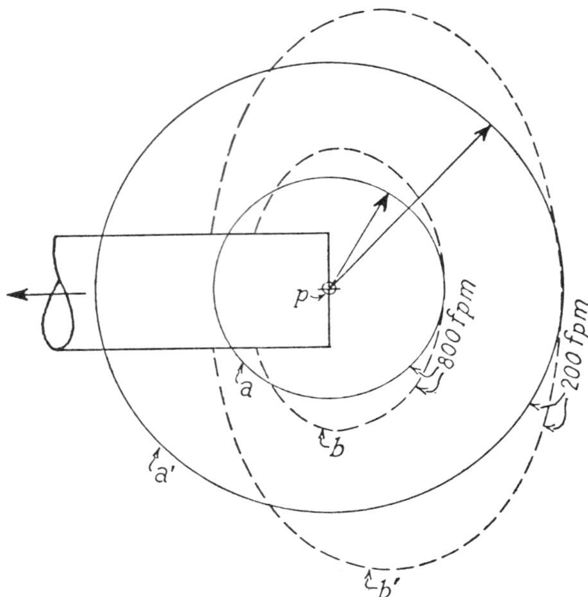

Fig. 2-1. Velocity contours of point source of suction at open pipe mouth.

a round pipe or hood.[5] The direction lines represent the paths of air particles entering the hood. Because of the symmetry of round hoods, a single diagram represents all of the contours and direction lines of all centerline planes.

Inspection of Fig. 2-2, part a, discloses that the velocity drops rapidly as the distance from the hood increases. This is more graphically illustrated in Fig. 2-2, part b, in which distances are expressed as percentages of hood-face diameter and velocities as percentages of hood-face average velocity. At outward distances greater than 0.5 diameter, the velocities are closely inversely proportional to the squares of the distances from the plane of the hood face.

LOCAL HOODS

Effectiveness of Suction Openings

From Fig. 2-2 it is evident why a suction hood cannot be expected to influence the behavior of a dust particle at a considerable distance from the

[5] The principal work in this field has been reported by DallaValle and Hatch in the following paper and others: "Studies in the Design of Local Exhaust Hoods," by J. M. DallaValle and T. Hatch, *A.S.M.E. Transactions*, Vol. 54, 1932.

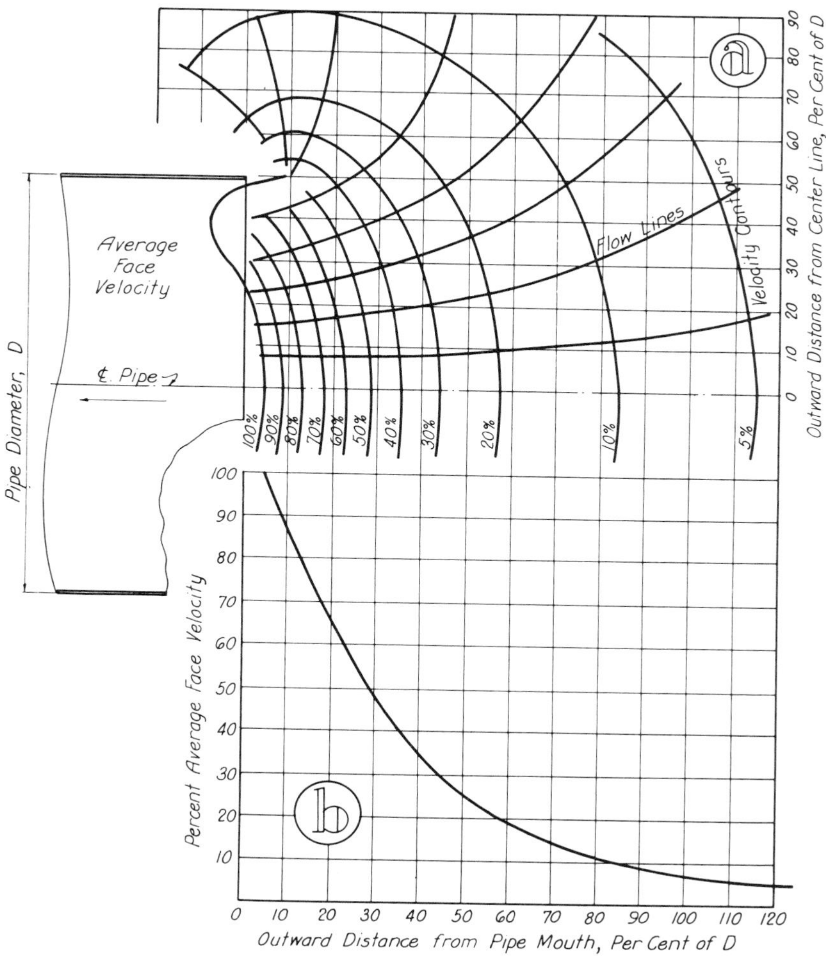

Fig. 2-2. Velocity contours and flow directional-lines in front of circular suction pipe.

hood mouth. Assume a dust particle flying in space and requiring an air velocity of 1,000 fpm to deflect it into the hood. With a 6-in. diameter pipe let the hood mouth be but one diameter, or 6 in. away from the particle, and let the face velocity be 4,000 fpm. Then note from Fig. 2-2 b, at 100 percent on the horizontal axis, that at 6 in. from the hood the velocity will be 7 percent of 4,000 fpm, or 280 fpm. This is plainly insufficient to capture the particle. The hood must approach the flying particle to within a distance of 3 in. or less before the kinetic energy of the latter can be counteracted by the inrushing air.

The zone of influence of exhaust currents is narrowly restricted to the immediate region of the hood face. This is in sharp contrast to the ability of a pressure jet to "reach out" to relatively great distances from a nozzle. (See Fig. 2-3.) Consequently, exhaust hoods must be placed very close to the source of dust; must embrace it; must be placed so that the natural

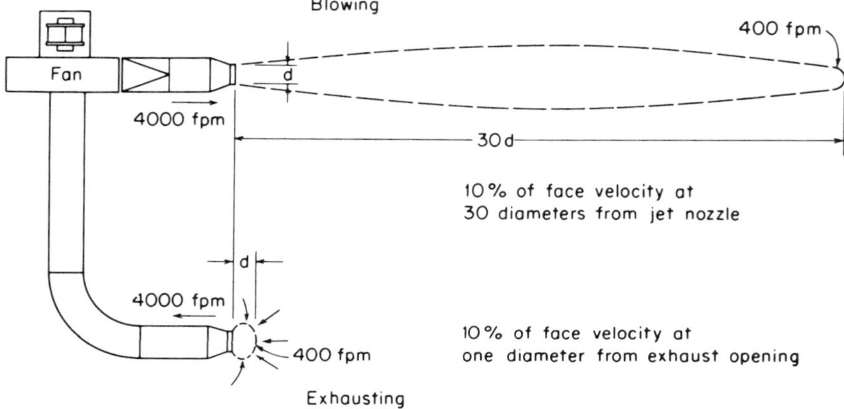

Fig. 2-3. Contrast in zones of influence of pressure-jet and exhaust inlet.

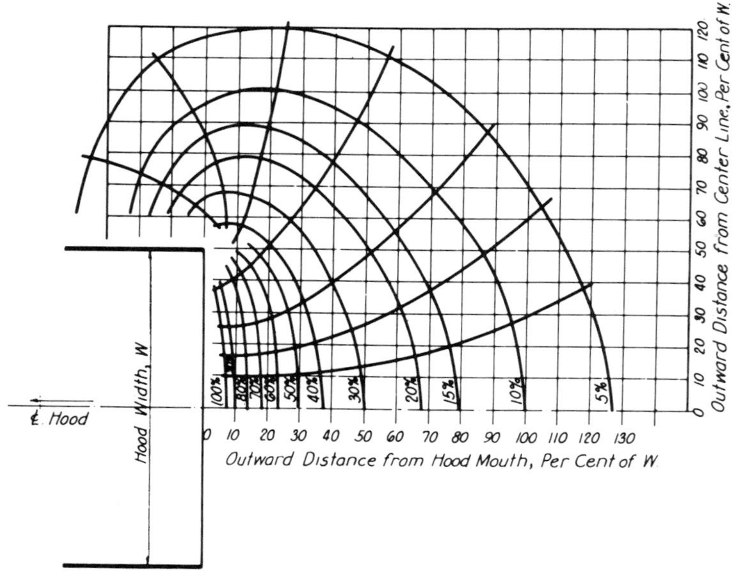

Fig. 2-4. Velocity contours and flow directional-lines in centerline plane of square suction hood.

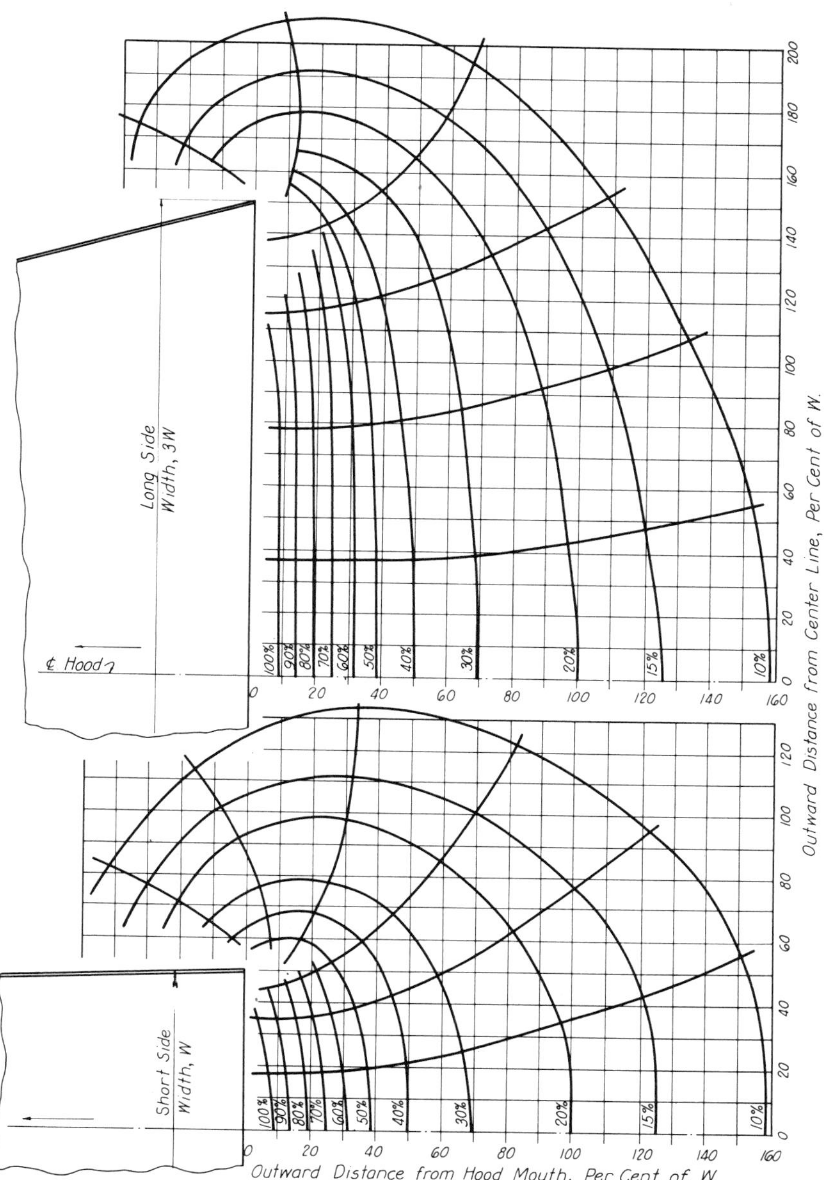

Fig. 2-5. Velocity contours and flow directional-lines in principal centerline planes of rectangular suction hood with side ratio 1:3.

trajectories of the particles terminate in the hood mouth; or must develop significant air flow patterns as workspace air moves toward the hood to satisfy exhaust demand.

Typical Hood Contours

Figures 2-4 and 2-5 show contour and direction lines along the principal axial planes of square and rectangular hoods. While the location of the contours along the axis varies somewhat with the shape of hood, it will be observed that the contours of all shapes of simple openings are similar. When the hood opening is round or square, a simple curve such as Fig. 2-2 b is sufficient to define its centerline characteristics. Rectangular hoods with elongated openings produce elongated contours conforming somewhat to the shape of the opening. It is possible, of course, to explore the whole field of influence of a hood and to prepare a three-dimensional model of velocities. Experience shows, however, that contours drawn for the two axial planes perpendicular to the hood sides are sufficient for design and application purposes.

Relation of Face Area to Velocity

DallaValle's experiments have demonstrated that centerline velocities are affected not only by the distance from the hood face but also by the hood-face area. A given contour is located farther from the hood face with a large hood than with a small one, everything else being equal. DallaValle derives an approximate relation between face area, velocity, and distance as follows:

$$y/(100 - y) = 0.1a/x^2$$

where:

y = velocity in % of face velocity,
a = hood face area,
x = distance from hood face.

This equation is often expressed as:

$$V = \frac{Q}{10x^2 + a}$$

where:

V = velocity at distance x from hood face,
a = hood face area,
Q = cfm exhausted.

Both a and x are expressed in the same linear units, The nomogram, Fig. 2-6, has been constructed from this equation to simplify calculation of the centerline velocity.

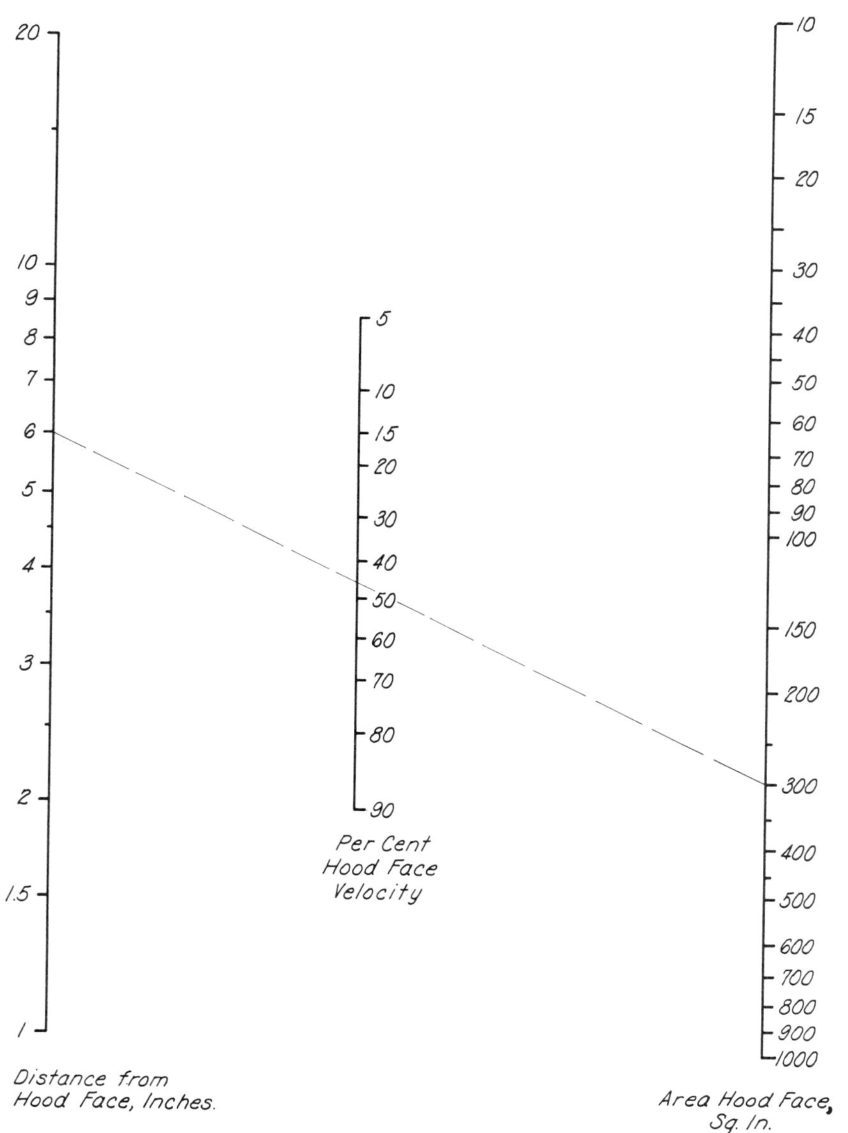

Fig. 2-6. Nomogram for determination of centerline velocity of suction hoods.

Summary of Hood Face Characteristics

Several conclusions can be drawn from the experimental studies just discussed and from the typical contour diagrams.

1. All suction openings regardless of size or shape tend to draw air equally from all directions. Departure from this ideal is caused by the presence of obstructions to flow such as the hood and pipe and by the fact that the suction source is a plane surface rather than a point in space.
2. The tendency for the contour surfaces to approach sphericity increases with the distance from the hood.
3. For a given hood shape, regardless of face velocity, the shape of the contour lines is nearly identical for all hood sizes.
4. When velocities are expressed in terms of face velocity, and distances in terms of hood dimensions, a single pattern of contours is representative of all hoods of the same shape.
5. Larger hoods are effective over greater distances than small hoods. Contours representing the same percentage of face velocity lie farther from the hood face.
6. Velocity contours are not far from parallel to the hood face over the area projected by the face.

The chief value of this discussion of hood flow characteristics is the emphasis it places on visualization of what happens when a hood is subjected to suction. The designer will have but little occasion to plot precise contours or flow lines. He will find that by study of the diagrams and by locating the intersections of the contours with the centerline, he can draw freehand contours and flow direction lines which are sufficiently accurate for most purposes. Practice in drawing contours will stimulate the development of air flow "sense" to a considerable degree.

Effect of Hood Structure in Rear of Face

The hood face is seldom of the same shape as the cross-section of the branch pipe. The two are joined by tapered section or by box-like pieces. It has been shown by DallaValle and Hatch that the shape of the taper and its proportions have little or no influence on the shape of the velocity contours outside the hood mouth. It has an important bearing on the pressure loss at entry. See Chapter 4.

Flanged Hood Faces

Flanges surrounding a hood opening as in Fig. 2-7, tend to push the velocity contours farther from the hood face by forcing air to flow from the zone directly in front of the hood. The flange reduces the flow from the ineffective regions. The flange width should be such that it intercepts the

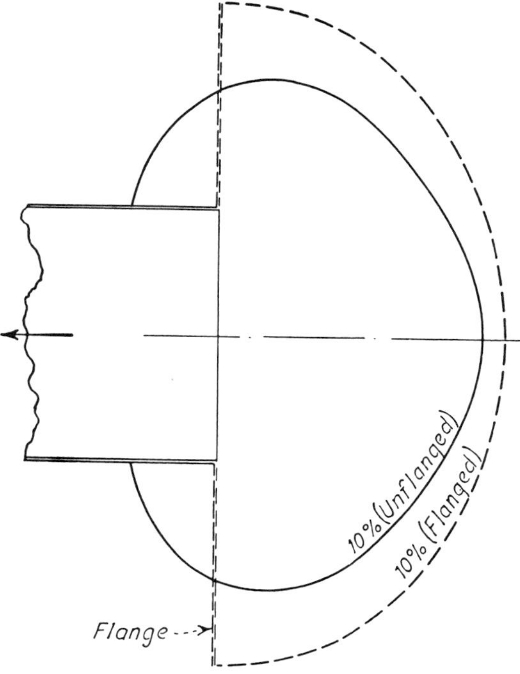

Fig. 2-7. Effect of hood flanges on velocity contours.

10% contour line of the unflanged hood if possible. For usual applications a flange width equal to hood side or diameter, but not more than 6″, will be sufficient. If so constructed, the 30% contour will be pushed outward about 14% and the 10% contour about 9%. For a given velocity in the effective zone, the flanged hood requires only about 70% of the air volume of an unflanged opening.

The increase in exhaust air effectiveness from use of the flange decreases as the area of the hood increases. For hoods in the side draft or booth categories no appreciable help can be expected although a flange around the opening is often a desirable structural detail.

Influence of Adjacent Planes

A hood lying on a large, flat surface such as a machine table, requires only about 75% of the air volume of a similar hood in space to produce the same effective velocity. Such a hood is shown in Fig. 2-8. Its velocity contours are identical with those of one-half of a hood or twice the depth of opening. The designer may imagine an identical hood, *a*, shown dotted, adjacent to the hood in question. The velocity contours of the latter are one-half of those of the combined openings of the real and imaginary hoods.

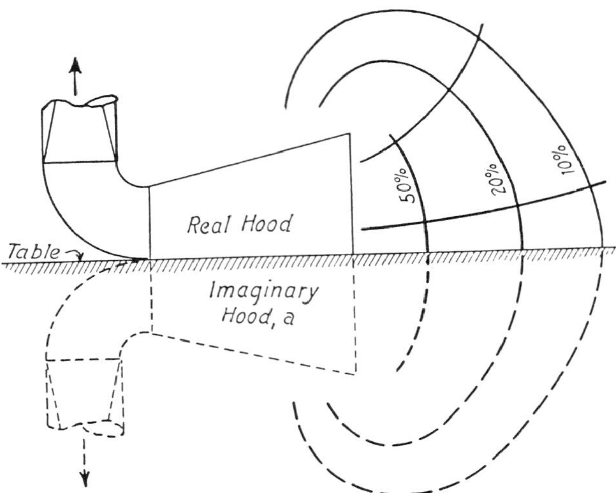

Fig. 2-8. Velocity contours of hood resting on table.

Hoods for Hand Tools

Dust released from portable hand tools and fumes from welding and brazing operations appear to be logical applications for local exhaust hoods; especially for those operations conducted on work benches or other horizontal surface. Portable hoods (Fig. 2-9), located close to the source, can be effective with control rates of 300 to 600 cfm. For vertical operations and large parts, suspension of the hood by counterweighted arms is sometimes employed. A major drawback is the need for positioning and relocating by the worker, a task that requires such constant policing by supervisors, that local exhaust hoods have lost favor and more expensive ventilated work tables, booths, or other larger exhaust-volume systems have become the usual control device.

Stimulated by work done in England by the British Steel Castings' Research Association, the use of high-velocity, low-volume exhaust from hand tools, surface grinders and sanders, wire brushes, and similar operations

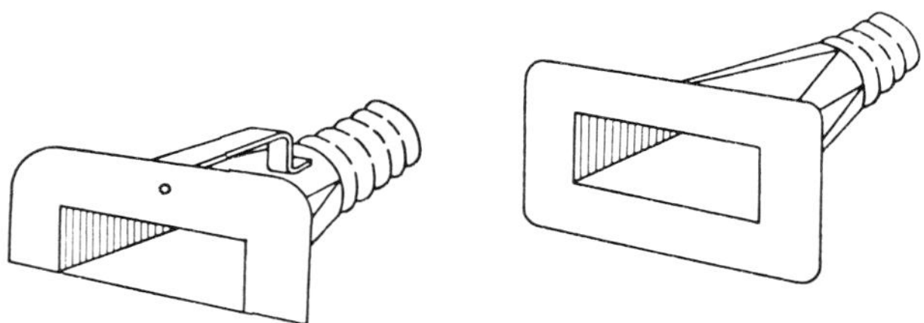

Fig. 2-9. Portable hoods for hand tools.

has increased. The vacuum-cleaner concept of very high velocities, 10,000 to 15,000 fpm, through small hoods close to the source, utilizes hoods attached to or part of the tool, or attached to a fixture on a machine tool.

One to two inch flexible hose is usual. Hose length must be short, usually less than 10 feet, before the duct is expanded into larger rigid piping because of the high pressure loss. High-pressure blowers of the industrial vacuum cleaning design, producing 8-inches and higher Hg pressure, are usually applied.

Figure 2-10 shows hood applications to a cup-shaped portable grinding wheel and a disk sander. Industry acceptance of the concept has been very limited, basically to those operations where small diameter flexible hose is adequate, and in some cases, where flat surfaces are finished. Shortcomings include the awkwardness of the exhaust hose, especially when 1 in. or larger diameters are required, and reduced productivity due to difficulty in reaching irregular surfaces, pockets, or corners. A similar concept involves the surrounding of the electrode on welding applications involving continuous feed.

Venting vapors during drum filling is another example of hood uses. See Fig. 2-11. The small volume required reduces problems of interference or lack of flexibility.

Hoods for the Capture of Coarse Particles

Thus far, the discussion has been confined to a type of local hood whose chief function is to create a general air flow away from the workman and past the dust source. Its principal effectiveness is in removing airborne particulates. Large particles thrown with considerable speed and possessing substantial kinetic energy cannot be captured economically by this type of hood—remote from the dust source—unless the particles follow a single

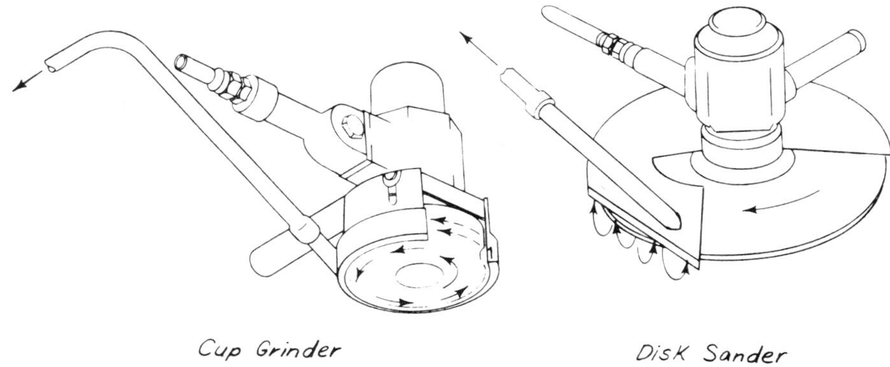

Fig. 2-10. High-velocity, low-volume hoods.

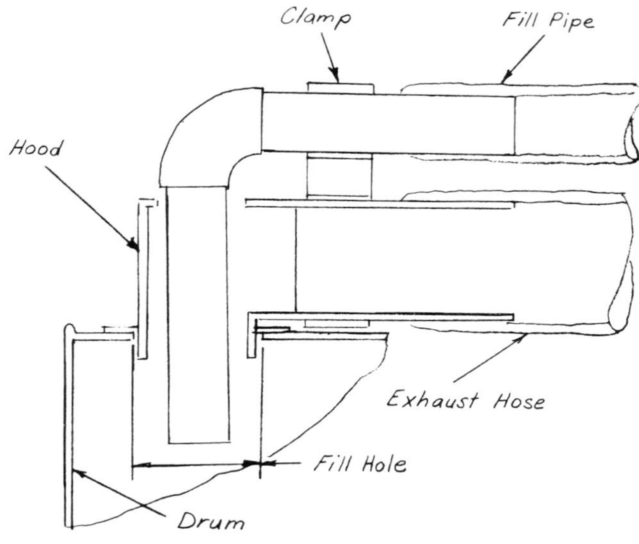

Fig. 2-11. Drum filling.

predictable sheaf of trajectories. Therefore, most machine operations producing large quantities of dust and refuse are provided with enclosing hoods if the refuse is to be air-conveyed by the exhaust system. A single rule covers the design of most hoods for this purpose:

Design the hood so that the material is thrown by the machine into the zone of highest air-velocity; preferably the mouth of the branch pipe.

Where this cannot be done, there are operations where the trajectory can be intercepted with a fixed barrier, permitting the stalled material to fall into a hood located below the flight pattern.

The influence of this principle will be seen in many of the hoods shown in succeeding illustrations. Certain exceptions will be mentioned wherein a departure is justified by operating or maintenance considerations. It should be emphasized again that such hood designs will carry off not only the large particles, but the minute ones as well.

A few local hoods from the woodworking and metalworking industries are illustrated in the following pages. These sketches conform to the principles enumerated and indicate the direction that local hood design can follow for other applications where machines perform similar functions.

Hoods for Woodworking Machinery

Woodworking exhaust systems are installed for waste removal purposes rather than for health protection. The emphasis is on the removal of large quantities of coarse materials rather than on the entrapment of microscopic particles. Consequently, most of the woodworking hoods illustrated are shaped to conform to the trajectories of flying chips. They depend for their success upon effective shape and placement with respect to chip trajectories rather than upon velocities external to the hood mouth.

Each hood must be provided with an adequate air inlet. While woodworking hoods should fit tightly in non-working areas, sufficient air must be admitted to transport the chips. The air inlet area seldom should be less than twice the branch pipe area. As a general rule, it should be so located that the air stream will pass through the dust generating zone in the direction of chip travel.

Like most hoods, the average woodworking hood receives severe usage. Heavy construction and generous reinforcement are essential. Doors, telescoping members, and sliding parts should be made of No. 16 gage steel, or heavier. Battered hoods fail to fit properly; are ineffective; are difficult to adjust; and are an annoyance to the workman.

Saw Hoods

Figure 2-12 (left) is a typical band-saw hood. The hardwood sloping bottom is slotted for passage of the saw. All saw hoods must admit sufficient air through the table slot and other openings and by leakage around the door to provide branch-pipe velocities sufficient to convey the sawdust after it is thrown into the pipe. Secondary air may be admitted to the floor-level

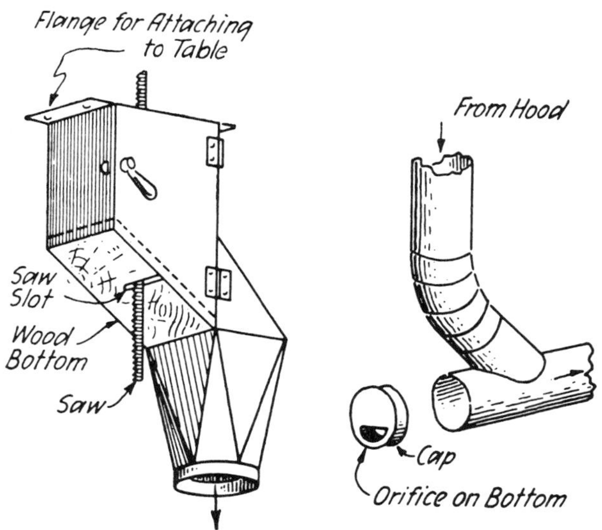

Fig. 2-12. (Left) Band-saw hood, and (Right) hood connection to branch with secondary air inlet.

branch as in Fig. 2-12 (right). The dead end of the branch is closed by a removable cleanout cap having an inlet orifice enlarged to a size just sufficient to prevent clogging. The orifice is aligned with the bottom of the pipe so that the entering air will sweep the bottom clean.

Large self-feed saws and band resaws are usually equipped with two suction pipes, one on the down-run of the saw and the other at the lower rear portion of a housing completely covering the lower band wheel. The first hood removes the bulk of the coarse dust and the second pipe handles the finer dust which follows the blade.

An inexpensive hood for small circular saws is the doorless hopper in Fig. 2-13. Circular resaws and other high production saws are provided with hoods equipped with side doors for easy removal of heavy saws as well as to provide access to the pipe mouth for removing blocks and edgings.

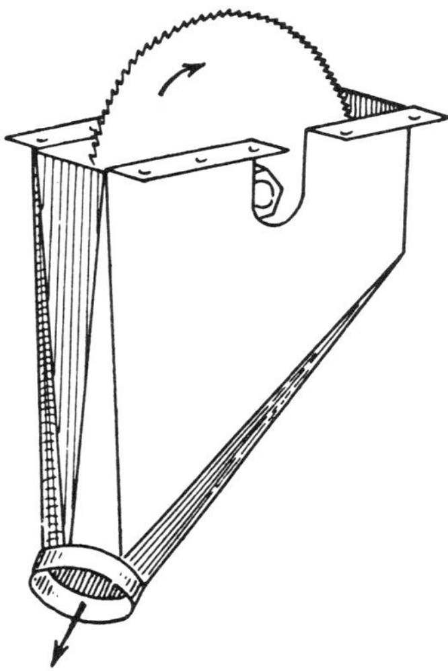

Fig. 2-13. Table-saw hood.

The bottom of the swing-saw hood, Fig. 2-14, slopes to the rear at an angle from the horizontal which is preferably 45° or more. When the angle is less than 45° or when the area of the saw slot in the table is too small to supply the necessary flow rate to keep the hood and branch pipe clean, a secondary air inlet may be cut in the end of the hood opposite to the branch pipe.

Shaper Hoods

There is no more difficult machine to hood than the vertical spindle shaper used for jobbing work. Because of its adapatability to both inside and outside cuts on pieces of almost any shape, the variety of work that comes to the

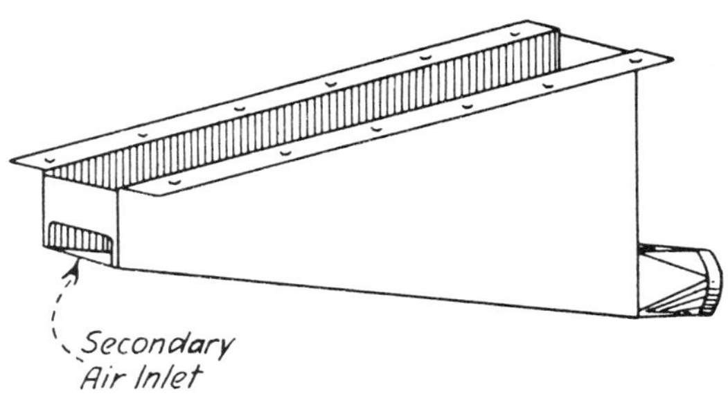

Fig. 2-14. Swing-saw hood.

shaper requires that the hood be fully adjustable and that it impose no restriction on the flexibility of the machine. Enclosing hoods can be applied only to single-purpose machines. On all others an open hood is clamped to the table as close to the knife as the work will permit and in line with the chip trajectory. Ball and telescoping pipe joints or hose are required in the connection to the main.

The effectiveness of a shaper hood depends upon the care with which it is adjusted for each job. A hood pushed back out of the way cannot collect chips. Because of the likelihood of improper adjustment as well as the essential difficulty of satisfactory all-purpose design, a high static suction and corresponding velocity are necessary to compensate for unfavorable conditions.

A typical shaper hood is shown in Fig. 2-15. The velocity contour characteristics of open hoods indicate improved performance when the hood mouth is flanged as shown in the alternate design at the right.

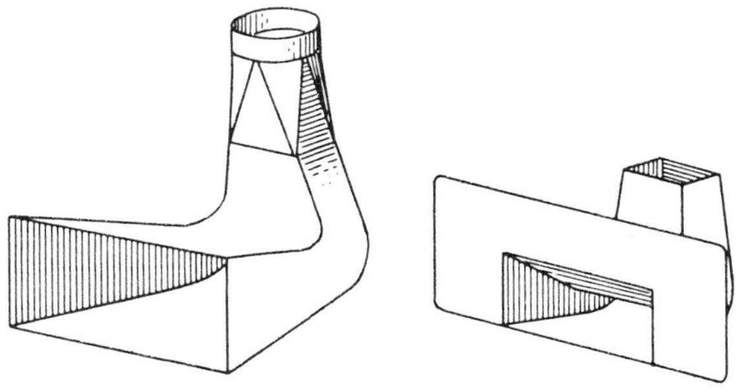

Fig. 2-15. Shaper hood.

Planer Hoods

The planer is representative of a large class of machinery whose operating principle depends upon high-speed rotating knives. Molders, stickers, tenoners, jointers, and others are identical with planers so far as hood problems are concerned.

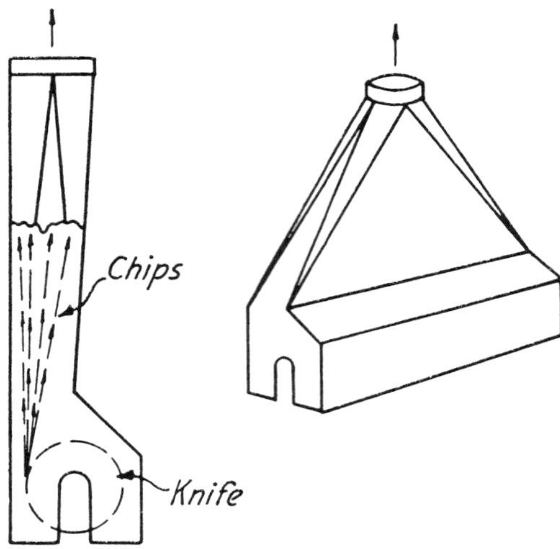

Fig. 2-16. Planer hood.

When the chip breaker of a planer is so constructed that the chips are thrown vertically from the knife as in Fig. 2-16, the hood is shaped like an inverted hopper. A chip breaker which causes a curved trajectory across the top of the cutter requires a hood shaped as in Fig. 2-17. The hood walls conform closely to the sheaf of chip trajectories so that the chips are thrown into the pipe mouth. Those which strike the hood do so at an acute angle, never more than 60°, so as to cause ricochet into the pipe.

Planer hood contours must be developed from actual chip trajectories. The existing hood, if any, should be removed and a few boards run through the

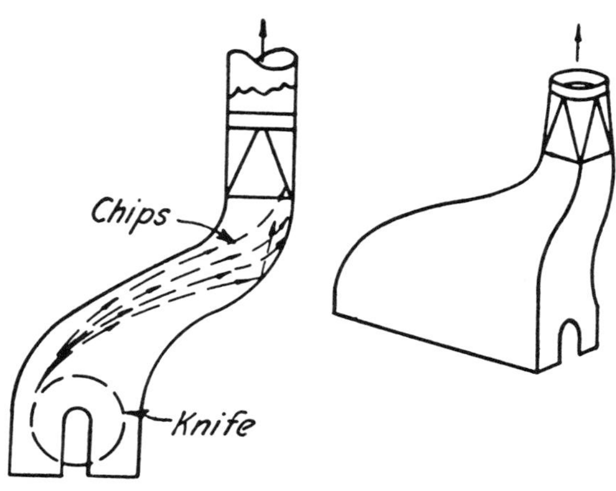

Fig. 2-17. Planer hood.

machine. Coordinates of points on the trajectory can be obtained by simple measurements while the chips are flying. The enveloping outlines of the hood can then be established so that most of the chips are thrown into the narrow high-velocity section and the remainder strike the hood walls at acute angles of incidence.

While many machines are now received with factory-made hoods, the design should be checked by observing the actual chip paths.

Sander Hoods

Wood sanding operations often produce greater volumes of dust than do metal grinding processes. Moreover, the natural abrasives often employed create greater hazard than do the artificial abrasives in general use in the metal trades.

Common sand drums projecting through tables are hooded from below with simple hoppers as in Fig. 2-18. The spindle sander hood resembles that for the variety shaper. Its face area may be made greater, however, and the face velocity lower. Large air volumes at low velocities are superior to low volumes at high velocities. The horizontal belt sander, Fig. 2-19, is typical of many belt sanders. An outlet at each pulley to catch dust thrown from the belt by centrifugal force is almost essential for production belt sanders. Patternmaker's sanders, used intermittently, may require only the exhaust at the head pulley.

ENCLOSURES, PARTIAL ENCLOSURES

Hoods are designed to confine a contaminant as completely as possible, and prevent its escape to the workroom. This is best achieved by a complete enclosure having a minimum of openings. For practical reasons this ideal

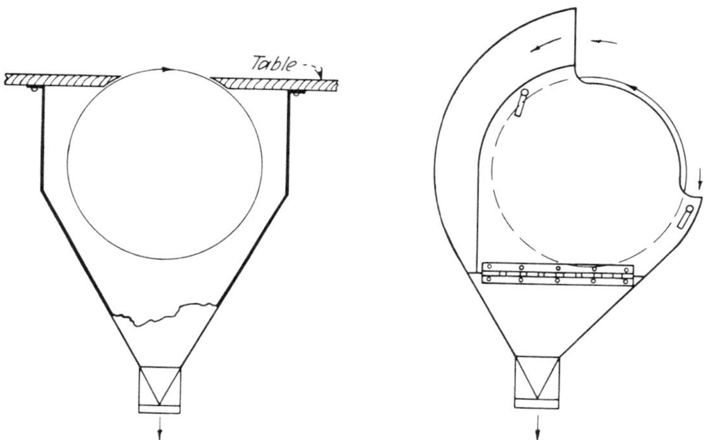

Fig. 2-18. Drum sander hoods.

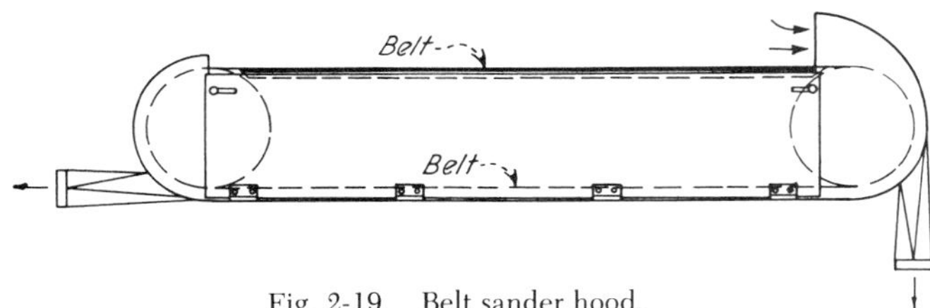

Fig. 2-19. Belt sander hood.

often cannot be attained. Material must be introduced to and removed from the process, manual operations must be performed and access must be had to the processing element for adjustment, maintenance, or other purposes. The hood must present the least possible interference with these functions yet at the same time contribute to good contaminant control. The hoods described as "booth," "side," "overhead," "canopy," or "downdraft" are merely variants of the "complete enclosure" in which one or more of the confining surfaces are missing. The further a hood departs from a complete enclosure, the greater the difficulty of effective contaminant control and the greater the size, cost, and power of the exhaust system.

Complete Enclosure

Most designers confronted with a new operation that requires confinement of a contaminant start by mentally putting the operation or the source of contaminant release in a complete enclosure. For many applications, the equipment, itself, provides such a ready-made enclosure or permits the addition of the missing surfaces. Complete enclosures are usual for abrasive blasting equipment, tumbling mills, mixers, bucket elevators, storage bins, glove boxes for clean rooms or toxic material operation, vibrating and rotary screens, automatic buffing, foundry shakeout, automatic painting and dipping, crucible and heat-treating furnaces. In many operations permanent openings through which indraft must be maintained are provided for observation of process or for material handling of the parts involved. Larger hinged doors and/or removable panels are provided to facilitate maintenance and repair. Exhaust connection can be so located that settlement within the enclosure is at a minimum. Exhaust volume must be sufficient to create effective inflow through openings and also to maintain a high enough negative pressure to prevent leakage at remote corners or cracks due to localized pressure-buildup.

Booth or Tunnel

The booth enclosure is basically a complete enclosure except for one open side. Exhaust air flow is usually horizontal toward the exhaust connection located opposite the open side. The booth concept can be used not only for the usual paint spray application, but also for many industrial applications such as benchwork, laboratory hoods, bagging machines, weigh stations, swing frame and portable grinding, finishing and welding.

Tunnel type enclosures are usually long in relation to their width. Exhaust volumes will be the same as for booth enclosures of equal open areas unless both ends are open or workmen are located along the long dimension. In the latter case, airflow is usually vertical to keep worker as free as possible from contaminated zones. Tunnel enclosures are frequent in automotive body and appliance finishing, the cleaning and painting of large cast or fabricated parts, the confinement of contaminant released from inline or conveyorized manufacturing or assembly.

Side Hood

A booth type of enclosure becomes a side hood when substantial portions of the top and sides must be removed. Exhaust air requirements are increased and control is subject to disruptions from cross drafts and stray air-currents in the vicinity.

Side hoods are usual at pouring stations, large foundry shakeouts, plating and cleaning tanks, bench operations, barrel-filling and upsetting.

Downdraft Hood

As the name implies, exhaust of contaminant is downward, usually through a floor grille or a grille in a workbench top. Performance is best where contaminant is released close to the grille and where side shields can direct the downflow of air over the work area and reduce short circuiting. Downdraft will tend to aspirate and entrain more materials than other hood types. Often the effective area of the grille is blocked by the operation at the time when maximum contaminant release occurs, making effective control difficult.

Overhead or Canopy Hood

While a canopy hood could be considered an enclosure without side walls, its usual application is over hot processes where convection produces a vertical thrust to the contaminant. The rising gas stream acts as a jet inducing sizable quantities of room air to join the upward flow. Exhaust volumes for control increase with the temperature of the process and the distance to hood mouth. Spill from a canopy hood is usually due to insufficient exhaust capacity to handle the induced air-volume in the mixture. Double hoods, or orifice plates within the hood are useful only to produce more uniform distribution, but have little influence on the volume needed for control. Performance of canopy hoods without side shields is at the mercy of cross drafts.

Air Flow Distribution Within Hoods or Enclosures

The need for incorporation of an air distribution device within the hood or enclosure will vary with the contaminant; the process; and the hood size, shape, and location.

For side hoods the use of one or more horizontal slots can produce excellent distribution for most industrial applications where ample plenum space behind the slots exists and an SP differential across the slot of 1/8 in. is maintained. Slots should be designed to produce a sharp edge orifice effect, so velocities in the 1,200-1,500 fpm range will produce such a pressure drop. (Bell-shaped or curved slot edges are difficult to justify as the lower entrance loss requires higher slot velocity and, consequently, narrower slots to accomplish the same air flow distribution.) Trash screens over the openings will protect the exhaust system. Flattened expanded metal or heavy gage ¾-in. mesh is suitable material. Slot dimensions should compensate for the free area reduction imposed by the protective covering.

Small side hoods, such as those used in place of downdraft hoods for workbench operations, need no distribution slots where the work station is relatively fixed. A single slot at the elevation of the more usual zone of dust generation will be ample where operations are not concentrated at one location. See Fig. 2-21b.

For long hoods, such as plating tanks, pouring line, foundry shakeout, sorting conveyor operations, usually a single horizontal slot located at the height of the more usual zone of contaminant release will suffice. See Fig. 2-21c. Where there is a thermal stack effect created from hot processes, the use of a second slot at the top of the hood exhausting 10-15% of the total volume will recapture stray smokes and fumes creeping upward along the hood face. See Fig. 2-21d. (Closely spaced multiple slots, either vertical or horizontal, offer little improvement over single or double slot designs and introduce increased fabrication costs.)

For long hoods, branch ducts connected to the plenum every 10-15 ft will help the distribution and reduce the cross section of the manifold. Where the need exists, more refined adjustments can be made by the addition of sliding shutters to vary the exhaust openings. Shutters can be either vertical or horizontal and are especially helpful to compensate for prevailing cross drafts. For smaller hoods, the shutter can have a double taper to increase air flow at the ends of the slot, restricting the slot area close to an exhaust connection at the center of the hood.

For booths the need for an arrangement of distribution slots or grids will vary with the location and method of contaminant generation. For mechanically generated dust, such as swing frame or portable grinding, chipping and sanding, a horizontal exhaust port near the floor, Figs. 2-20a and b, is a popular detail. Where metallic fumes are released with an upward thermal thrust, such as welding, torch cutting, powder burning, arc air operation, the

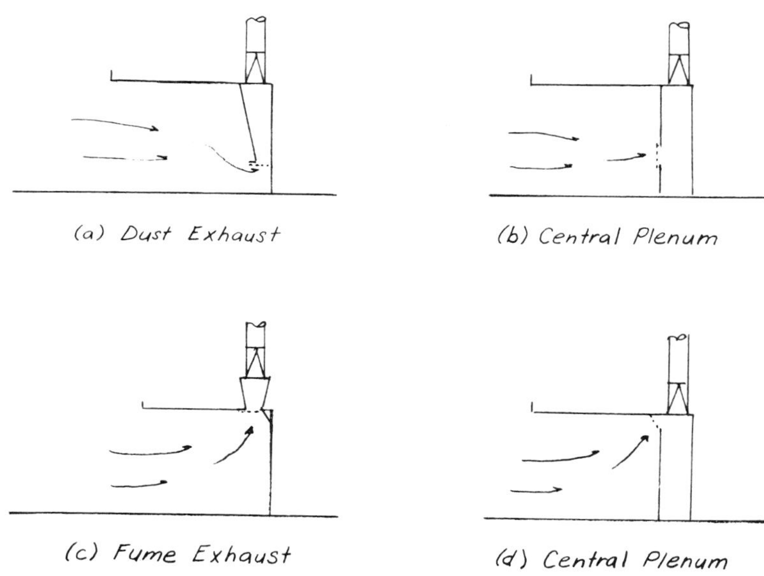

Fig. 2-20. Booth exhaust locations.

location of the exhaust slot at the top of the booth wall, Figs. 2-20c and d, is preferred. For spraying operations, a horizontal slot formed by the water wall overspray collector gives good distribution for larger booths. For shallow or smaller spray booths or cabinets the use of filters or grids to give uniform distribution horizontally and vertically is suggested.

Where several booths are located side by side, a common plenum, Figs. 2-20b and d, simplifies exhaust duct connections and permits easy relocation of exhaust ports to meet changing requirements.

Where booths enclose floor grilles, Fig. 2-23d, an exhaust slot at the higher elevations indicated in Fig. 2-21d will minimize pick up of usable material as dry material is fed through the floor openings.

With downdraft exhaust the hood is incorporated with and becomes part of the material-receiving hopper. For large downdraft grilles, slots in the exhaust headers, Fig. 2-23a and b, are usual. Slots are located in the underside of the duct to prevent accumulations at the far end. With downdraft benches, the exhaust slot can be a part of the bench design. See Fig. 2-21a.

For complete enclosures it is the indraft through the access or inspection openings that prevent escapement. Exhaust duct location or locations are selected to cause the flow pattern to sweep the contaminant generation area in a way that will lower fallout within the enclosure to reduce housekeeping.

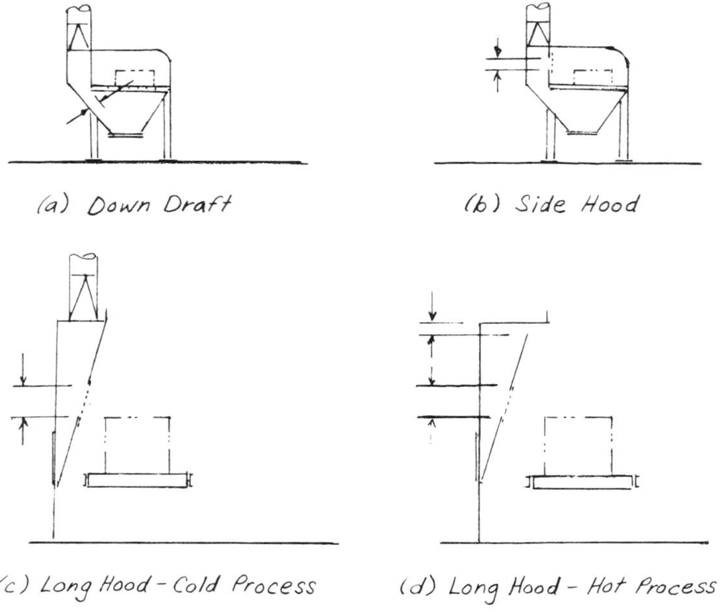

Fig. 2-21. Slots for exhaust distribution.

Overhead hoods are usually selected to intercept contaminants released in an upward direction. Where side shields can be installed on two or three adjacent sides, distribution slots are seldom needed. Without slide shields, baffling as illustrated in Figs. 2-32b, c, and d are used as air flow distributors and as a means of compensating for prevailing cross drafts.

HOOD SELECTION

Local conditions often determine the hood design, as can be noted in the following discussion of frequently encountered applications.

Hoods for Material Handling

The material handling system, Fig. 2-22, is supplied by truckloads of dusty material dumped through a grating at floor level to a surge bin below. Air is induced by the material as the product flows from truck body to hopper. The induced air, unless exhausted, will boil back out of the hopper carrying the dust cloud into the workroom. First reaction, especially from production people, will be to encourage downdraft control, Fig. 2-23a. It involves no obstructions above the floor that could interfere with other use of the space or cause damage during the dumping operation.

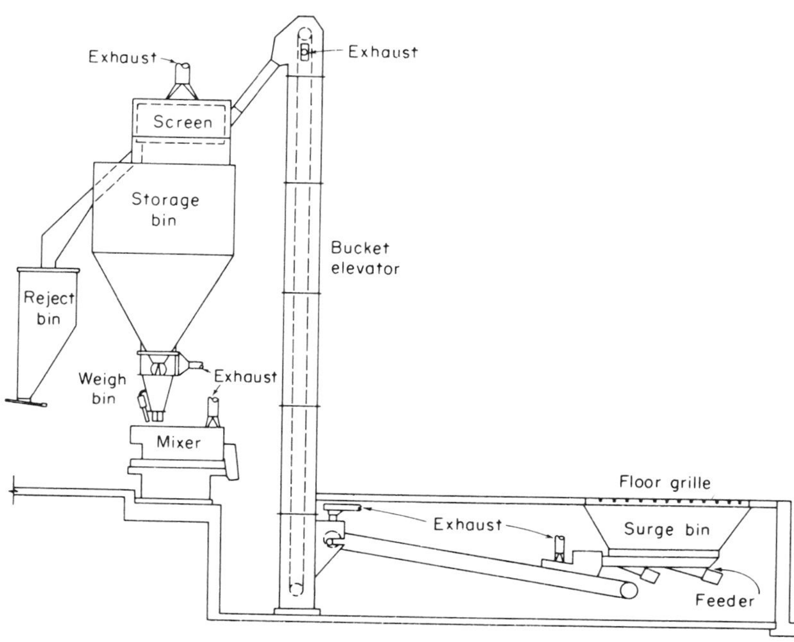

Fig. 2-22. Hoods for material handling.

Downdraft control, however, has several disadvantages. Regardless of how well the exhaust headers are shielded, the pickup of usable material by the exhaust system will be excessive. If supply gets ahead of production, the surge bin can become full, burying the exhaust takeoffs with material. When trucks are unloaded inside a plant, the logical location for the floor opening is close to a door introducing the probability of strong cross drafts. Addition of side shields, Fig. 2-23b, on three sides would help offset the cross-drafts but would not reduce the other disadvantages. A booth type of exhaust, Fig. 2-23d, or side hood design, Fig. 2-23c, will be required to overcome the disadvantages of downdraft. The booth is most effective but will be the most easily damaged and is a major obstruction. The side hood approach would be a logical compromise, especially if the cycle is a relatively infrequent one.

Hoods at conveyor feed and discharge points approach complete enclosures. At the feed point, extending the hood in the direction of belt travel by four to eight feet is important because dust is released for some distance downstream. The higher the hood cover is located above the belt, the lower will be the pickup of usable material; and the faster the belt speed, the longer the hood extension should be. Exhaust takeoff at the feed point to a belt conveyer indicated in Figs. 2-22 and 2-23 is typical of a conventional exhaust location. When located so close to the zone of dust generation, excessive pickup of usable material is likely.

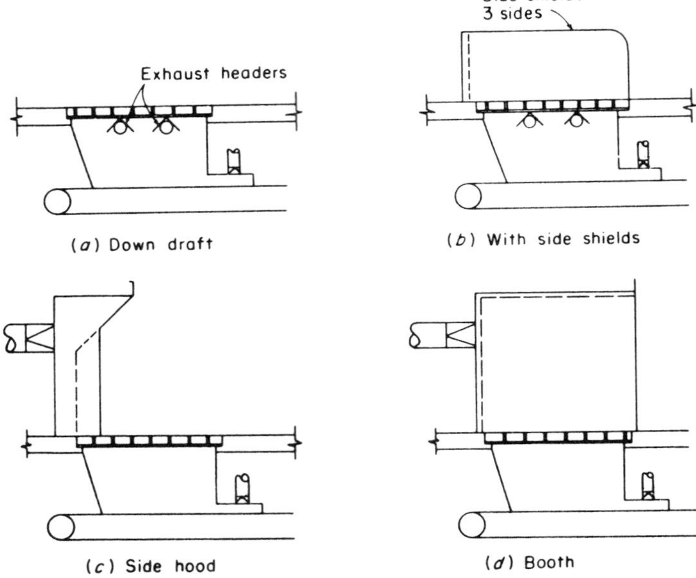

Fig. 2-23. Floor grille exhaust.

Expanding the hood to allow maximum fall out would reduce loss of usable material. See Figs. 2-24a and b. Note that the traditional hood at the head pulley has been eliminated in Fig. 2-24b. The downdraft induced by the falling material makes the need for exhaust at the head pulley questionable.

With high-speed belts (in excess of 200 fpm) heavily loaded, the induced air caused by the falling material is substantial. Reducing the height of fall or interrupting its free fall, will make significant reductions in exhaust requirements.

Belt conveyors located indoors will seldom need hoods or covers except at feed and discharge points, unless removal of heat or steam is needed. The bucket elevator can readily be provided with a complete enclosure and such construction is usual where dry particulates are elevated. The rotating buckets on their endless conveyor set up a fan action within the casing. In addition, stack effect, especially in tall elevators or in those transporting hot materials, adds to localized internal pressure areas. Major point-of-pressure relief and exhaust to keep elevator casing under negative pressure is at the elevator head. By locating exhaust connection under the head pulley and between the up and down run of the belt, a minimum of usable material will be entrained. Some designers plan the exhaust at head pulley as a means of maintaining indraft at the feed connection. Unless such feed is from a closed chute, exhaust at the boot is also recommended and conforms to usual

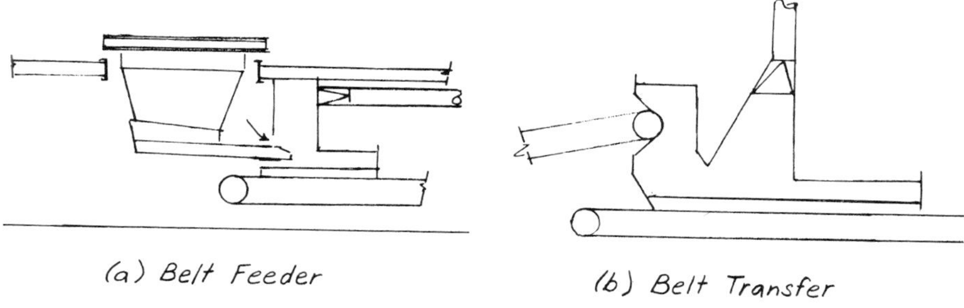

Fig. 2-24. Modified conveyor hoods.

practice. It is difficult to confine air entrained by the falling material at the feed to an elevator from a remote suction connection at the elevator head. Where materials are hot and moist, keeping exhaust duct at elevator head in service becomes a problem because of condensation and plugging. Where dust loads are not excessive, venting the elevator directly to the atmosphere, above the roof line, will help.

Screens, either flat deck or cylindrical, can be completely enclosed. Often they are located at the bin top where exhaust of bin and screen can be accomplished with the same exhaust connection. A flat deck screen can be provided with cover plates and exhausted by a flexible connection. However, substantially less material will be picked up by the exhaust air when the screen is housed and exhaust take-off can be located a greater distance from the screen surface.

Bins are a source of substantial induced-air motion because of the height of fall, especially when bin level is low. If the bin is tight and covered, the induced-air flow that must be exhausted will be that caused by the drop of material from point of discharge to top of bin. The fall below the bin top causes internal air circulation that increases quantities of airborne particulates but does not greatly influence exhaust volumes needed for bin control.

Mixers are frequently used items of process material handling, to mix or blend a number of different ingredients. The ingredients are usually dry and agitation produces airborne particulates. Usually, a dust hood attached to the mixer shell is feasible for control. Openings for inspection and for feed of ingredients are provided, and exhaust volume must be sufficient to produce an indraft into the hood through such open areas.

A weigh hopper and transfer car can introduce an intermediate operation between storage bins and mixer feed, for which exhaust is required. Hood designs can range from small side hoods at each station to a tunnel or booth-type of enclosure encompassing the entire transfer. When liquids are added at the mixer, local exhaust ventilation may not be needed for the material handling of the mixed product. Where mixed material is dry, control similar to that on the raw side will be required.

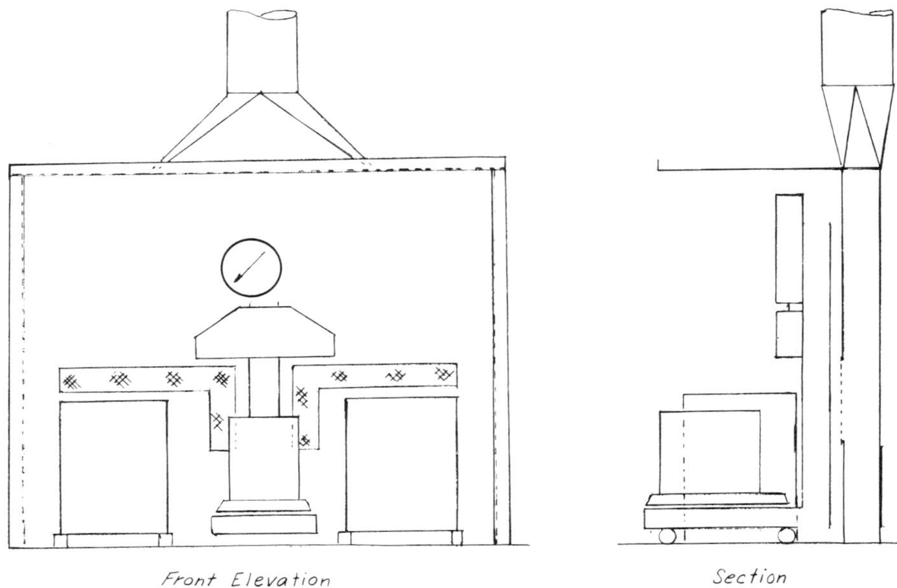

Fig. 2-25. Scale booth.

In many cases, dry materials are added in small quantities, or the whole batch can be a blend of a number of dry products (chemicals, pigments, bonding materials, etc.) weighed from bins, drums, or bags and transferred to the mixer. The loading of small open-top bins from drums or bags can be a dusty but intermittent operation. Use of side hoods, Fig. 2-21b, or booths, Fig. 2-25, at the scales and bins is often possible. Where paper bags are involved, incorporating the bag slitter within a ventilated booth, Fig. 2-26, has merit.

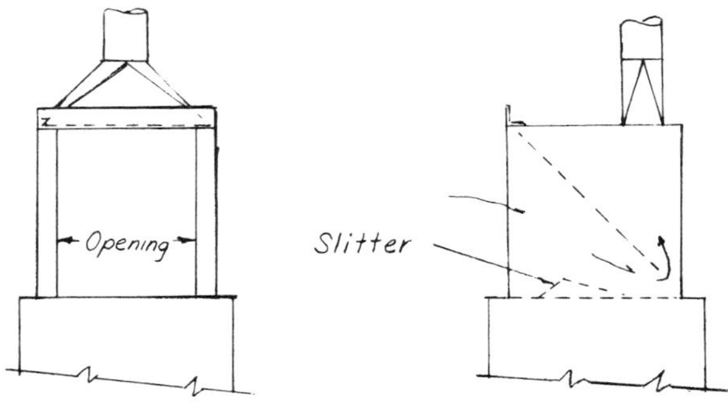

Fig. 2-26. Bag breaker booth.

Empty paper bags can be a dusty material handling problem as they are often accumulated on the mixer deck or thrown to a tote box on the floor below. Each time the bags are handled, dry dust generation can be visible. While it is possible to pneumatically convey them from mixer or blender deck to a remote collection bin, the exhaust duct must be 16–20 inches in diameter and free from sheet metal screws, burrs, etc., where a bulky bag could get hooked and form a dam. Other suggested solutions have included misting the inside surfaces of a bag after emptying; feeding the bags to a wet-type pulper; substituting plastic for paper; or using pneumatic material transport from remote bulk storage bins.

A frequently overlooked source of significant dust dispersion from material handling operations is the collection of refuse from bins, the head end of belt or vibrating conveyors, or dry dust collector hoppers. Either a booth or overhead hood is the usual effective solution. The booth enclosure, Fig. 2-27a, is a more positive arrangement requiring modest exhaust volumes. The drawback is the lack of lift truck accuracy tending to destroy the structure. An overhead hood, Fig. 2-27b, provides more latitude for positioning the tote box and is the more frequent arrangement.

When quantities permit, dust collector hoppers can be connected to sealed drums as indicated in Figs. 2-27c and d. For larger tote boxes a flexible duct from hopper or screw conveyor to tote box cover facilitates handling. In critical areas a second duct connected to the exhaust system will keep the container under negative pressure. See Fig. 2-27e. Hinging a section of a fixed cover will permit upsetting at the disposal site with a minimum of fugitive dust release.

Hoods for Bench Operations

Many times, operations on smaller parts conducted at workbench stations require control through local exhaust. The local hood illustrated in Fig. 2-9 could be effective for several problems if workers can be trained to keep the hood mouth in the proper position relative to the contaminant release. Because of this human equation, larger exhaust volumes through fixed hoods are the more reliable; usually in the form of a downdraft grille, Fig. 2-28a, or a booth as in Fig. 2-28b. For downdraft control, shields on three sides increase the effectiveness. For most applications, lateral exhaust, using the back wall as the mouth of a side hood, will be as effective as downdraft when the exhaust volume is in the same range. For booths, sides may require cut-outs to facilitate flow of parts to and from the work space. For larger items where contaminant is released over a wide area, enclosure in a tunnel-type of hood, Fig. 2-28c, isolates the operation yet keeps exhaust airflow direction such that worker is protected. For critical or hazardous operations complete enclosures such as the glove box, Fig. 2-28d, or the laboratory hood, Fig. 2-28e, justify the slower production pace by providing the highest degree of

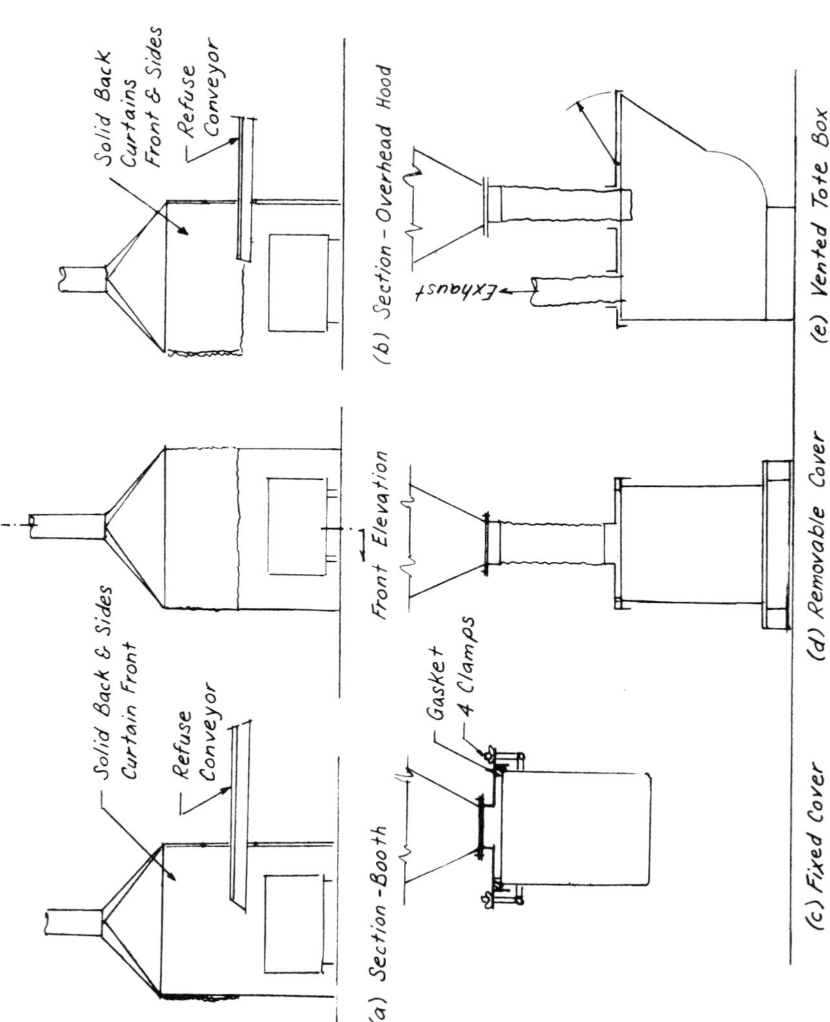

Fig. 2-27. Refuse and dust disposal.

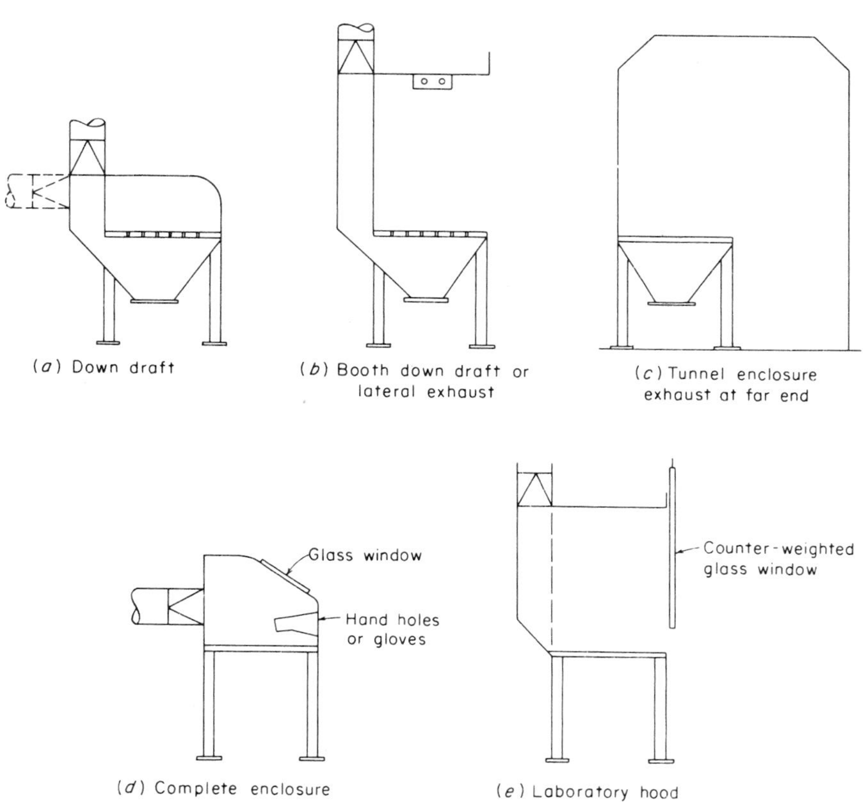

Fig. 2-28. Hoods for bench operations.

contaminant removal and the minimum exposure of the worker to the process.

Hoods for Melting-Furnaces

Smokes and metallic oxides from metallurgical operations have been difficult to control, and have caused in-plant and atmospheric contamination. They do, however, illustrate the evolution that can occur as engineering concentration on means of confinement and exhaust are applied. The industry has produced many innovations as it has changed from general ventilation through roof fans or roof monitors to the application of local exhaust-hoods.

The Elecric-arc Furnace used in the basic steel and the foundry industries furnishes an excellent case history. Early control efforts relied on general roof exhaust or at best, a canopy hood (Fig. 2-29a) located in the roof truss

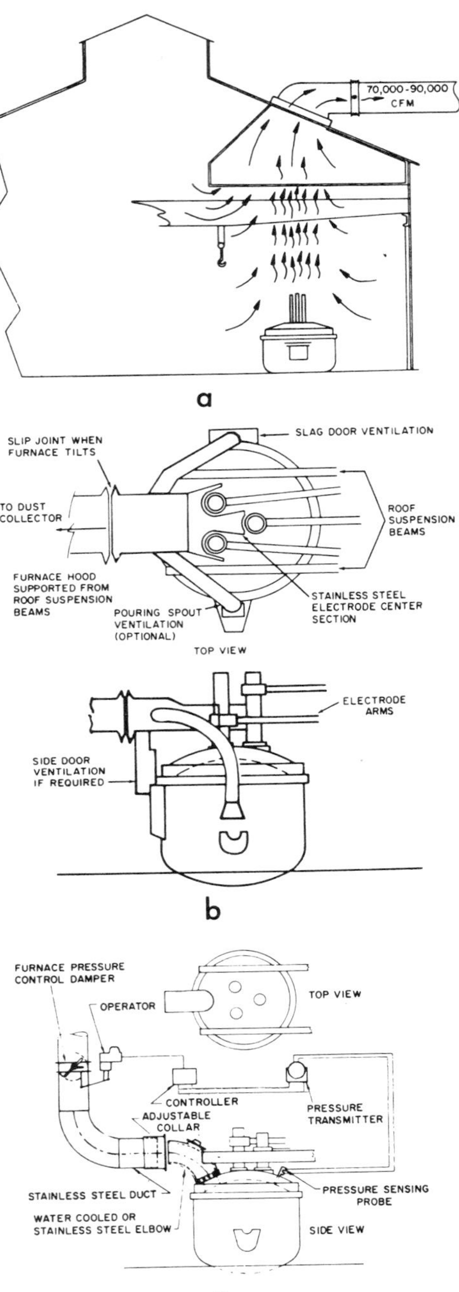

Fig. 2-29. Exhaust hoods for electric-arc furnace, a. Canopy hood; b. Local hood; c. Enclosure. By permission Wheelabrator Corporation.

and above the crane rails. Exhaust volumes were substantial because of the induced air set in motion by the thermal stack effect. If make-up air was provided, in-plant control was economically feasible as long as the substantial volumes could be exhausted to atmosphere without passing through fume collectors.

With emphasis on air pollution and with the greater fume production from oxygen addition, the need for fume collection accelerated the use of local exhaust hoods (Fig. 2-29b) at the points of fume release around the electrode cooling glands, the slagging door, and the pouring spout. Application of local exhaust principles reduced the exhaust volume to about 20 to 25 percent of that of general ventilation and provided superior in-plant control. A later refinement, Fig. 2-29c, used the furnace shell as a complete enclosure type of hood, where, by maintaining a slight indraft into the furnace shell exhaust volume needed for control was reduced further.

Crucible Furnaces used extensively in the nonferrous casting industry are

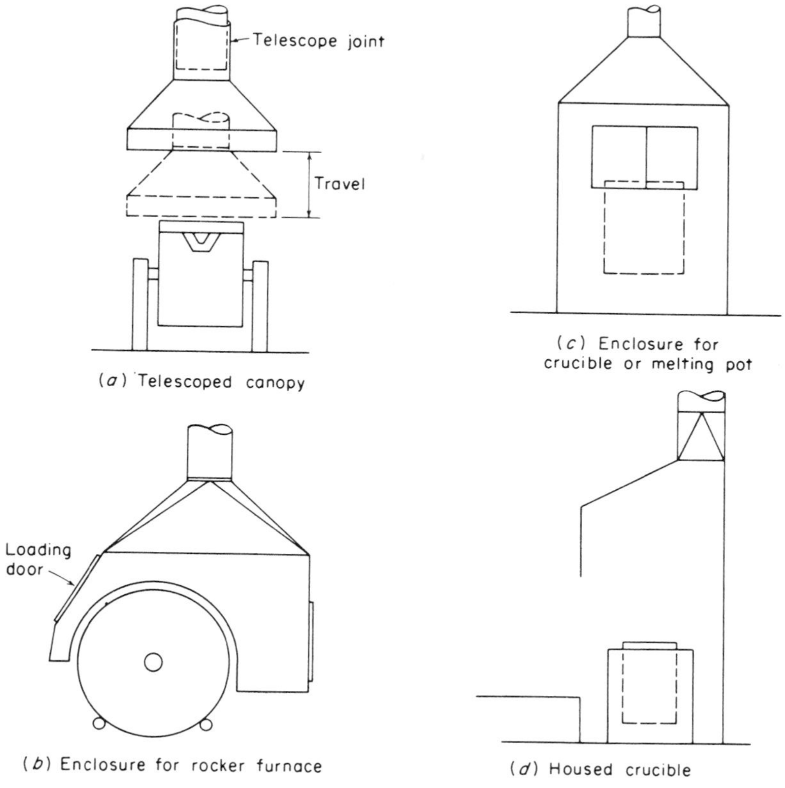

Fig. 2-30. Hoods for melting-furnaces.

smaller melting units that can be exhausted by a variety of hood designs.[6] Counterweighted canopy hoods (Fig. 2-30a) are practical for some operations. A canopy hood extending over the pouring spout (Fig. 2-30b) provides control where furnaces are tilted for pouring. Where the crucible is removed from a stationary furnace or metal is ladled from it, complete enclosure (Fig. 2-30c) or booth type (Fig. 2-30d) hoods will be effective.

For larger melting rates, the reverb and induction melting designs are popular (the induction melting furnace is used in place of the cupola in a number of gray and ductile iron foundries also). Exhaust of the reverb furnace requires only an exhaust chimney at the discharge flue to exhaust hot gases and metallic fumes. The induction furnace may be exhausted through roof fans and general ventilation or with a local exhaust hood attached to the furnace roof. A proprietary design keeps the exhaust system in operation during charging and pouring as well as melting.

Copper-based alloys contain varying percentages of zinc and lead, both metals having lower melting points than the copper. Visible clouds of the oxide are released while filling ladles during hot metal transport, at the skimming station, and while pouring. With the sharp reduction in the standards for acceptable exposures to lead inhalation, the problems of control have been magnified. In some instances, a local exhaust hood attached to the ladle bail, Fig. 2-31, can provide continuous exhaust through a moving

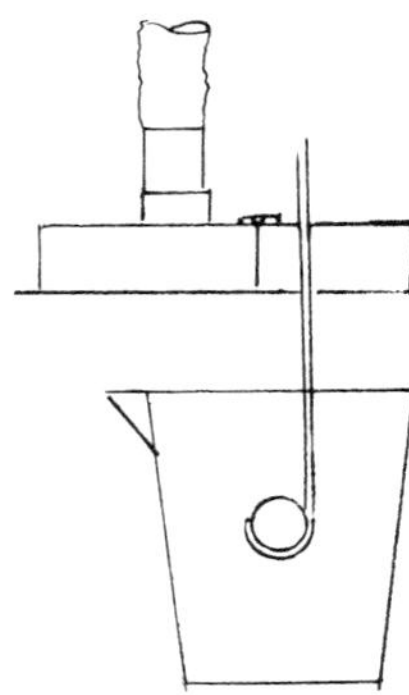

Fig. 2-31. Local hood for ladle.

exhaust shoe connected to an exhaust plenum paralleling the hot metal transfer ladles for all or part of the cycle.

Local exhaust hoods are also applicable at skimming stations; ladle covers will reduce fume release during transfer from furnace to mold pouring line. Permanent side draft exhaust hoods are applicable where molds can be

[6] John M. Kane. "Scrapbook of Exhaust Hood Designs," *Heating and Ventilating*, February, 1951.

poured within a fixed conveyor length—an exhaust mechanism that is frequently installed in ferrous foundry practice.

Hoods for Surface Treatment Operations

Many surface treatment operations like degreasing, pickling, electropolishing, etching, electro-plating, and stripping involve open tank-type equipment from which gases, vapors, and mists are released, often from hot solutions. Where contaminant is not hazardous, and material handling permits, the canopy hood is frequently selected, especially where hot materials are involved, producing an upward, thermal-stack type of release.

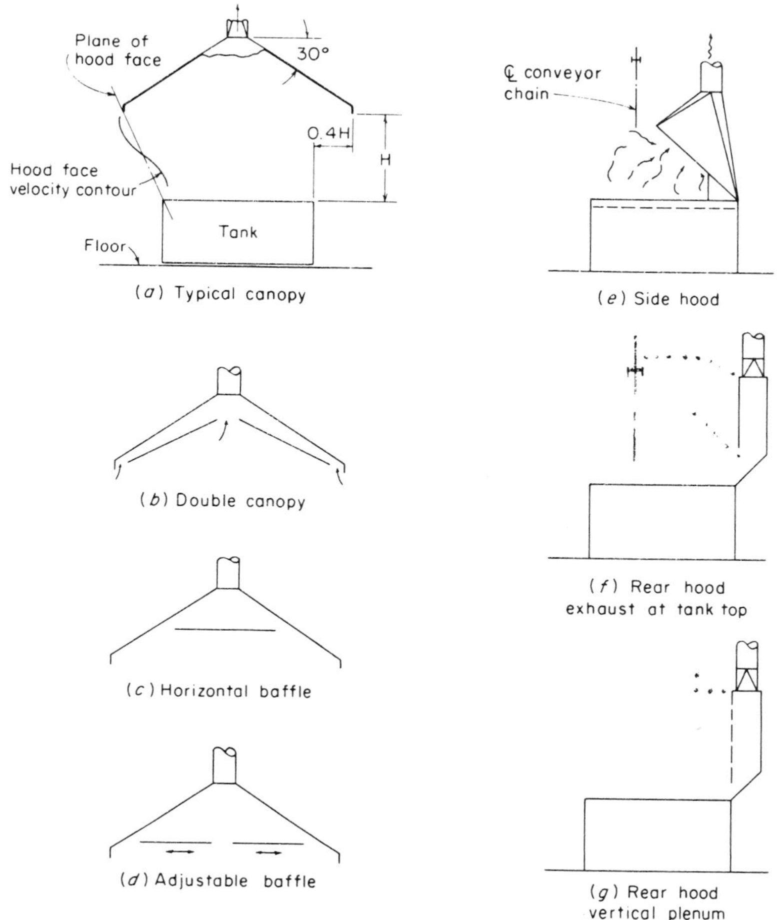

Fig. 2-32. Hoods for surface treatment.

Historical hood dimensions in relation to surface area of the operation are shown in Fig. 2-32a.

Double hoods (Fig. 2-32b) or horizontal baffles (Figs. 2-32c and d) produce better distribution over the perimeter of the hood. Velocities in the slots are in the 1,000 to 2,000 fpm range. Baffles will not eliminate "spill" where induced airflow caused by thermal effects exceeds the exhaust capacity of the connecting pipe. Adjustable baffles (Fig. 2-32d) do permit some compensation for cross drafts where direction can be predicted, by concentrating exhaust volume downwind.

Because performance from such hoods is disturbed by cross drafts and the

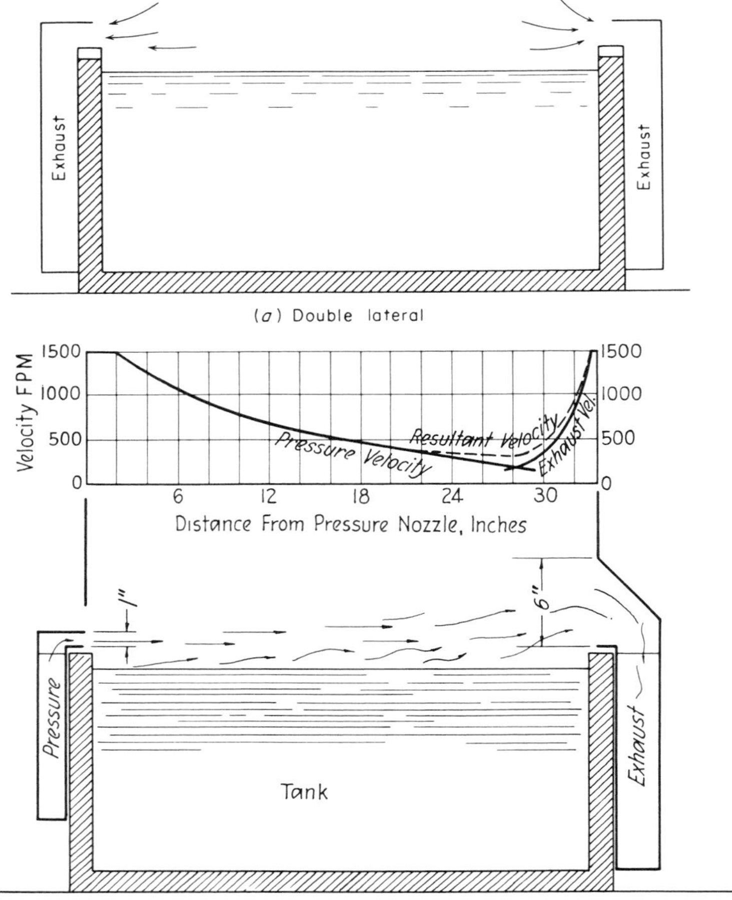

Fig. 2-33. Lateral hoods.

open area between process and hood is so great, the exhaust volume will be high compared to that when side shields are used.

The classic hood dimensions reported in Fig. 2-32a should be used with care. When distance *H* is moderate, possibly less than 5 feet, an indraft can be maintained that will prevent fume dispersion, and plan dimensions can approach those of the tank. An overhang can increase worker exposure if the worker is stationed near the perimeter of the tank.

For greater distances between tank and hood, the hood does become a gathering device to intercept the plume with the aspirated secondary volume induced by the thermal thrust of the hot surface. See discussion in Chapter 12.

Material handling systems often compel other hooding methods because a canopy hood located high above the conveyor or crane supports would be ineffective. A side hood (Fig. 2-32e) or rear hood (Fig. 2-32f) will eliminate interference under those conditions. Where contaminant is released with product in a raised position for transfer or drainage, rear hood (Fig. 2-32g) can produce a more effective control pattern of exhaust airflow than the slot at the tank top (Fig. 2-32f). Velocities in the 1,500 to 2,500 fpm range will provide reasonable distribution over the hood length.

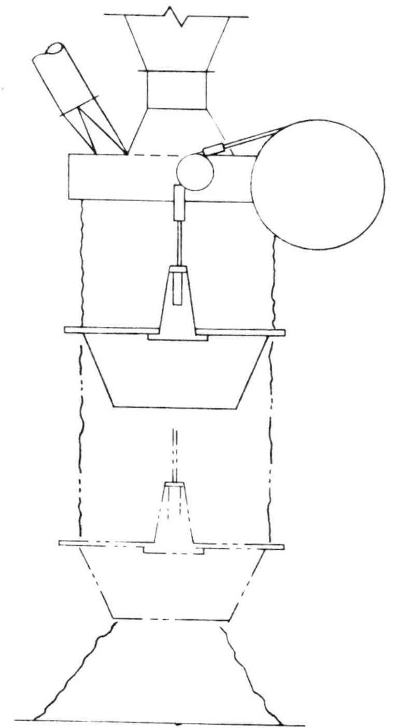

Fig. 2-34. Bulk loading exhaust. By permission Midwest Division, Ron Par Enterprises, Inc.

Often a compromise between the side hood, Fig. 2-32e, and the rear hood is possible. For many applications an extension from the rear hood is feasible and can be useful either to decrease exhaust volume or to increase effectiveness. See dotted extensions on Figs. 2-32f and g. Extension of the back wall and addition to the roof above the conveyor monorail is also a frequent option that could reduce exhaust requirements by one-fourth to one-third. See Fig. 2-32f.

The double lateral hood (Fig. 2-33a) is attractive to production personnel because there is no obstruction on either side of the operation. Control, however, is subject to disruptions from cross drafts and material handling. Area of minimum velocity contour is on the centerline between the two lateral hoods which is the area of maximum contaminant release.

The push–pull lateral hood, Fig. 2-33b, finds application also. See discussion in Chapter 3 and Fig. 3-5.

Hoods for Bulk Loading

Fugitive dust escapement during the bulk loading of dry dusty materials into a truck, rail car, barge, ship, or open or enclosed stockpile is a frequent source of public nuisance complaints.

In the loading of closed body trucks and rail cars, the body can be used as the enclosure, locating the exhaust connection at an unused loading door. The exhaust must be sufficient to maintain an indraft through the loading hatch and exhaust the entrained air volume. A similar approach has been taken in ship loading by the use of tarps to cover the hold opening. An exhaust hood is either incorporated with the loading boom mechanism or located separately, remote from the loading spout.

Where open body trucks are loaded, enclosing the truck in a booth or room-type enclosure is an option, although the exhaust volume needed to prevent dust escapement is substantial.

An interesting and effective application of local exhaust for the entire range of bulk loading operations is illustrated in Fig. 2-34. The loading spout diameter is large enough to serve as the exhaust duct. By keeping the spout located close to the top of the load, exhaust volumes in the 1,000–4,000 cfm range have proved effective.

CHAPTER 3

Local Exhaust Systems— Exhaust Volume Determinations

The air volume to be drawn through a hood can be computed only after the general shape and location of the hood are established. The minimum basis for the necessary assumptions is a free-hand sketch reasonably true to scale. The preparation of this sketch must take into account most of the factors treated in Chapter 2 and summarized in the following paragraphs.

Unnecessary air contamination should be eliminated at the source. Dust-dispersing air currents should be minimized or should be controlled by baffles or shields.

The hood should draw dusty air away from the operator and away from the breathing zone. Convection currents and other dust-dispersing agencies should be opposed by exhaust currents of greater intensity. The exhaust velocity at all points in the zone of dust generation must exceed the velocity of escape. Hoods handling large particles projected at high speeds must be so located that the material is thrown into the hood mouth. Open hoods similar to Figs. 2-4 and 2-5 should be shaped to conform to the area of dust generation and should be proportioned to produce flat velocity contours in this area. The face velocity should be the lowest consistent with the required velocity in the dusty area. Side flanges and baffles promote economy by reducing airflow from the rear of the hood and from other unimportant areas.

Fortunately, for many operations field research has established guidelines to usual exhaust volume requirements stated either in terms of capture velocity, indraft velocities, or mass air movement. Likewise, the comparison of an operation with a similar one where control values have been established will provide a check on exhaust volume design calculations for uncharted processes.

Capture Velocity

For small local hoods the capture velocity selected must be sufficient to immediately deflect the contaminant into the higher velocity contours closer to the hood face. Because the exhaust volume is low, there is no sustained air flow pattern beyond the immediate area, and normal room ventilation currents can disperse stray airborne material. Capture velocities in the range reported in Table 3-1 would apply. Plotting velocity contours as discussed in Chapter 2 is desirable.

Table 3-1. Indraft Velocities

Method of Generation	Usual, fpm	Typical Applications
Released without noticeable movement	50 to 100	Evaporation of vapors, exhaust from pickling, washing, de-greasing, plating, welding.
Released with low velocity	100 to 200	Paint spraying in booth; inspection, sorting, weighing, packaging; low-speed conveyor transfer points; rotating mixtures; barrel filling.
Active generation	200 to 500	Foundry shakeout; high-speed conveyor transfer points; crushers, screens.
Released with great force	500 to 2000 and higher	Grinding; tumbling mills; abrasive cleaning; metal working.

For larger downdraft, side, or overhead hoods the sizable exhaust volumes create a mass movement of air toward the exhaust area and tend to nullify the problems of stray room air patterns. Consequently, capture velocities can be much lower as the aerodynamic drag will slow the particle and redirect it toward the exhaust opening. See footnote 4, Chapter 2. For this group of applications velocity contour development has limited applicability. Selection of an adequate air movement based on cfm per square foot of plan area of contaminant generation is the more usual approach. Judgment factors do become involved, but for cold processes 150-250 cfm per square foot is the usual range. This range also applies to hot processes controlled by overhead hoods located reasonably close to the process. For side hood or downdraft control of contaminants generated from hot processes the likely range would be 300-600 cfm per square foot.

Indraft Velocity—Booths and Enclosures

For complete enclosures and for booth or tunnel hoods, selection of an indraft velocity sufficient to prevent contaminant escapement will be the first step in air volume determinations. The range of velocities reported in Table 3-1 were catalogued by early investigators and are still valid within certain parameters:

50 to 100 fpm is at the extreme lower range for booths or enclosures; 100 fpm is only slightly more than 1 mile per hour and control can be nullified by cross drafts, air supply grilles, etc.

Where operators work in a booth type of enclosure, maintenance of uniform air flow over the cross section is unlikely with flow rates in the 50-75-fpm range. Table 3-2 reports the variations measured in an 18 ft by 16 ft booth designed for 50 fpm indraft. At such low face velocities removal of contaminant is slow and air flow patterns are disrupted by movement of people and material as well as by spray gun jets, air tool exhausts, and the like. Consequently, the protection of persons working within the booth may be seriously impaired.

100 to 200 fpm is the usual range for most industrial operations housed in enclosures or booths, with the 150-200-fpm range predominating.

200 to 500 fpm is indicated in Table 3-1 for the typical processes listed. The higher velocities would likely be selected for enclosures with limited size access or inspection openings.

500 to 2000 fpm will be appropriate where air flow must counteract high velocity particulate trajectories such as local hoods for woodworking and metalworking; for air supply to abrasive blast rooms and tumbling mills.

Enclosures require a minimum exhaust volume to prevent localized pressures from producing dust escapement and to minimize housekeeping. A volume of five air changes a minute is a good starting point and can require the addition of strategically located air supply ports in enclosures with limited open area for access or inspection.

Table 3-2. Ventilation Traverse of 18 × 16 ft Spray Booth (Values in fpm)

25	70	75	50	40	30	20	60
25	80	80	55	50	40	20	50
30	80	75	50	60	50	10	60
20	70	80	50	50	50	10	55

Field Determination of Exhaust Volumes

In the solution of inplant and atmospheric air pollution problems, the use of field research can pay substantial dividends. The size and cost of a control system can be minimized and high costs for correction of an inadequate solution can be avoided.

The necessary hood-face velocities for local hood control in a specific situation may be determined experimentally by means of simple exploratory apparatus.

For larger sources, hood construction can be completed or a temporary mock-up made. A vaneaxial fan attached to the exhaust opening includes sufficient straight duct to measure air flow and a means of throttling. Such field studies will illustrate the control to be obtained for the hood construction selected and will reduce the usual factors of safety that are added to system capacity. Where larger volumes are involved and expensive air-cleaning equipment is to be procured, savings in exhaust-system cost will justify this extra research.

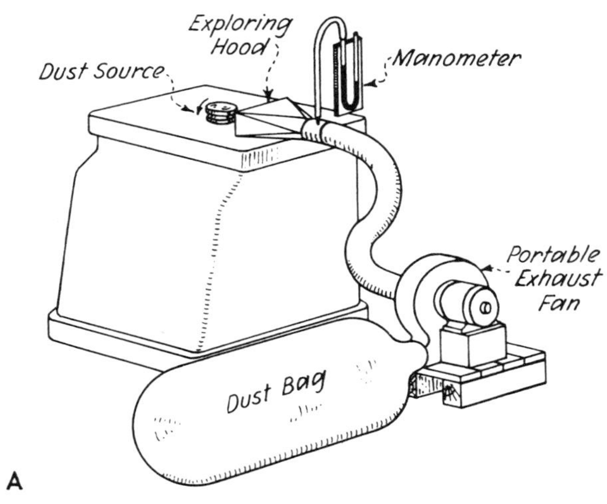

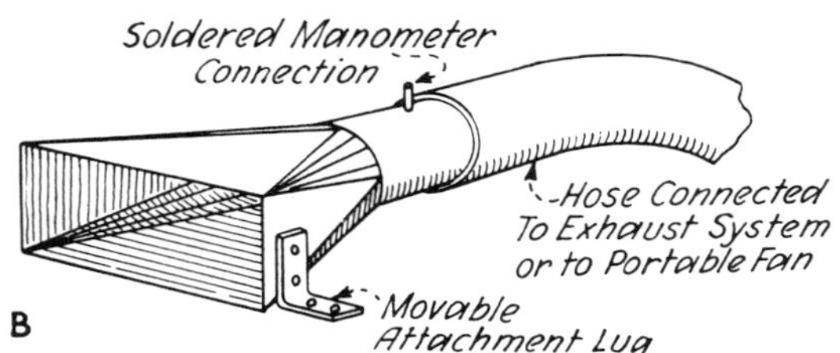

Fig. 3-1. Test assembly. (A) Portable exploratory apparatus; and (B) Calibrated exploring hood.

Full-scale try-out of small hoods or mockups also is advisable if many identical units are required. By this means, not only can over-engineering be avoided with its attendant expense, but equally important, practical refinements can be made which enhance convenience for the operator.

For local hoods a portable exploratory system, Fig. 3-1, is useful. Connected to a portable exhaust fan, hood dimensions and location can be determined. Volume can be calculated using a manometer and the hood suction estimate of velocity pressure. For the hood illustrated, the manometer reading would approximate 1.25 VP. A blast gate at the fan inlet or outlet will permit adjustment to the optimum volume.

For most applications, a paddle wheel centrifugal fan, 6 in. inlet diameter connected to 6 in. or smaller flexible hose would be a good selection, capacity 900 cfm at 4 in. SP. Air can be discharged into a cloth bag of 25 to 40 square feet or can be discharged to atmosphere if the location permits. Actually, discharged air could be directed toward the roof trusses without collection equipment for the short duration of the test program for many situations.

Figure 3-2 shows a similar field study with a large hood in a chemical process department that has a number of open tanks expelling fumes and vapors. The duct fan had a capacity for 8,000 cfm—the equivalent of 200 cfm per square foot of hood face. Field tests indicated an exhaust of 5,000 cfm as ample for the application.

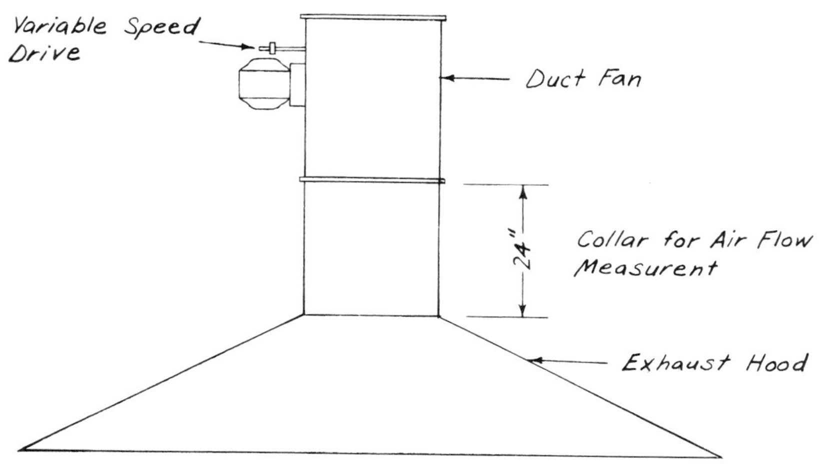

Fig. 3-2. Test overhead hood.

Figure 3-3[1] illustrates the use of field research to correct an ineffective exhaust system on a gray iron foundry squeezer line. The exhaust at the work stations from an existing downdraft exhaust plenum was inadequate.

[1] "Field Test before Purchase of Dust Control Systems," by J.M. Kane, *Plant Engineering*, September, 1970.

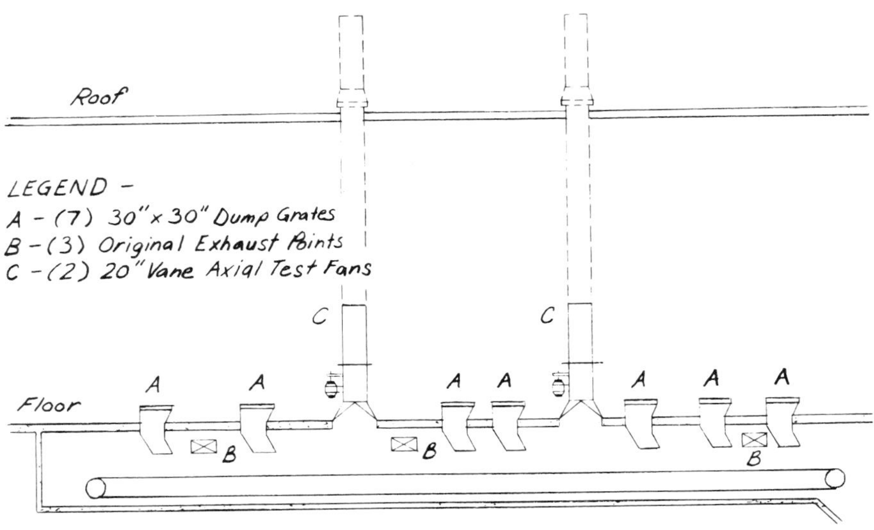

Fig. 3-3. Exhaust study. From John M. Kane, "Before Buying an Exhaust System, Test of Dust Control." PLANT ENGINEERING Magazine, September 17, 1970.

Two duct fans were "borrowed" from an adjacent pouring hood and connected through short stub stacks. The volume was adjusted to minimum effective values of 7,500 cfm at each takeoff. The study:

1. Eliminated a grievance and corrected poor dust control within 3 days.
2. Determined optimum exhaust volume before an expensive dust collector was purchased.
3. Provided a temporary solution short circuiting the long lead times involved to purchase, ship, and install permanent equipment.

Figure 3-4[2] provides another example of where field testing prevented an expensive and time delaying mistake. The thermal thrust from the hot escaping gases during cast iron chip melting in an electric arc furnace produced an in-plant problem from fume leakage through the joints in a movable exhaust enclosure roof in spite of an exhaust of 62,000 cfm. Escapement through an existing wall fan to the atmosphere also caused an external air pollution situation.

Before the purchase of air pollution control equipment, a second 65,000 cfm exhauster was connected to make 130,000 cfm available. Fume escapement into the plant continued because the increased exhaust volume was not enough to overcome the positive pressure under the roof. The study demonstrated that a solution would require either

[2] *Ibid.*

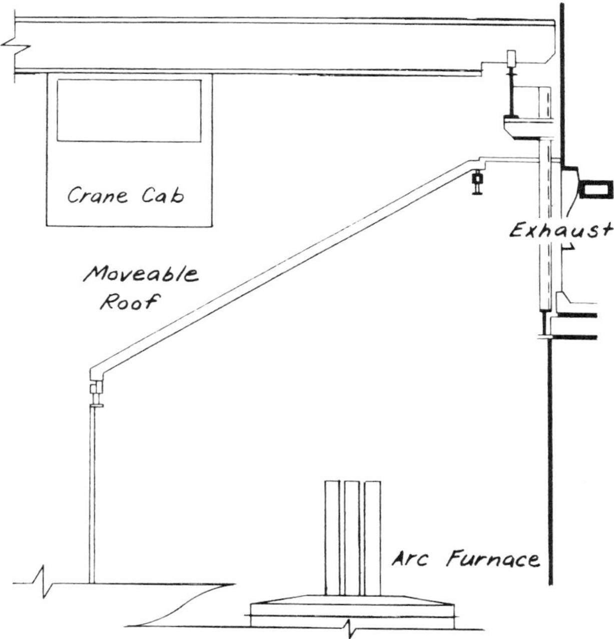

Fig. 3-4. Thermal thrust study. From John M. Kane, "Before Buying an Exhaust System, Test of Dust Control," PLANT ENGINEERING Magazine, September 17, 1970.

(a) a substantial additional increase in exhaust with comparable increase in air pollution control equipment cost and makeup air needs;

(b) the development of a dust-tight roof construction to prevent leakage of fume to the in-plant area; or

(c) to restrict air inlet openings at the working and inspection stations so that the orifice loss from the indraft velocity would be sufficient to offset the positive pressure developed from the thermal thrust, and keep the pressure within the enclosure negative.

Hood modifications to accomplish the conditions described in Item (c) were developed and leakage through the roof joints was eliminated with an exhaust volume of 120,000 cfm.

Usual Exhaust Volumes for Typical Operations

Table 3-3 gives usual exhaust volumes for a wide range of industrial operations with recommended conveying velocities for average conditions. A more detailed discussion for a number of the operations listed follows.

Woodworking. The usual exhaust volumes for woodworking operations are shown in Table 3-4A. Branch duct sizes reported are based on 4,000 fpm

Table 3-3. Usual Exhaust Volumes and Conveying Velocities for Dust-Producing Equipment

Dust-Producing Equipment	Exhaust Hood	Exhaust Requirements	Conveying Velocities, fpm Branch	Conveying Velocities, fpm Main	References and Notes
Abrasive blast rooms (sand, grit, or shot)	Tight enclosure with air inlets (usually in roof)	60 to 100 fpm downdraft (long rooms of tunnel proportions 100 fpm cross-draft)	3500	3500	Exhaust volume should be sufficient to provide visibility for operator. Sand as abrasive or castings with cores or heavy moulding sand deposits require highest range.
Abrasive blast cabinets	Tight enclosure with access openings	20 air changes per minute but not less than 500 fpm through all openings	3500	3500	AFS Code
Bagging machines	Booth or enclosure (provide spillage hopper)	Paper bags—100 cfm per sq ft open area Cloth bags—200 cfm per sq ft open area	3500	3500	New York Code 34 for silica dust in stone-crushing operations
Barrels (for filling or removing material)	Local hood 120F around top of barrel	Through 24 in. dia.—4 in. branch Over 24 in. dia.—5 in. branch	3500	3500	
Belt conveyors	Hoods at transfer point	Belt speeds less than 200 fpm—350 cfm per foot of belt width, but not less than 150 fpm through open area. Belt speeds over 200 fpm—500 cfm per foot of belt width, but not less than 200 fpm through open area	3500	3500	"Foundry Dust Control," *The Foundry*, January 1938.
Belt wipers (may be required with high-speed belts)	Tight-fitting hood held against underside of belt	200 cfm per foot of belt width	3500	3500	Requires high hood suction and high conveying velocities. Mechanical brushing or wiping often used in conjunction with hood.

Bins (closed bin top)	Connect to bin top away from feed point	150 to 200 fpm through open area at feed points.	3500	3500	
Bucket elevators	Tight casing required	100 cfm per sq ft of elevator casing cross section. (Exhaust from elevator head)	3500	3500	To maintain indraft in casing only. Additional exhaust at elevator boot and discharge unless tight connections are employed.
Ceramics Dry Pan Dry Press	Local Hoods	See Mixers Automatic feed, 1-5 in. dia. branch at die Manual feed, 1-5 in. dia. branch at supply bin; 1-5 in. dia. branch at die	3500 3000	3500 3000	
Fettling, brushing, sagger filling and unloading	Downdraft or side hood	100 to 150 cfm per sq ft of plan area of dust producing operation	3500	3500	
Grinders Polishing, buffing, etc.	Standard wheel hood	See Table 3-3B	4500	3500	
Grinders swing frame	Booth	100 to 150 fpm indraft through opening in booth face	3000	3000	"Swing-Frame Grinder Dust Control," *The Foundry*, August 1944.
Grinders Portable and flexible shaft	Downdraft grilles. Use side shields where possible	Bench type, 200 to 400 cfm per sq ft of exhaust grille but not less than 150 cfm per sq ft of plan working area Floor grille, 200 to 400 cfm per sq ft of exhaust grille but not less than 100 cfm per sq ft of plan working area	3500 3500	3500 3500	

Table 3-3 (Continued). Usual Exhaust Volumes and Conveying Velocities for Dust-Producing Equipment

Dust-Producing Equipment	Exhaust Hood	Exhaust Requirements	Conveying Velocities, fpm Branch	Conveying Velocities, fpm Main	References and Notes
Tumbling Mills Hollow trunnion type	Exhaust connection by manufacturer	Use branch diameter same size as exhaust outlet. For round mills branch dia. should be 1/6 dia. of mill; for square mills, branch dia. should be 1 in. plus 1/6 side dimension of mill	5000	4000	
Mixer	Enclosure	100 to 200 fpm through working and inspection openings	3500	3500	Where mixer causes pronounced agitation, use indraft velocities in the higher range listed
Pharmaceuticals Coating pans	Narrow side hood	Through 16 in. dia. opening—200 cfm Over 16 in. dia. through 22 in.—300 cfm Over 22 in. dia. through 26 in.—400 cfm	3000	3000	Assumes no heated air supplied to coating pan. Increase exhaust volume by cfm of heated air where supplied
Shakeouts Foundry—Vibrating deck	Enclosure	200 fpm through all openings in enclosure, but not less than 200 cfm per sq ft of grate area	3500	3500	
	Side Hood (use side shields whenever possible)	400 to 600 cfm per sq ft of shakeout grate area	3500	3500	

Screens Vibrating, Flat deck	Enclosure	150 to 200 fpm indraft through hood openings, but not less than 25 to 50 cfm per sq ft of screen area	3500	3500	Use single deck area where screen has two or more decks
Cylindrical	Enclosure	100 cfm per sq ft of circular cross section but not less than 400 fpm indraft through openings in enclosure	3500	3500	Table 3-4
Spraying	Booth	125–200 fpm for small booths 100–150 fpm for usual spray booth	500 2500	1500 2500	For very large booths or airless spraying; see text.
Woodworking		See Table 3-4A	4000	3500	
Miscellaneous Packaging machines, granulators, enclosed dust-producing units	Complete enclosure	100 to 400 fpm indraft through inspection or working openings, but not less than 25 cfm per sq ft of enclosed plan area	3000	3000	Volume will normally be insufficient to prevent dust settling on floor and equipment within enclosure
Packaging, weighing, container filling, inspection	Booth	50 to 150 cfm per sq ft of open face area	3000	3000	
	Downdraft	75 to 150 cfm per sq ft of dust-producing plan area	3500	3500	

Table 3-4. Usual Branch Sizes and Exhaust Volumes

Machine	Size		Branch Pipe No.	Branch Pipe Dia, In.	cfm
A—Woodworking Machinery—4,000 fpm, Branch Velocity					
Single Planers	Knife Length, Inches	Up to 20	1	6	790
		Over 20 to 26	1	7	1,070
		Over 26 to 36	1	8	1,400
		Over 32 to 38	1	9	1,770
		Over 38	1	10	2,180
Double Planers	Knife Length, Inches	To 20, Top head	1	6	790
		To 20, Bottom head	1	5	550
		20 to 26, Top head	1	7	1,070
		20 to 26, Bottom head	1	6	790
		26 to 32, Top head	1	8	1,400
		26 to 32, Bottom head	1	7	1,070
		32 to 38, Top head	1	9	1,770
		32 to 38, Bottom head	1	8	1,400
		Over 38, Top head	1	10	2,180
		Over 38, Bottom head	1	8	1,400
Single Drum Sanders	Surface, Sq. In.	Up to 200 sq in. surface and 10 in. dia	1	4	350
		Under 400 sq in. surface, over 10 in. dia	1	5	550
		Over 400 to 700	1	6	790
		Over 700 to 1,400	1	7	1,070
		Over 1,400 to 2,400	1	8	1,400
Spindle Sanders		. . .	1	3	200
Triple Drum	Drum Length, In.	Up to 30, each roll	1	6	790
		Over 30 to 42, each roll	1	7	1,070
		Over 42 to 48, each roll	1	8	1,400
		Over 48 to 60, each roll	1	10	2,180
		Brush roll	1	5	550
Horizontal Belt Sanders	Width, Inches	Up to 6, Top	1	4	350
		Up to 6, Bottom	1	4	350
		Over 6 to 9, Top	1	4	350
		Over 6 to 9, Bottom	1	4-1/2	440
		Over 9 to 14, Top	1	4-1/2	440
		Over 9 to 14, Bottom	1	5	550
		Over 14, Top	1	5	550
		Over 14, Bottom	1	7	1,070
Vertical Belt Sanders	Width, Inches	Up to 6	1	4-1/2	440
		Over 6 to 9	1	5	550
		Over 9 to 14	1	6	790
		Over 14	1	7	1,070
Arm Sanders		. . .	1	4-1/2	440

Table 3-4 (Continued). Usual Branch Sizes and Exhaust Volumes

A—Woodworking Machinery—4,000 fpm, Branch Velocity					
Machine	Size		Branch Pipe		cfm
			No.	Dia, In.	
Disc Sanders	Diameter, Inches	Up to 12 Over 12 to 18 Over 18 to 26 Over 26 to 32 Over 32 to 38 Over 38 to 48	1 1 1 2 2 3	4 4-1/2 5 4 4-1/2 4-1/2	350 440 550 700 880 1,320
Rip, Table, Mitre, Cut-Off and Variety Saws	Diameter, Inches	Up to 16 Over 16 to 24 Over 24	1 1 1	4 4-1/2 5	350 440 550
Variety Saw with Dado Head	Diameter, Inches	. . .	1	5	550
Swing Saws	Diameter, Inches	Up to 20 Over 20	1 1	4 4-1/2	350 440
Self-Feed Table Saws	Diameter, Inches	Up to 16 Over 16	2 2	4-1/2 & 4 5 & 4	790 900
Self-Feed Rip Saw, Wet Lumber	Diameter, Inches	Over 24	2	6 & 5	1,340
Gang Rip Saws	Diameter, Inches	Up to 24 Over 24 to 36 Over 36 to 48 Over 48	2 2 2 2	5 & 4 6 & 4-1/2 7 & 5 8 & 5-1/2	900 1,230 1,620 2,060
Band Saws	Blade Width, In.	Up to 2 Over 2 to 3 Over 3 to 4 Over 4 to 6 (Resaw) Over 6 to 8 (Resaw)	1 1* 1* 2 2	4 5 6 7 & 5 8 & 5	350 550 790 1,620 1,950
Jig Saws		. . .	1	4	350
Sash Stickers		Each head	1	5	550
Hogs		Up to 12 Over 12	1 1	8 12	1,400 3,100
Floor Sweeps			1	6 to 8	790 to 1,400

*Sometimes equipped with 3-1/2- or 4-in. pipe on up-run side of blade at lower wheel.

Table 3-4 (Continued). Usual Branch Sizes and Exhaust Volumes

Machine	Size		Branch Pipe No.	Branch Pipe Dia, In.	cfm
A—Woodworking Machinery—4,000 fpm, Branch Velocity					
Jointers	Knife Length, Inches	Up to 6	1	4	350
		Over 6 to 12	1	4-1/2	440
		Over 12 to 20	1	5	550
		Over 20	1	6	790
Moulders, Matchers, Tenoner, and Sizers		Up to 7, Top head	1	5	550
		Up to 7, Bottom head	1	4-1/2	440
		Up to 7, Side head	2	4	700
		Over 7 to 12,			
		Top head	1	6	790
		Bottom head	1	5	550
		Side head	2	4-1/2	880
		Over 12 to 18,			
		Top head	1	7	1,070
		Bottom head	1	6	790
		Side head	2	5	1,100
		Over 18 to 24,			
		Top head	1	8	1,400
		Bottom head	1	7	1,070
		Side head	2	6	1,580
		Over 24, Top head	1	9	1,770
		Over 24, Bottom head	1	8	1,400
		Over 24, Side head	2	7	2,140

Type of Abrasive	Size: Diameter, Inches	Size: Thickness, Inches, Not Over	Branch Pipe No.	Branch Pipe Dia, In.	cfm
B—Abrasive Wheels, Discs, and Belts—4,500 fpm, Branch Velocity					
Grinding or Abrasive Cutting-Off Wheels‡ (6500 sfm and under)	Up to 10	1-1/2	1	3	220
	Over 10 to 14	2	1	3-1/2	300
	Over 14 to 16	2	1	4	390
	Over 16 to 20	3	1	4-1/2	500
	Over 20 to 24	4	1	5	610
	Over 24 to 30	5	1	6	880
Grinding or Abrasive Cutting-Off Wheels‡ (Over 6500 sfm)	Up to 10	1-1/2	1	4	390
	Over 10 to 14	2	1	4-1/2	500
	Over 14 to 16	2	1	5	610
	Over 16 to 20	3	1	5-1/2	740
	Over 20 to 24	4	1	6	880
	Over 24 to 30	5	1	7	1,200
Buffing, Polishing, and Scratch Brushing Wheels‡	Up to 9	2	1	3-1/2	300
	Over 9 to 16	3	1	4-1/2	500
	Over 16 to 19	4	1	5	610
	Over 19 to 24	5	1	5-1/2	740
	Over 24 to 30	6	1	6-1/2	1,040

Table 3-4 (Continued). Usual Branch Sizes and Exhaust Volumes

B—Abrasive Wheels, Discs, and Belts—4,500 fpm, Branch Velocity					
Type of Abrasive	Size		Branch Pipe		cfm
	Diameter, Inches	Thickness, Inches, Not Over	No.	Dia, In.	
Horizontal Single Spindle Disc Grinders	Up to 19	...	1	4	390
	Over 19 to 30	...	1	5	610
	Over 30 to 36	...	1	6	880
Horizontal Double Spindle Disc Grinders	Up to 19	...	1	5	610
	Over 19 to 25	...	1	6	880
	Over 25 to 30	...	1	7	1,200
	Over 30 to 53	...	2	6	1,760
	Over 53 to 72	...	4	8	6,280
Vertical Single Spindle Disc Grinders Where top of disc is covered not less than half.	Up to 20	...	1	4-1/2	500
	Over 20 to 30	...	2	4	780
	Over 30 to 53	...	2	6	1,760
	Over 53 to 72	...	2	8	3,140
Vertical Single Spindle Disc Grinders Where top of disc is uncovered.	Up to 20	...	2	4	780
	Over 20 to 30	...	2	5-1/2	1,480
	Over 30 to 53	...	4	6	3,520
	Over 53 to 72		5	7	6,000
Belts and Abrasive Straps	Up to 2	...	1	4	390
	Over 2 to 5	...	1	4-1/2	500
	Over 5 to 8	...	1	5	610
	Over 8	...	1	5-1/2	740

‡For each inch increase in wheel width over values listed, increase diameter of branch pipe 0.3 in. to next larger 1/2 in.

conveying velocities, a value established many years ago to meet the then existing state codes requiring a 2 in. hood suction. The usual 3,500 fpm velocities used in main ducts should be equally acceptable for branch ducts if hood outlets provided by the machinery manufacturer are of sufficient size or can be modified.

Grinding, Polishing, Etc.

The usual exhaust volumes for grinding, polishing, scratch brushing, and related operations are shown in Table 3-4B. Usual good hood enclosures have been assumed.

Table 3-5. Ventilation Rates for Open-Surface Tanks

Process	Minimum Ventilation Rate cfm per sq ft Hood Opening				Minimum Ventilation Rate cfm per sq ft Tank Area Lateral Exhaust (Note) $W/L = \frac{\text{Tank Width}}{\text{Tank Length}}$ Ratio					
	Enclosing Hood		Canopy Hood		W/L 00-.24		W/L 0.25-0.49		W/L 0.50-1.0	
	Open Sides									
	One	Two	Three	Four	A	B	A	B	A	B
Plating										
Chromium (Chromic Acid Mist)	75	100	125	175	125	175	150	200	175	225
Arsenic (Arsine)	65	90	100	150	90	130	110	150	130	170
Hydrogen Cyanide	75	100	125	175	125	175	150	200	175	225
Cadmium	75	100	125	175	125	175	150	200	175	225
Anodizing	75	100	125	175	125	175	150	200	175	225
Metal Cleaning (Pickling)										
Cold Acid	65	90	100	150	90	130	110	150	130	170
Hot Acid	75	100	125	175	125	175	150	200	175	225
Nitric and Sulfuric Acid	75	100	125	175	125	175	150	200	175	225
Nitric and Hydrofluoric Acid	75	100	125	175	125	175	150	200	175	225
Metal Cleaning (Degreasing)										
Trichloroethylene	75	100	125	175	125	175	150	200	175	225
Ethylene Dichloride	75	100	125	175	125	175	150	200	175	225
Carbon Tetrachloride	75	100	125	175	125	175	150	200	175	225
Metal Cleaning (Caustic or Electrolytic)										
Not Boiling	65	90	100	150	90	130	110	150	130	170
Boiling	75	100	125	175	125	175	150	200	175	225
Bright Dip (Nitric Acid)	75	100	125	175	125	175	150	200	175	225
Stripping										
Concentrated Nitric Acid	75	100	125	175	125	175	150	200	175	225
Conc. Nitric and Sulfuric Acid	75	100	125	175	125	175	150	200	175	225
Salt Baths (Molten Salt)	50	75	75	125	60	90	75	100	90	110
Salt Solution (Parkerize, Bonderize, etc.)										
Not Boiling	90	90	100	150	90	130	110	150	130	170
Boiling	75	100	125	175	125	175	150	200	175	225
Hot Water (if vent. desired)										
Not Boiling	50	75	75	125	60	90	75	100	90	110
Boiling	75	100	125	175	125	175	150	200	175	225

NOTE—Column A refers to tank with hoods along one side, or two parallel sides, when one hood is against a wall or a baffle running length of tank and as high as tank is wide; also to tanks with exhaust manifold along center line with W/Z becoming tank width in W/L ratio. Column B refers to free-standing tank with hood along one side or two parallel sides.

Abrasive grinding exhaust recommendations are shown for two categories: those below 6,500 sfm (surface speed in fpm), which is about the maximum speed that parts being finished can be held by hand; and above 6,500 sfm where the hood must incorporate a rest to support the part. With very high surface speeds, such as 12,500 sfm, the fan action of the wheel can upset exhaust air flow patterns and in the case of ferrous parts cast in silica sand molds, the local exhaust may require supplemental ventilation or isolation to prevent concentrations embedded in the casting surfaces from causing excessive worker exposure to airborne silica concentrations.

Branch pipe sizes shown are based on 4,500 fpm conveying velocity, a value established many years ago to meet the then existing state codes requiring a 2 in. hood suction. Since such regulations have been superceded by exhaust volume values, the usual 3,500 fpm velocities used in main ducts are equally acceptable for branches, resulting in a measurable energy savings. Unfortunately, most manufacturers provide combination wheel guards and hood with outlets sized for the 4,500 fpm velocity. With the heavy construction involved, increasing the size of the outlet can be difficult. Energy savings can still be realized by expanding the branch diameter to at least reduce friction losses.

Standards for small diameter wheels permit exhaust volumes as low as 300 cfm. However, the high duct resistance of a 3 or 3½ in. pipe suggests increasing the branch and exhaust volume to that of a 4 in. or larger pipe for lower system pressure losses and better balance where a number of larger diameter branches are connected to the same system.

Belt sanders are used for a variety of operations including sanding of horizontal, vertical, and peripheral surfaces. The influence of belt width on exhaust volumes shows little correlation when compared to similar influences of grinding or buffing wheel widths.

Recommendations are based on an analysis of the variations reported in various texts. The exhaust of belt sanders in the woodworking industry, see Table 3-4A, includes an exhaust at the tail pulley as well as at the head pulley. While similar practice does not appear usual in the metalworking applications, the need for such a second exhaust point deserves evaluation, especially when aluminum, magnesium, and other low flash point dusts are generated.

Open Surface Tanks

Table 3-5 is a condensation of an elaborate ASA Code, Z-9.1, published in 1951 and adopted by the National Consensus Standards program of OSHA in 1971. Air volumes have been adjusted for exhaust hooding and, in the case of lateral exhaust hoods, on the aspect ratio of tank width to length. In spite of four categories of hazard potential, there is only a slight difference in the exhaust rate, as can be noted from inspection of the various operations listed in Table 3-5.

For wide tanks, improved control of vapors has been reported by combining the long range of a pressure jet with an opposing exhaust hood. This constitutes the blow-and-exhaust or "push-pull" system, where clean air blows from the pressure hood across the liquid surface to the exhaust hood. Both hoods extend the full length of the tank. Additional exhaust openings at the end of the tank may aid in preventing escape of vapors.

Figure 3-5 gives data for sizing the pressure slot and the exhaust hood as well as a method for calculating the air supply volume.

A major factor not included in the evaluation is the influence of tank size and number of tanks involved. The larger the exhaust volume moved from

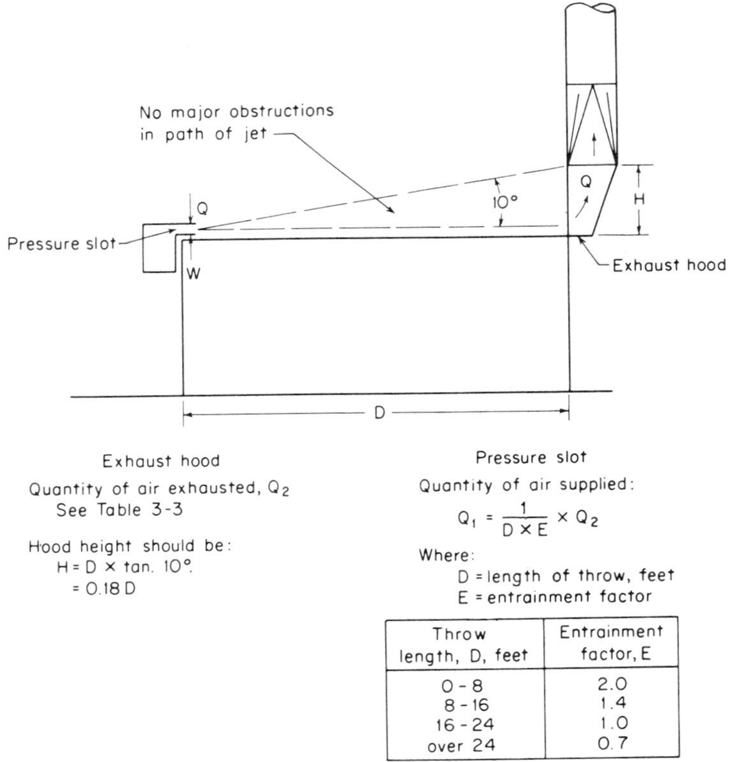

Throw length, D, feet	Entrainment factor, E
0 - 8	2.0
8 - 16	1.4
16 - 24	1.0
over 24	0.7

Fig. 3-5 Push-pull hoods. By permission from ACGIH, *Industrial Ventilation Manual* (January 1968), and "Practical Pointers on Industrial Exhaust Systems," by Benjamin S. Malin, *Heating and Ventilation* (February 1943), pp. 42, 75.

an area, the lower the unit volume per square foot of tank surface need be. Likewise, a concentration of tanks against a plant wall superimposes an overriding side hood effect from the flow of supply air toward the exhaust demand of the hoods.

For new installations and in the absence of paralleling field experience, use of the exhaust volumes listed is advisable. Capital costs of oversized systems are not great unless scrubbers are included, and the absence of solids permits throttling to lower volumes without concern for settling within the duct system.

Spray Booths

For booths where the operator is positioned at or near the booth face, indraft velocities of from 125 to 200 fpm are usual. The higher flow rates apply to smaller booths, possibly those which are less than 10 square feet in cross section. Lower ranges can be used for airless spraying because of the reduced amount of aeration and reduced quantities of over-spray.

For large walk-in booths, large objects will reduce the net cross section and permit lower volumes calculated on the total booth cross section. Such lower volumes can prove marginal if small parts are also processed. See Table 3-3.

CHAPTER 4

Air Flow Through Hoods

After the exhaust volume has been determined and the exhaust hood has been designed, the static pressure that must be developed to maintain the flow of air through the exhaust hood to the connecting branch can be calculated.

Air Volume Entering Hood

The volume rate of flow into a hood can be computed from the pipe size, static suction, and a factor which may be termed the coefficient of entry. The coefficient of entry, C_e, may be defined as the ratio of the actual flow to the theoretical as computed from the base flow formula:

$$v = \sqrt{2gH}$$

The volume entering the branch is:

$$Q = C_e AV$$

where:

Q = volume rate of flow, cfm
A = area of branch pipe, sq ft
V = velocity corresponding to static pressure in pipe if completely converted to velocity pressure, fpm.

When the static section is measured in inches of water:

$$V = 60\sqrt{\frac{2gWh}{12w}} = 4005\sqrt{h}$$

where:

W = weight of 1.0 cu ft of water at 70F = 63.32 lb,
g = acceleration due to gravity = 32.17 ft per sec^2,
h = static pressure in pipe, in. water,
w = density of standard air = 0.075 lb per cu ft

The volume entering the branch then becomes

$$Q = 4005\, C_e A\sqrt{h}$$

from which the nomogram in Fig. 4-1 has been constructed.

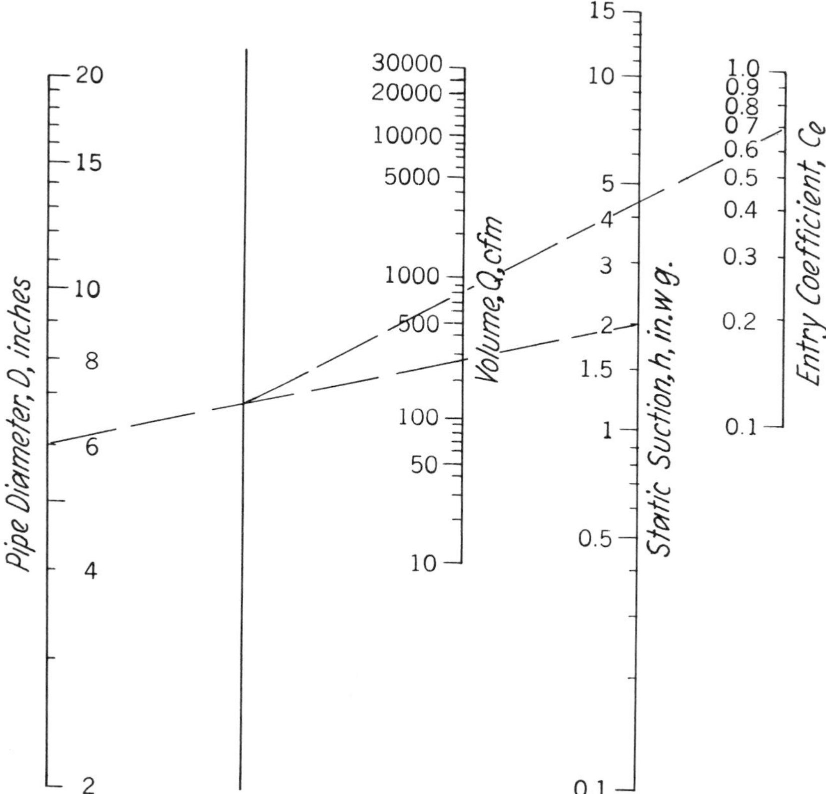

Fig. 4-1. Nomogram for determination of air flow into suction pipes.

The relation between the entry loss and the coefficient of entry is:

$$h_L = \frac{1 - C_e^2}{C_e^2} h_v. \quad \text{or}$$

$$C_e = \sqrt{\frac{h_v}{h_v + h_L}}$$

Coefficient of Entry

The physical significance of the coefficient of entry is worthy of brief consideration. In Fig. 4-2 is shown a thin-walled sheet metal box under suction into which air flows from the atmosphere through a round hole in one wall. The outer filaments of the entering stream curve inwardly at the plane of the orifice and maintain their convergence for some distance downstream. Consequently, the diameter of the jet a short distance within

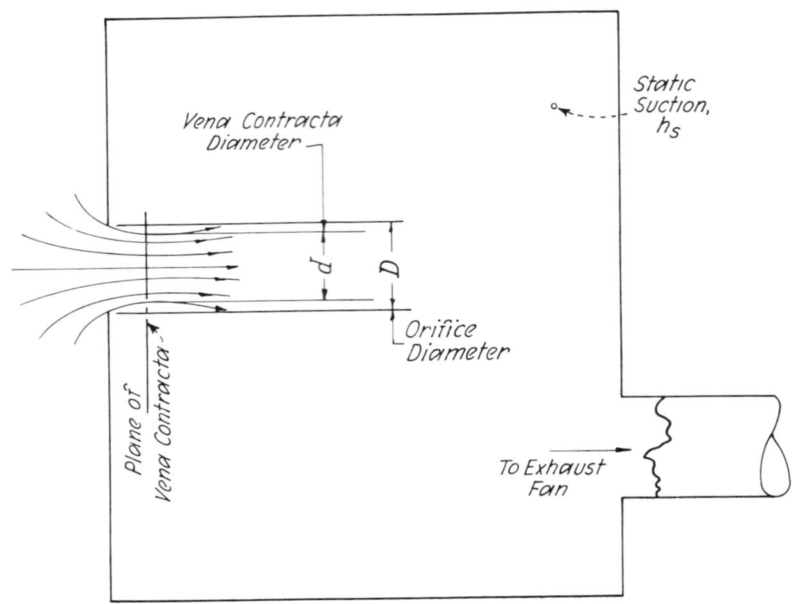

Fig. 4-2. Flow through elementary thin-plate orifice.

the box is somewhat smaller than the diameter of the orifice through which it entered. The plane in which the jet has parallel boundaries locates the "vena contracta" or region of smallest jet diameter.

The velocity at the vena contracta is very nearly that to be expected from theoretically perfect conversion of pressure to velocity. Since this velocity is present only over the reduced area of the vena contracta, it is evident that the velocity in the plane of the orifice will be lower in inverse proportion to the areas. The vena contracta velocity is about 97½% of that calculated from the expression $V = 4005\sqrt{h}$ and the vena contracta area is found to be about 62% of that of the thin plate orifice. The flow through the orifice, then, is:

$$Q = 0.975 \times 0.62 \times 4005\, A \sqrt{h}$$

where A is the orifice area and h is the pressure in the box. For thin-plate orifices, the coefficient of entry is about 0.60.

The coefficient of entry is identical in value with the coefficient of discharge for the same form of orifice or nozzle. In both cases, of course, flow takes place in the direction of pressure drop. The term "coefficient of entry" is more descriptive of flow conditions at suction hoods and will be used, therefore, in preference to the more common hydraulic designation.

Typical Orifices and Nozzles

In Fig. 4-3 are arranged the more common forms of orifice. The thin plate orifice just described is shown in its more customary form at *g*. The outline of the jet and the vena contracta are indicated by the flow lines. If the jet be confined within solid boundaries conforming to its free shape, the orifice becomes the well-rounded nozzle illustrated at *a*. In this form the jet does not leave the pipe wall and the diameter of what would otherwise be the vena contracta now becomes the pipe diameter. Straighten the smooth-flowing curved lines of the well-rounded nozzle and we have the flanged cone inlet at *b*. Contract the conical side and the flanged pipe, *c*, results. The unflanged cone, *d*, is a less refined form of *b*. Likewise, the loss of the flange from *c* produces the plain pipe inlet, *e*.

Even without supporting experimental facts, intuition would tell us that the bell-mouthed orifice, *a*, would have a coefficient approaching unity since the jet conforms to its solid envelope and no vena contracta is formed. In the flanged cone inlet, *b*, a small vena contracta is formed at the junction of the flange and the cone. A second contraction occurs where the cone joins the pipe. These combine to reduce the flow somewhat so that a lower coefficient is to be expected.

Because of the more acute angle between flange and pipe in form *c*, the jet contraction is still greater, resulting in a still lower coefficient. The unflanged cone and the plain inlet pipe present still greater contractions and, therefore, progressively lower entry coefficients.

The coefficients of entry of orifices *a* to *e*, inclusive, have been based on the pipe area at the cylindrical section. Since *f*, *g*, and *h* constitute orifices discharging into large chambers, the coefficients are calculated from the area of the orifice proper. In each case the jet is heavily contracted. Type *f* differs from *c* in that the cylindrical pipe is too short to permit expansion of the jet and conversion of pressure. Its coefficient therefore becomes the same as that of the thin plate orifice, *g*. Contraction of the jet entering the short re-entrant pipe, *h*, sometimes called "Borda's mouthpiece," is greater than that of other forms such as *f* or *g*. Hence the coefficient of entry is lower.

Figure 4-4[1] lists the entry losses and coefficients for round and square inlets of the general forms of Fig. 4-3b and d, probably accurate to about ±5%. It will be seen that the losses are lowest and the coefficients highest when the included angle is in the neighborhood of 40 to 50°. At smaller angles the influence of the entrance contraction is dominant whereas at the higher angles, the contraction at the pipe mouth is the more important. The ratio of the area of the hood face to that of the pipe also affects the entry loss. The tabular values are reasonably valid for all ratios greater than 2:1. At lower ratios, however, the loss rapidly approaches that of an open-flanged pipe. The presence or absence of flanges appears to make little difference in the entry losses of tapered hoods although the effect on plain pipes is substantial.

[1] Figure 4-4 has been adapted from tests reported in "Energy Losses at Suction Hoods," by A. D. Brandt and R. J. Steffy. *ASHVE Transactions*, Vol. 52, Paper No. 1295 (1946), 205-236. The higher values of the coefficients have been reduced slightly.

SYMBOL	TYPE OF ORIFICE	DESCRIPTION	COEFFICIENT OF ENTRY, C_e	LOSS IN % OF VELOCITY HEAD, h_L
a	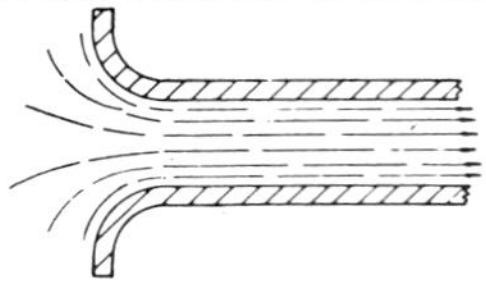	Smooth well rounded	0.98	4
b	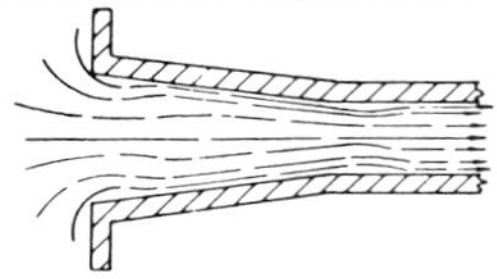	Flanged cone	See Fig. 4-6	
c	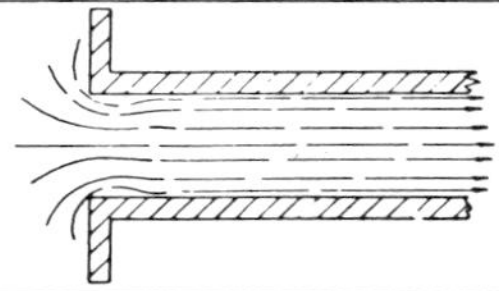	Flanged pipe	0.82	49
d	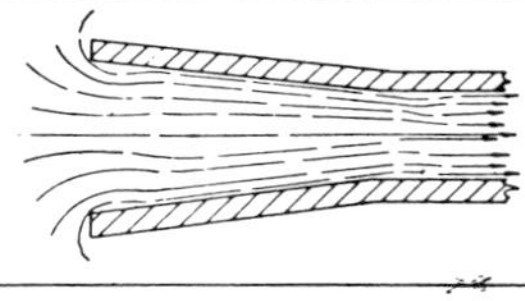	Unflanged cone	See Fig. 4-6	
e	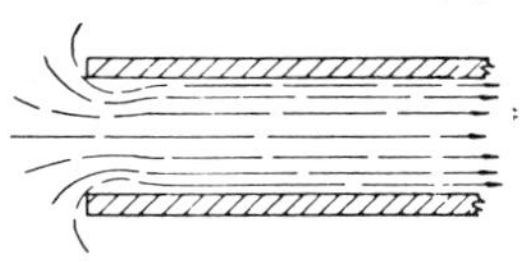	Unflanged pipe	0.72	93
f	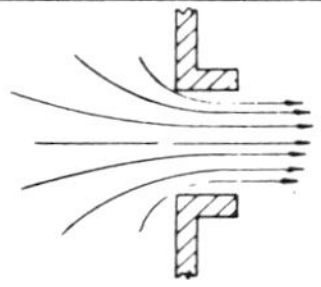	Short flanged pipe, less than 1½ diameters long	0.60	178
g	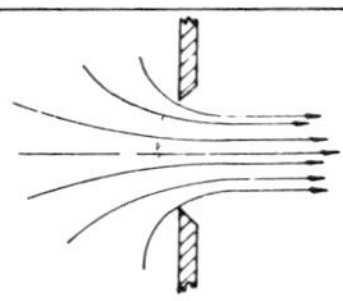	Thin-plate orifice	0.60	178
h	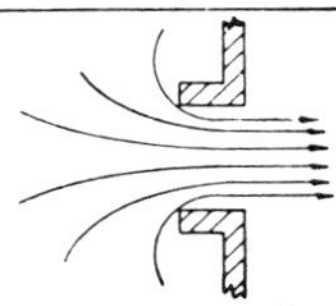	Short re-entrant pipe, less than 1½ diameters long	0.53	256

Fig. 4-3. Properties of orifices and nozzles.

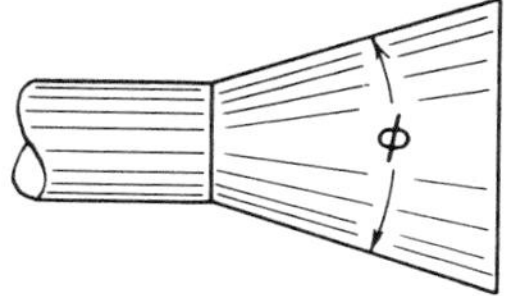

Face area at least 2× pipe area

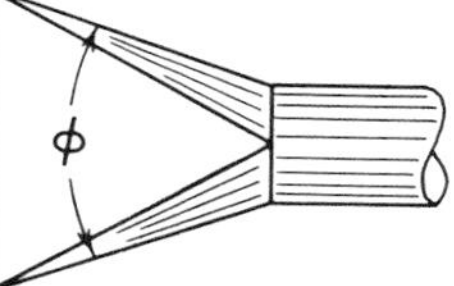

φ Incl. Angle, Degrees	Round Opening		Square and Rectangular Openings	
	h_e, Loss, Velocity Heads	C_e Coeff. of Entry	h_e, Loss, Velocity Heads	C_e Coeff. of Entry
0*	0.93	0.72	0.93	0.72
10	0.32	0.87	0.49	0.82
20	0.13	0.94	0.21	0.91
30	0.11	0.95	0.18	0.92
40	0.08	0.96	0.16	0.93
50	0.08	0.96	0.16	0.93
60	0.11	0.95	0.18	0.92
70	0.11	0.95	0.18	0.92
80	0.13	0.94	0.21	0.91
90	0.18	0.92	0.26	0.89
100	0.21	0.91	0.29	0.88
110	0.23	0.90	0.32	0.87
120	0.26	0.89	0.35	0.86
130	0.29	0.88	0.38	0.85
140	0.32	0.87	0.42	0.84
150	0.38	0.85	0.45	0.83
160	0.42	0.84	0.49	0.82
170	0.45	0.83	0.45	0.81
180†	0.49	0.82	0.56	0.80

* Unflanged pipe
† Flanged pipe

Fig. 4-4. Entry losses and coefficients of entry for tapered hoods.

As stated in Chapter 2, flanges have a marked influence on the velocity pattern in front of the hood opening and, therefore, on its ability to capture contaminants.

The loss at entry h_L, expressed in percentage of the velocity head, has been included in Fig. 4-4, and plotted separately in Fig. 4-5. This factor is useful when it is necessary to find the suction required to produce a given average velocity at the pipe mouth. The coefficient of entry, on the other hand, is convenient when the static suction is known and the pipe velocity is required.

Examples: Pipe form, *e*, Fig. 4-3.

$$C_e = 0.72$$
$$h_L = 0.93\,h_v$$

Given: average pipe velocity V = 4,000 fpm

$$h_v = 1.0 \text{ in. water}$$
$$h_L = 0.93 \times 1.0 = 0.93 \text{ in. of water}$$
$$h_s = 1.0 + 0.93 = 1.93 \text{ in. of water}$$

Given: static suction, h_s = 2.0 in. of water.

$$V = 0.72 \times 4005\sqrt{2.0}$$
$$= 4080 \text{ fpm}$$

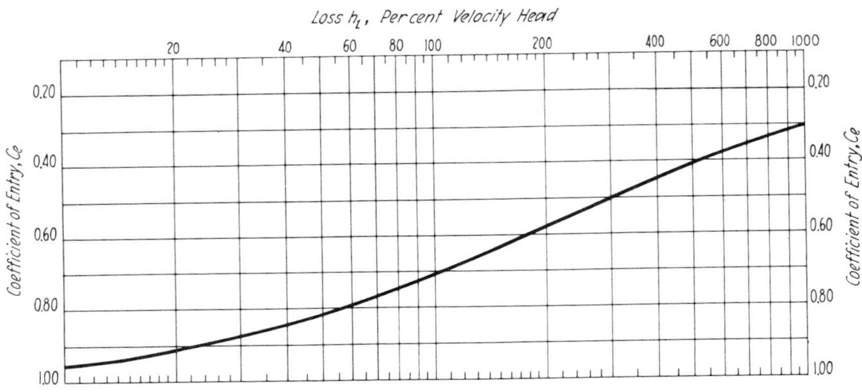

Fig. 4-5. Orifice losses expressed in velocity head corresponding to values of entry coefficient.

The well-rounded nozzle, *a*, and the thin plate orifice, *g*, are used extensively for metering purposes, consequently, their properties have been investigated thoroughly. The coefficients of the other forms are not so well established. Nevertheless, Fig. 4-4 can be used with confidence with the possible exception that the tabular loss values for square and rectangular hoods should be increased by, perhaps, 4 or 5% for long, narrow hood openings.

Static Pressures at a Suction Opening

The progressive changes in static pressure occurring in a suction pipe are plotted in Fig. 4-6. The mechanism of flow at the mouth of a suction opening is an excellent application of Bernoulli's theorem which states that the sums

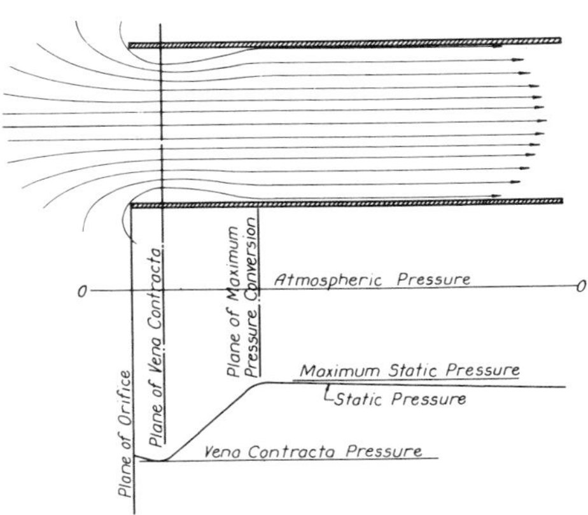

Fig. 4-6. Static pressures at entrance to suction pipe.

of the static and velocity pressures at various planes in a given pipe are constant if energy is neither gained nor lost (see Chapter 1).

The negative pressure in the plane of the orifice causes air to flow from the atmosphere toward the opening with increasing velocity as the latter is approached. Between the pipe mouth and the vena contracta the stream accelerates and the increase in velocity is accompanied by a drop in static pressure. The latter reaches its minimum in the plane of the vena contracta where the cross sectional area of the stream is the least and the velocity is greatest. Thereafter, the jet expands to fill the pipe, the velocity diminishes, and the static pressure rises to a maximum. Friction loss causes the static pressure to fall progressively from this point to the fan inlet unless there is a substantial increase in velocity in a downstream section. (Total pressure must fall as it approaches the fan inlet regardless of velocity pressure-static pressure variations.) In a cylindrical pipe the plane of the vena contracta is located about 0.2 diameter downstream from the orifice and the plane of maximum static pressure about 0.8 diameter.[2] The exact locations of these significant planes depend upon the nature and degree of constriction of the opening at the pipe mouth and, probably, upon the velocity. If the entrance orifice were a perfect bell mouth having no entry loss, the static and velocity pressures would be numerically equal. Since the velocity pressure is positive and the static pressure negative their sum (the total pressure) would be zero or atmospheric—the same as the pressure of still air outside the orifice.

Effect of Suppressed Contraction

The formation of a vena contracta is always accompanied by a reduction of volumetric flow from that to be expected solely from the static suction and the pipe area. It tends to decrease hood efficiency in the sense that maximum flow from a given pressure constitutes maximum efficiency. While the velocity at the vena contracta closely approaches that to be expected from complete conversion, differing only by the amount of the loss, perhaps 2½%, the vena contracta area is substantially smaller than the pipe area. The combination of the velocity loss and the reduction of effective area reduces the entry coefficient to less than unity. The greater the contraction of the stream, the lower is the coefficient and the smaller the flow. Consequently, any circumstance which suppresses jet contraction is beneficial to hood effectiveness.

In Fig. 4-3e, the boundary flow lines curl through an included angle of approximately 180°, whereas those in Fig. 4-3c do not bend more than 90°. The lessened inward angular curvature of the latter results in partial suppression of the jet contraction. Contraction is also reduced when several thin-plate orifices lie close together as in a perforated sheet metal grille. An

[2] "The Intake Orifice and a Proposed Method for Testing Exhaust Fans." by N. C. Ebaugh and R. Whitfield, *ASME Transactions*, Vol. 56, No. 12 (December, 1934), 903-911.

increase in flow through orifices so arranged of the order of 5% to 10% has been observed. The presence of planes adjacent to the mouth has a similar effect. Thus, the coefficient of discharge of a metering orifice on the wall of a plenum chamber is raised measurably when the orifice is located within 3 diameters of a side wall. Still more pronounced suppression takes place when closely adjacent planes form a practical continuation of the sides of a suction opening. A common example is that of a hood resting on a machine table as illustrated in Fig. 4-7. The flow lines indicate that practically no contraction takes place on the side of the mouth nearest the table. The influence of the lessened contraction on the orifice coefficient and, hence, the rate of flow, is proportional to the fraction of the orifice periphery over which suppression takes place. Thus,

$$C_e = c_e \left(1 + 0.12\frac{L}{p}\right)$$

where:

C_e = coefficient of entry of orifice with suppression
c_e = coefficient of entry of same orifice without suppression
L = length of side of orifice over which suppression takes place
p = periphery of orifice.

Thus, the entry coefficient of a square hood in which suppression takes place is increased about 3% for each side affected by suppressing planes arranged as in Fig. 4-7.

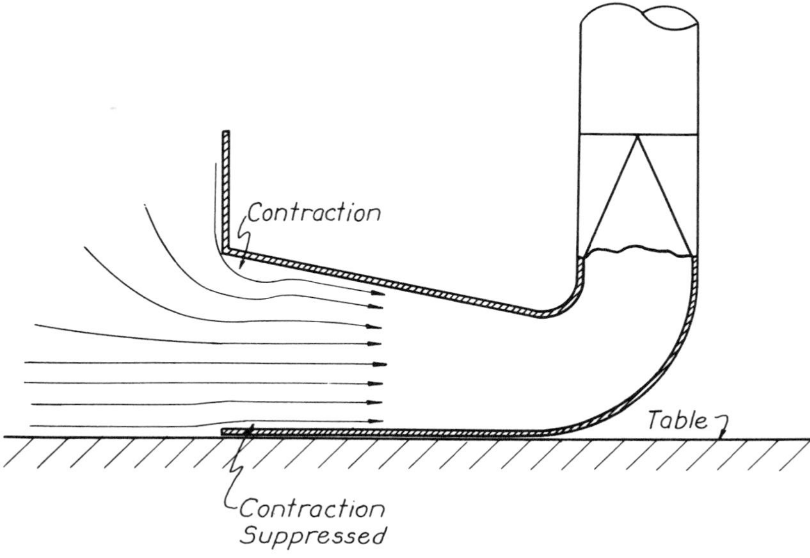

Fig. 4.7. Suppression of contraction by adjacent planes.

Entry Coefficients of Hoods

In the field or laboratory, entry coefficients are obtained by direct measurement of the branch pipe suction and corresponding volumetric flow rate. The engineer should neglect no opportunty to collect such hood data. A careful compilation of actual hood coefficients together with records of surrounding conditions is an essential to accurate estimating. Nevertheless, there are many occasions on which it is necessary to estimate the coefficients of hoods from contractor's sketches without the aid of actual tests of similar hoods. In such instances fair accuracy may be obtained in synthesizing the coefficients from the data provided in Fig. 4-3.

Synthetic Entry Coefficients

Hoods whose shapes are reasonably close to the simple geometrical forms of Fig. 4-3 will have coefficients departing but little from those tabulated. Thus, pyramidal or cone-shaped hoods or those whose air passages are without sudden expansion or contraction may be compared with flanged or unflanged pipes or cones. More complex forms may be treated as combinations of orifices, usually in tandem. Velocity changes are evaluated and pressure losses estimated for each unit of the combination. The total effect of the series of losses is then reflected in the resulting synthetic coefficient.

For example, the grinder hood, Fig. 4-8d, consists of two orifices in tandem. The first is the entrance from the atmosphere to the large chamber enclosing the wheel and the second is the junction of the branch pipe and chamber. The former is treated as an unflanged pipe, Fig. 4-3e, while the latter is similar to the flanged pipe, Fig. 4-3c, with partially suppressed contraction due to the presence of the hood walls. The suction set up in the large chamber must be deducted from the branch suction to obtain the effective pressure causing flow from the chamber into the pipe. The following steps illustrate the process of synthesizing the entry coefficient:

Given: Branch suction, 2.0 in. wg
Maximum chamber entrance velocity, 1300 fpm
Chamber entrance velocity pressure, Fig. 4-9, = 0.11 in. wg
Chamber suction = 0.11 + 0.10 = 0.21 in. wg
Effective branch suction = 2.0 − 0.21 = 1.79 in. wg
Corresponding velocity, Fig. 4-9, = 5360 fpm
C_e, flanged branch, no suppression, Fig. 4-3, = 0.82
Addition for suppression, estimated, = 0.01
C , flanged branch with suppression, = 0.83
Branch velocity = 5360 × 0.83 = 4450 fpm
Velocity corresponding to branch suction, Fig. 4-9, = 5670 fpm

$$C\text{, hood, } = \frac{4450}{5670} = 0.79$$

Hood Type	Entry Coefficient, C_e	Entry Loss Vel. Heads, h_L	Nearest Simple Orifice
 a. Canopy Hood	0.82	0.49	See Fig. 4-4
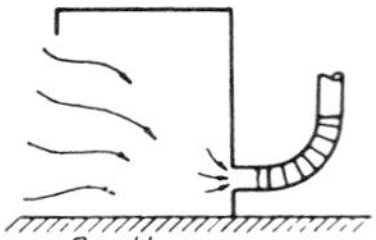 b. Booth	0.82	0.49	Flanged Pipe
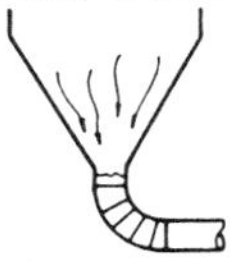 c. Hopper	0.82	0.49	90° Incl. Angle and Elbow
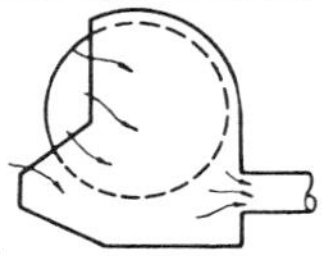 d. Grinder Hood	0.79	0.60	Flanged Pipe – Chamber Loss Reduces C_e –
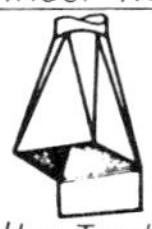 e. Lathe Top Hood	0.82	0.49	Unflanged Pipe
 f. Smoke Hood	0.57	2.08	Unflanged Pipe and Mitre Elbow ~ Suction Measured in Pipe
	0.72	0.93	Unflanged Pipe only ~ Suction Measured in Hood
 g. Floor Sweep	0.61	1.69	Unflanged Pipe and Square Throat Elbow ~ Suction Measured in Pipe
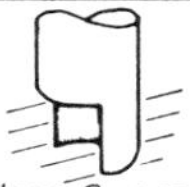 h. Floor Sweep	0.57	2.08	Unflanged Pipe and Mitre Elbow ~ Suction Measured in Pipe
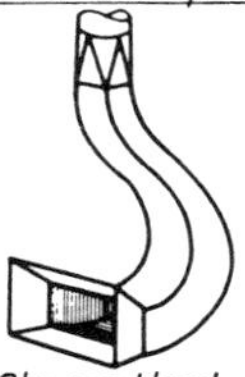 i. Shaper Hood	0.71	0.99	30° Unflanged Cone and 2 Elbows ~ Suction Measured in Pipe above Square-to-Round.

Fig. 4-8. Entry coefficients of typical hoods.

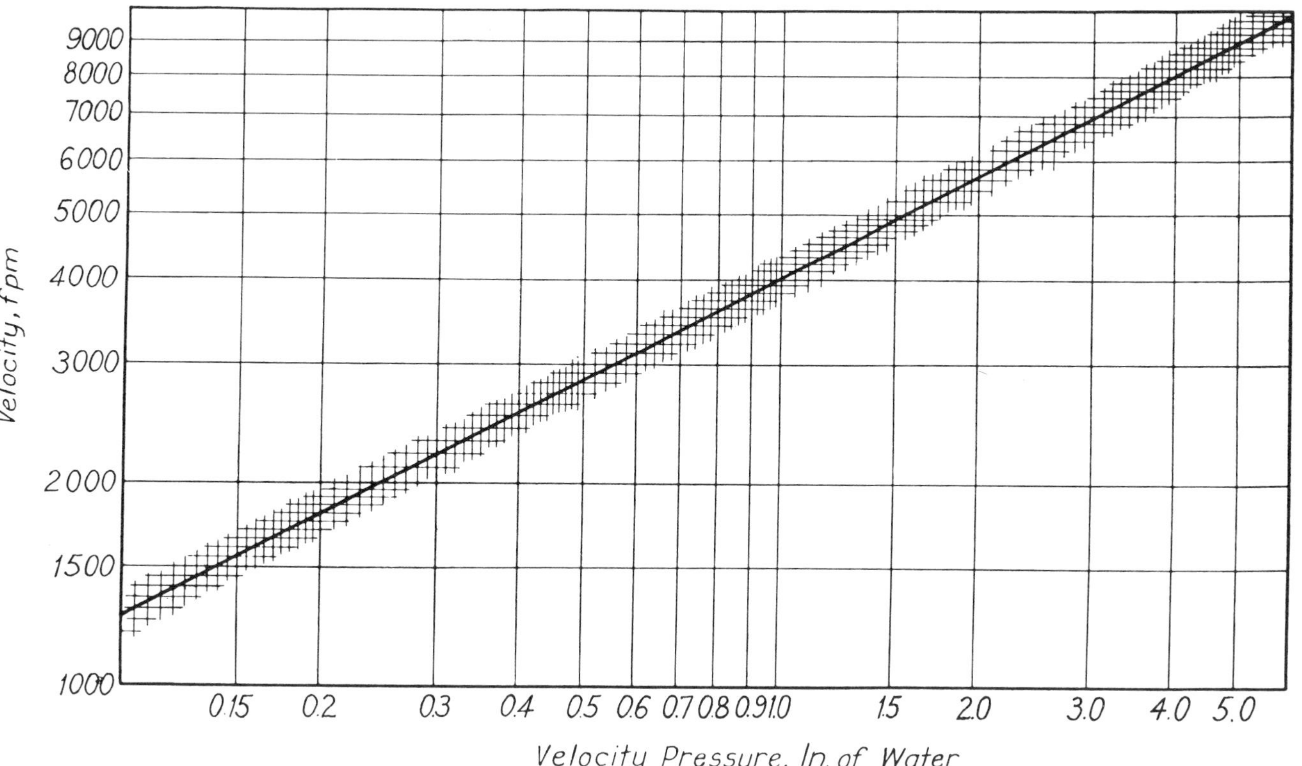

Fig. 4-9. Relation of velocity to velocity pressure (fpm = 4005 $\sqrt{VP}$).

With experience, the engineer will gain facility in estimating coefficients without the necessity for detailed calculations. He will find that for chamber-type hoods whose face velocities do not greatly exceed 1,000 fpm, an acceptable procedure is to select a coefficient appropriate for the branch connection and to reduce it by an estimated amount, say, from 3% to 5%, to allow for the mouth loss or chamber suction. Experience indicates that synthetic coefficients are more likely to be high than low because the actual hood is usually less favorable in form than the fundamental shapes in Fig. 4-3 from which its coefficient has been derived. Every effort should be made toward acquiring skill in estimating coefficients by inspection of freehand sketches of hoods and their surroundings.

Entry Coefficients of Typical Hoods

A number of common hood forms with their coefficients and losses are arranged in Fig. 4-8. The notes supply the basis on which coefficients may be synthesized. In each instance the simple orifice forms of Fig. 4-3 furnish the essential data for estimating workable coefficients. The reliability of synthetic entry coefficients is illustrated by the close agreement between synthetic and actual measured coefficients listed in Table 4-1.

Table 4-1. Comparison Between Synthetic and Actual Entry Coefficients

Hood Form, Fig. 4-8	Entry Coefficient	
	Synthetic	Actual
a	0.82	0.84
b	0.82	0.81
c	0.82	0.83
e	0.82	0.82
g	0.61	0.64
i	0.71	0.70

It will be observed that only Fig. 4-8a, b, and c resemble the elementary shapes shown in Fig. 4-3. The canopy hood, Fig. 4-8a, is pyramidal with an included angle of about 160°. The coefficient was taken from Fig. 4-4. Figure 4-8c is a square hopper of about 90° included angle. Measurements were taken beyond the elbow so that the latter was included in the hood loss. The face area of the lathe hood, Fig. 4-8e, is only 1.4 times that of the pipe. The resulting high velocity at the hood mouth, combined with the small included angle, indicates that the mouth loss is dominant and that the slight contraction at the throat is inconsequential. Hence, this hood is treated as a square hood with 10° included angle and whose loss is 0.49 velocity head. The face areas of g and h are 1.25 and 1.0 times the pipe area respectively.

Figure 4-8f shows a small local hood for exhausting soldering fumes. The mouth area is equal to the pipe area. Since the pipe joins the hood at a right angle, the elbow loss may be taken as being close to that of a mitre stovepipe elbow. When the suction is taken in the pipe, the elbow loss must be included in the hood loss. If the suction is measured in the hood, the elbow loss becomes part of the piping loss. In the first case the entry coefficient is low, while in the second it is higher because of the omission of the elbow loss. The hoods illustrated in Fig. 4-8 have been taken from actual installations and do not necessarily represent optimum designs.

Typical Flow Calculations

An early step in the design of every exhaust system is the computation of flow data for each hood of the system. This will include the volume rate of flow and the selection of conveying velocities for the branch pipe so that the

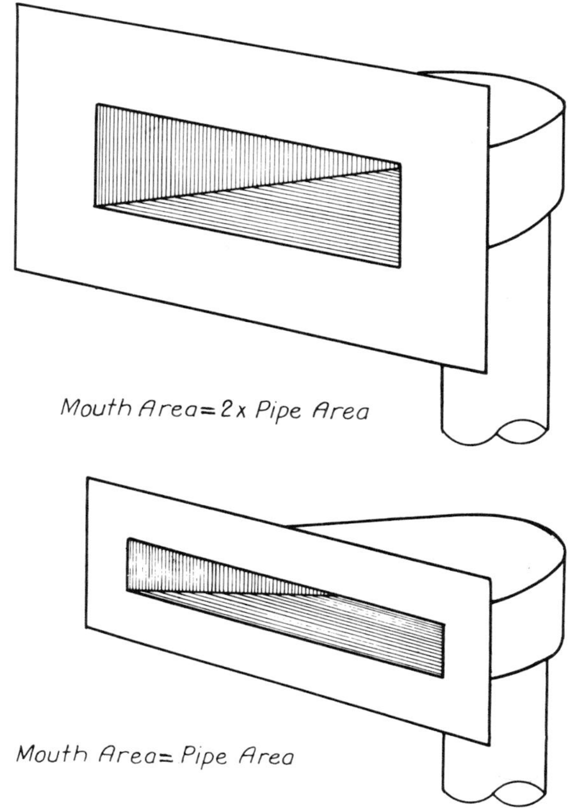

Fig. 4-10. Addition of face flanges to increase flow through smoke hood.

acceleration and turbulence losses through the hood and its connecting duct can be calculated. The selection can be guided by data in Tables 3-1, 3-3, 3-4, 3-5, and 5-1. Duct velocities can vary from recommended values by 15% or more since the tables include a liberal factor of safety.

Flow Calculations—Economical Hood Design

Any method of raising the entry coefficient and lowering the entrance loss will increase the flow through the hood. By this means the desired flow can be attained with less expenditure of power. Study of the elementary forms in Fig. 4-3 will indicate the more favorable shapes to follow. A further improvement is gained by the avoidance of repeated acceleration and deceleration of the air stream. A concrete example of improved flow conditions is the substitution of conical pipe inlets from booths and chambers for the more common straight pipe connections. An increase in flow of nearly 15 percent is possible. Similarly, the addition of flanges to the smoke hood, Fig. 4-8f, in the manner shown in Fig. 4-10 adds little to the cost and increases the flow about 14 percent. In addition, its velocity contours are shifted to improve the effectiveness of the hood as explained in Chapter 2, and shown in Fig. 2-7. If the face area of the same hood be increased without change in branch pipe diameter, a further increase in flow takes place. In general, doubling the face area will raise the flow rate by 20 to 30 percent. These refinements are useful only during the design stage. There is little to be gained by applying them to existing hoods, since the potential for increased exhaust volume is throttled by the increased pressure losses that would occur throughout the exhaust system.

While much of the material in this section has been prepared for the benefit of the exhaust system designer, it is no less useful for the engineer entrusted with the purchase of a system. He should insist that the contractor submit with his proposal sketches of the principal hoods together with the expected suction and other pertinent flow data. From these the purchaser can make an independent check on the aerodynamic efficiency of the hoods and can estimate their probable effectiveness in controlling dust.

CHAPTER 5

Pipe Resistance

Before the exhauster can be selected, the necessary exhaust volume must be known and also the pressure required to draw the air into the hood, and move it through the system. When the designer's freedom is not limited by legal requirements, he determines the minimum volume desired for each hood from sources such as Tables 3-1, 3-3, and 3-4 and selects the branch and main velocities from Tables 3-3 or 5-1, which indicate the usual values. Solids must be conveyed at velocities high enough to prevent dropout in the duct. On the other hand, when gases, mists, etc., are carried, the designer has a wide choice of velocities. The selection of the velocity depends upon the type of exhauster, the available space for ducts, and the balance between a small, and less costly installation and its higher resistance and power demand. A conveying velocity for dusts of 3,500 fpm through round pipes will satisfy most system requirements; for gases, mists, etc., velocities usually range from 1,000 to 2,500 fpm through round or rectangular pipes subject to the considerations mentioned above.

Conveying Velocity

The velocities maintained in branch pipes, mains, and discharge pipes should be low enough to minimize friction, yet high enough to prevent settlement of suspended solids. Table 5-1 lists a number of common materials handled by exhaust and low pressure conveying systems together with air velocities known to be adequate to transport them under ordinary circumstances.

Special Considerations

Finely divided organic solids such as: flour, grain dust, wood flour, and phenolic molding powder usually constitute an explosion hazard. The same is true of powdered aluminum and some other metals which burn readily in the flaked or pulverized states. Probably the best precaution

Table 5-1. Conveying Velocities for Dust Collecting

Material	Velocity, fpm	
	From	To
Wood flour — sander dust	1500	2000
Sawdust, light, dry	2000	3000
Sawdust, heavy, wet or green	3000	4000
Shavings, light, dry	2000	3000
Shavings, heavy, wet or green	3000	4000
Wood blocks, edgings, heavy, wet or green	3500	4500
Hog waste	3500	4500
Grinding dust	3000	4000
Foundry dust, tumbling barrel, shake-out	3500	5000
Sand blast dust	3500	4000
Buffing lint, dry	2500	3000
Buffing lint, sticky	3000	4000
Metal turnings	4000	5000
Lead dust	4000	5000
Cotton	2500	3000
Cotton lint, flyings	1500	2000
Wool	3000	4000
Jute lint, flyings	2800	3000
Jute picker stock, shredded bagging	3000	3300
Jute dust shaker waste	3100	3400
Jute butts (conveying)	3600	4500
Grain	2500	4000
Ground feed, 1/2-in. screen (conveying)	4500	5000
Grain dust	2000	3000
Coffee beans	3000	3500
Shoe dust	3000	4000
Rubber dust	2000	2500
Bakelite molding powder	3000	3500
Bakelite molding powder dust	2000	2500
Granite dust and surfacer chips	3000	4000

against fire and explosion hazard is the use of adequately high conveying velocities. It is false economy to attempt to save power through the medium of minimum velocities at the risk of increased hazard. Pockets formed by poorly proportioned enlargements must be avoided. Formation of eddies must be prevented to minimize stray deposits of material. These deposits may become explosion hazards or, in the case of poisonous dusts, health hazards to maintenance men.

Friction Loss in Round Pipes

The dimensional formula for friction (see Chapter 1) may be reduced to the form:

$$h_f = 0.0000747 \frac{fV^2}{D}$$

for standard air, where:

h_f = friction loss per 100 ft of round pipe, in. wg
f = friction factor
V = average velocity in pipe, fpm
D = pipe diameter, in.

Friction, therefore, varies inversely with the diameter, directly with the density and with the square of the velocity. Pressure losses increase rapidly with small pipes and excessive velocities.

To facilitate practical determination of friction loss, Fig. 5-1 has been prepared. It will be observed that this chart relates four factors: volume rate of flow, velocity, pipe diameter, and friction loss per 100 ft. From any two factors the other two may be obtained. Thus, if a 15-in. pipe carries 4,000 cfm, the velocity is close to 3,300 fpm and the friction loss per 100 ft of pipe about 0.91 in. wg. The charted values are based on 40 joints per 100 ft of clean round galvanized pipe and allow for all normal roughness. No further safety factor need be applied. No adjustment for density is required if the system habitually operates in the range of 32F to 100F.

Friction Loss in Rectangular Pipes

While rectangular pipes are used in exhaust systems much less frequently than are round pipes, conditions occur which are best satisfied by this form. Friction losses in rectangular, annular, and oval ducts may be obtained by finding from Fig. 5-1 the loss in an aerodynamically equivalent round pipe. For shapes other than round, a factor, m, known as the "hydraulic radius" may be substituted for the pipe diameter in the dimensional formula for friction. The hydraulic radius is defined as the ratio of the cross sectional area to the perimeter of the duct. When a and b are the width and depth, respectively, of the duct, expressed in units consistent with the formula:

$$m = \frac{ab}{2(a+b)} \text{ for rectangular pipes, and}$$

$$m = \frac{D}{4} \text{ for round pipes}$$

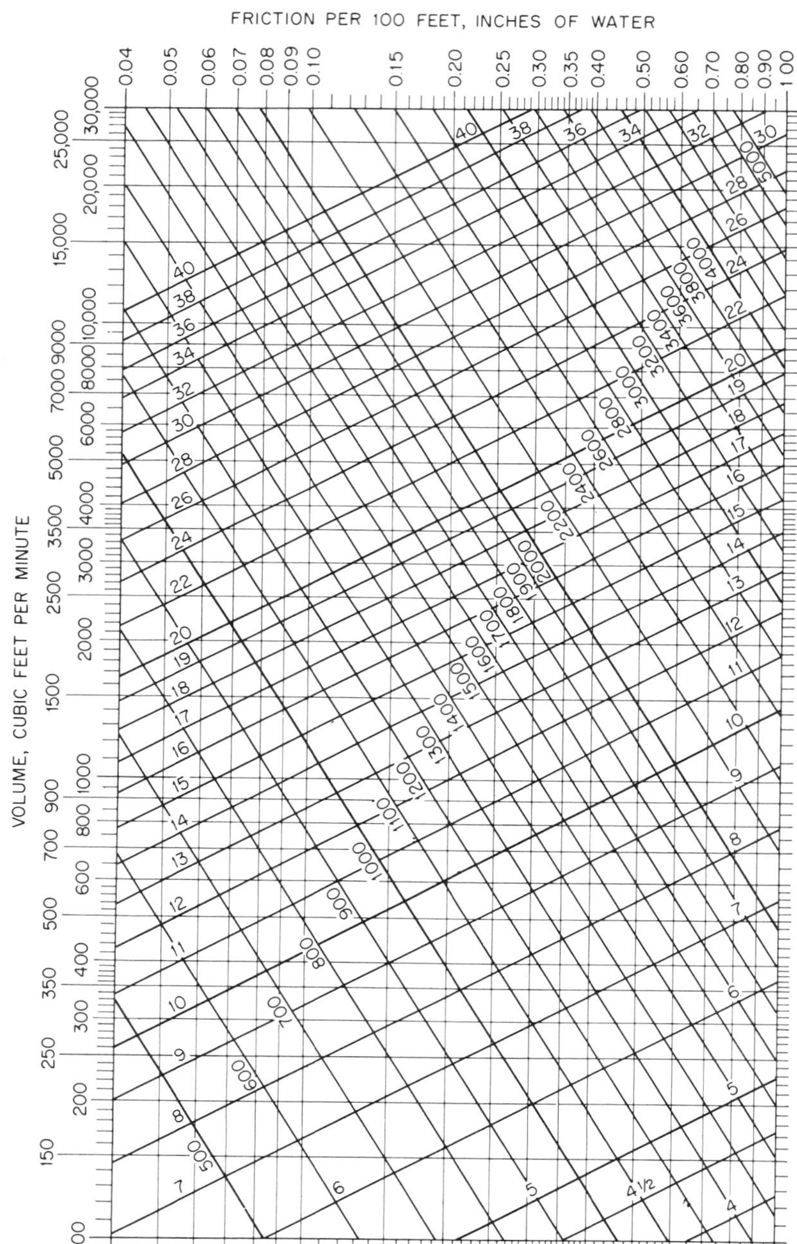

Fig. 5-1. Friction

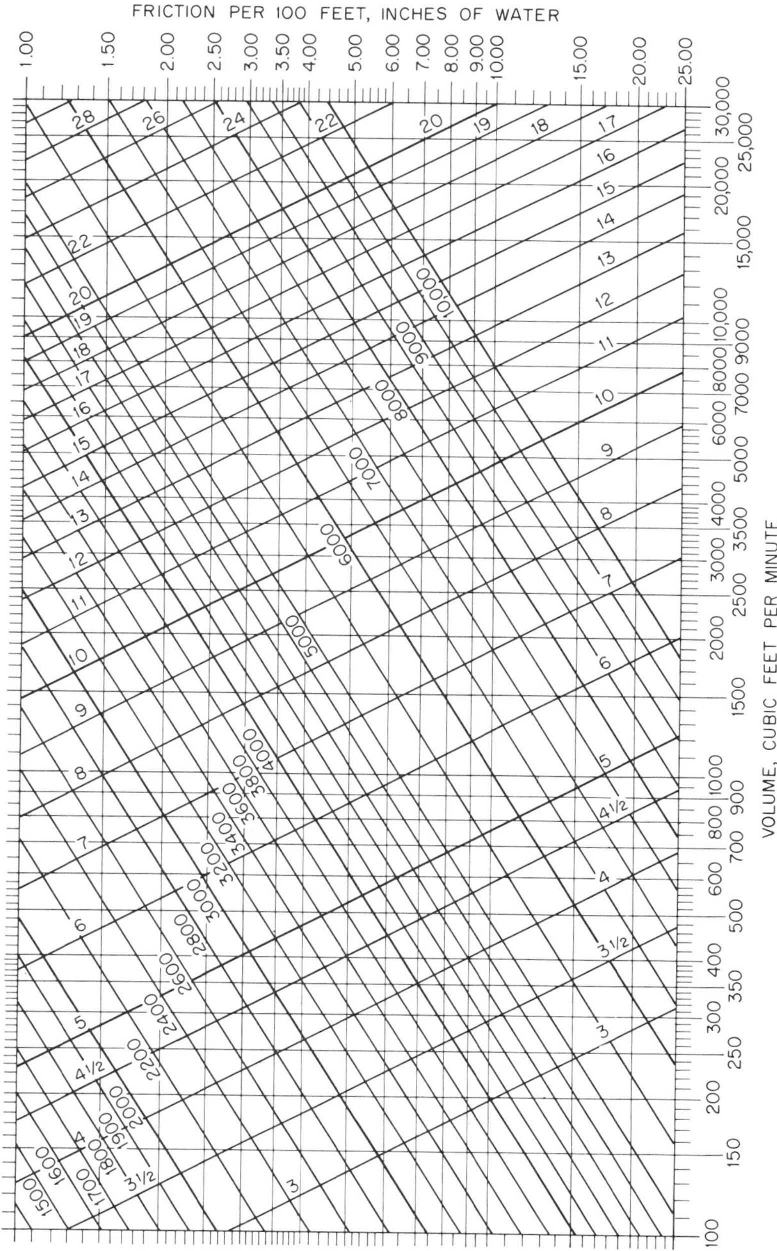

loss in round pipes.

A rectangular pipe is frictionally equivalent to a round pipe when the velocities in both pipes are the same and when the hydraulic radii are equal. Hence, the diameter of a round pipe equivalent to a given rectangular duct is:

$$D = \frac{2\,ab}{a + b}$$

when the friction losses per 100 ft are equal. Example: Rectangular duct, 15×30 in., $Q = 10{,}000$ cfm. Hence, $V = 3{,}200$ fpm. Find friction loss per 100 ft.

$$D = \frac{2 \times 15 \times 30}{15 + 30} = 20 \text{ in.}$$

From Fig. 5-1, friction loss per 100 ft of 20-in. pipe at 3,200 fpm is about 0.61 in. wg. This is also the required friction loss in the rectangular pipe.

Friction Loss of Mixtures

It was shown in Chapter 1, "Flow of Fluids," that the presence of suspended solids in the ordinary dust collecting concentrations can have but slight effect on friction losses or power consumption. Concentrations commonly found in low pressure conveying systems, on the other hand, materially affect pipe friction. For example, the pneumatic elevating system of a common hammer mill handled 16,000 lb of ground feed per hour through 5-in. diameter pipe with an airflow rate of 900 cfm. This is equal to 4 lb of solids per pound of air. It was observed that the friction loss at this conveying rate was approximately 2-1/2 times that when air alone was flowing.

Figure 5-2 has been constructed from data obtained from tests of grain and coal conveying systems. It should be applied with caution since there is conclusive evidence that it is valid only when the solids are completely suspended. When drifting takes place the friction may be as much as 2 or 3 times the charted values. Moreover, the available data are confined to granular materials and it is possible that other factors may control when the conveyed solids are greatly different. In spite of these uncertainties, the chart is useful if applied with discretion.

To obtain the approximate friction loss of a mixture, the loss when handling air only is read from Fig. 5-1. This then is multiplied by the appropriate factor from Fig. 5-2, corresponding to the expected weight of conveyed material per pound of conveying air.

"Velocity Head Rule" for Pipe Friction

A rule often quoted for the resistance of straight round pipes is that the static pressure drop in a length of, say, 50 diameters, is equal numerically to

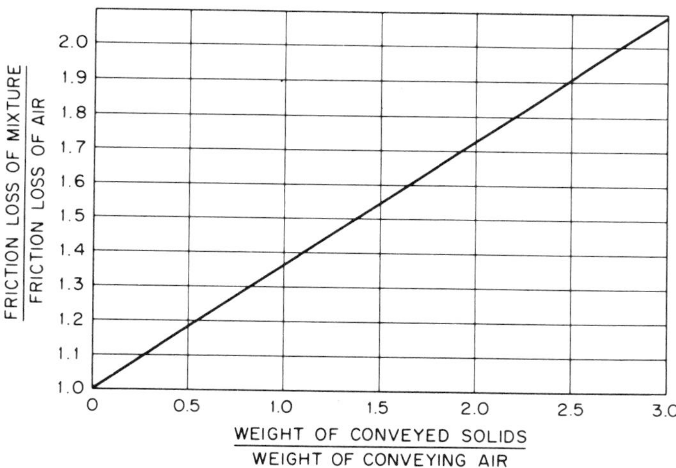

Fig. 5-2. Friction loss of mixture expressed in terms of friction loss of clean air.

one velocity head. While this rule has the virtue of simplicity, it must be used with discretion since it can be valid over a narrow range only. It has been shown in Chapter 1, "Flow of Fluids," that the friction factor, f, varies with the Reynolds number. It follows that the length of straight pipe, measured in diameters, to produce a loss of one velocity head also varies with the Reynolds number. Hence, no single value, such as 50 diameters, applies to the full range of pipe sizes and velocities common to exhaust systems.

If modified to use a sliding scale of equivalent lengths, the velocity head rule is useful in the rough estimation of pipe friction and also facilitates the combination of pipe and fitting losses into a single equivalent length of straight pipe thereby simplifying calculations. The diagram, Fig. 5-3, has been prepared from the same data as the friction loss chart, Fig. 5-1, and shows, for various velocities, the average equivalent length of pipe in diameters corresponding to the usual range of pipe sizes.

Friction Loss in Hose

Hose construction varies so widely that no single set of friction-loss data is applicable. Nevertheless, some guidance may be had from the chart in Fig. 5-4. The hose to which this chart applies is made of fabric, impregnated with neoprene and reinforced by a helical steel wire embedded in the structure. It is smooth inside, and while the internal corrugations are visible, they are relatively shallow. This is one of the better hoses for exhaust purposes.

PIPE	VELOCITY, FT PER MIN						
DIA, IN.	2000	2500	3000	3500	4000	4500	5000
3							
4			40 DIAMETERS				
5							
6			45 DIAMETERS				
7							
8							
9			50 DIAMETERS				
10							
11							
12			55 DIAMETERS				
13							
14							
15							
16							
17				60 DIAMETERS			
18							
19							
20							
22				65 DIAMETERS			
24							
26							
28							
30							
32					70 DIAMETERS		
34							
36							
	2000	2500	3000	3500	4000	4500	5000

Fig. 5-3. Average equivalent length of pipe in diameters for various velocities.

Hose is seldom used as straight pipe, thus accurate prediction of loss is further complicated by bends. The cross section at bends is likely to be flattened, and of less than full area. Where more accurate data are not available, estimate the friction as three times that of straight metal pipe; friction in a straight section can be twice the metal pipe friction and the irregularities of the run in service can account for the added amount. This hose may be bent to a throat radius of about 1.0 diameter. The pressure drop in 90° bends ranges from that of 5 to 10 diameters of straight hose when the throat radius varies from 6.0 to 1.0 diameters. If an accurate prediction of resistance is needed, a sample should be bent to the desired shape and the pressure drop measured under at least one rate of flow. The resistance at other velocities will be proportional to the squares of the velocities.

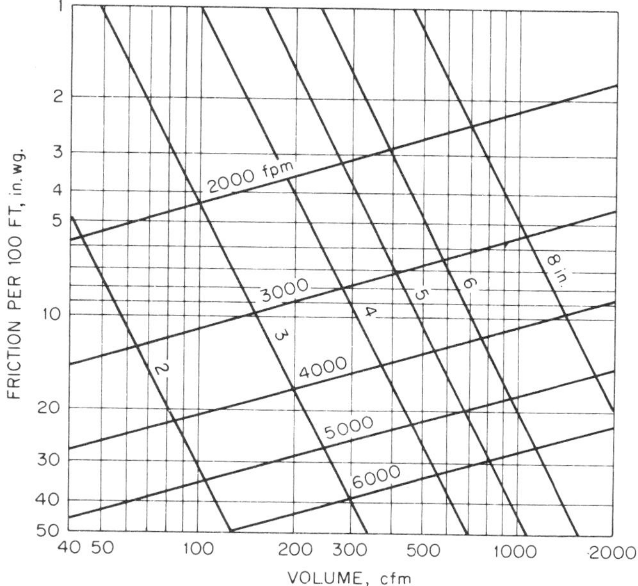

Fig. 5-4. Friction loss in hose.

Losses in Elbows

The degree of "hardness" of bend of an elbow is usually designated by expressing the centerline radius, or throat radius, in terms of pipe diameter. A "long-radius" elbow may be considered as one whose centerline radius is 2.0 diameters, or greater. The terms "radius ratio" and "curve ratio," illustrated in Fig. 5-5, are less often used to designate the character of the bend.

The velocity of air flowing along the outside of a bend is not only lower than that of the filaments nearer the throat but the stream, in addition, shows a pronounced tendency toward a double helical motion symmetrical about the plane of the bend. When the elbow is followed by a short length of straight pipe, there is a partial recovery of static pressure as the velocity diminishes and the helical flow subsides. When the elbow discharges directly to the atmosphere, no static pressure regain takes place. The loss in an elbow usually is expressed as a fraction of the velocity head. It also may be expressed as the equivalent length of straight pipe having equal resistance. Figure 5-6 gives the losses in velocity heads of round elbows of various radii. Centerline radii of 2.0 and 2.5 are common, the latter generally being restricted to small branch lines where the velocity and hence, the loss, is likely to be greatest. There is little merit in the use of longer radii except in high-velocity conveying systems

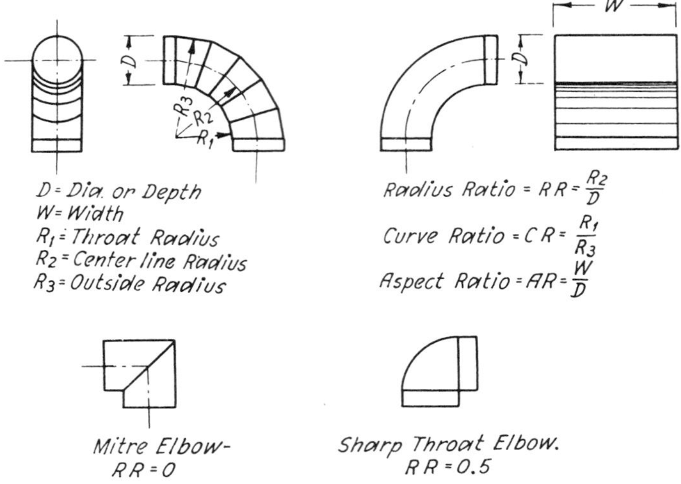

Fig. 5-5. Radius, curve, and aspect ratios of elbows.

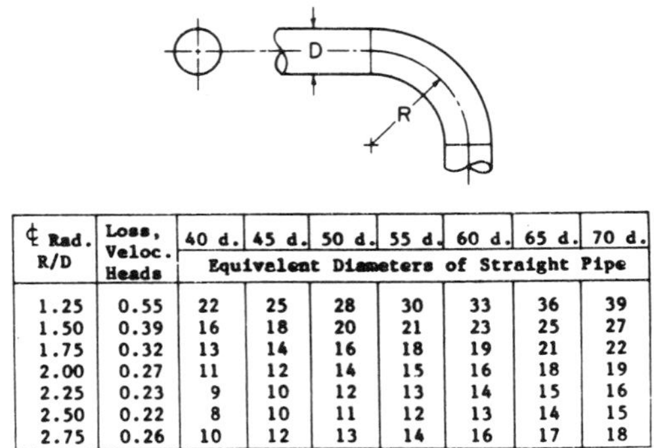

¢ Rad. R/D	Loss, Veloc. Heads	40 d.	45 d.	50 d.	55 d.	60 d.	65 d.	70 d.
		Equivalent Diameters of Straight Pipe						
1.25	0.55	22	25	28	30	33	36	39
1.50	0.39	16	18	20	21	23	25	27
1.75	0.32	13	14	16	18	19	21	22
2.00	0.27	11	12	14	15	16	18	19
2.25	0.23	9	10	12	13	14	15	16
2.50	0.22	8	10	11	12	13	14	15
2.75	0.26	10	12	13	14	16	17	18

Fig. 5-6. Resistance of 90° round elbows in velocity heads and equivalent diameters of straight pipe.

where the governing factor is erosion rather than friction loss. The mitre elbow and sharp-throat elbow have no place in a well-designed piping system. Their pressure losses are about 1.0 velocity head.

Figure 5-7 has been prepared as a convenience to simplify elbow calculations for average exhaust conditions. Since most common dusts are conveyed in the velocity range of 3,000 to 4,000 fpm, the table has been based on 3,500 fpm.

Influence of Aspect Ratio

The aspect ratio is a term expressing the width of an elbow cross-section

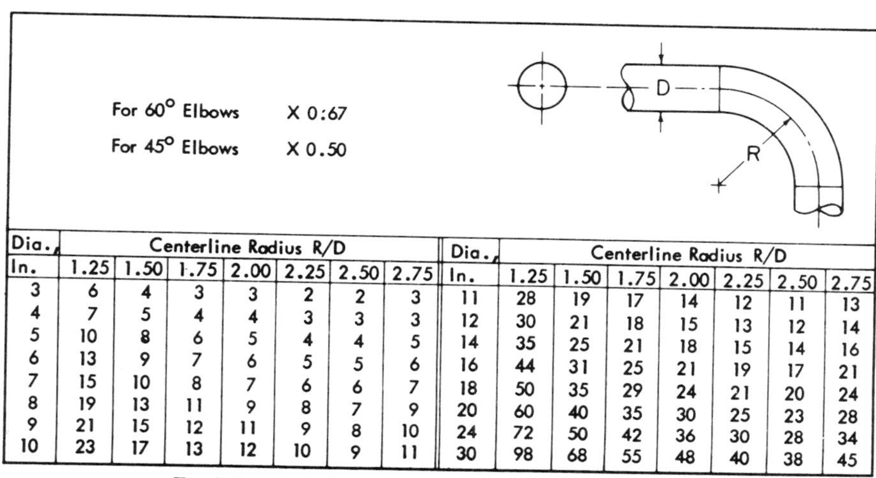

Dia., In.	Centerline Radius R/D 1.25	1.50	1.75	2.00	2.25	2.50	2.75	Dia., In.	Centerline Radius R/D 1.25	1.50	1.75	2.00	2.25	2.50	2.75
3	6	4	3	3	2	2	3	11	28	19	17	14	12	11	13
4	7	5	4	4	3	3	3	12	30	21	18	15	13	12	14
5	10	8	6	5	4	4	5	14	35	25	21	18	15	14	16
6	13	9	7	6	5	5	6	16	44	31	25	21	19	17	21
7	15	10	8	7	6	6	7	18	50	35	29	24	21	20	24
8	19	13	11	9	8	7	9	20	60	40	35	30	25	23	28
9	21	15	12	11	9	8	10	24	72	50	42	36	30	28	34
10	23	17	13	12	10	9	11	30	98	68	55	48	40	38	45

Fig. 5-7. Feet of straight pipe equivalent to 90° elbows.

in terms of its depth as shown in Fig. 5-5. It applies to rectangular elbows only. Square elbows have an aspect ratio of 1.0. "Easy" turns have aspect ratios greater than 1.0. Figure 5-8 shows that high aspect ratios are accompanied by low elbow losses.

Influence of Angle of Turn

Figures 5-6 and 5-7 refer only to 90° elbows. In Table 5-2 is shown the variation of resistance with the angle of bend.

Table 5-2. Effect of Angle of Bend on Elbow Resistance

Angle of Bend, Degrees	Relative Resistance of Elbow Followed by Duct	Angle of Bend, Degrees	Relative Resistance of Elbow Followed by Duct
15	0.18	90	1.00
30	0.34	120	1.27
45	0.52	150	1.50
60	0.68	180	1.65
75	0.84	. . .	. . .

It will be observed that the losses in bends greater than 90° are less than would be expected from direct proportionality. For the angles below 90°, no significant error is introduced by using the proportion that the angle bears to 90°. Thus, a 45° bend may be taken as one-half of a 90° elbow.

R/D	Aspect Ratio, W/D					
	0.25	0.5	1.0	2.0	3.0	4.0
0.5	1.36	1.21	1.05	0.95	0.84	0.79
1.0	0.45	0.28	0.21	0.21	0.20	0.19
1.5	0.28	0.18	0.13	0.13	0.12	0.12
2.0	0.24	0.15	0.11	0.11	0.10	0.10
3.0	0.24	0.15	0.11	0.11	0.10	0.10

Fig. 5-8. Loss in velocity heads in square and rectangular elbows.

Influence of Approach Velocity

If the velocity distribution in the pipe approaching the elbow departs materially from the nearly parabolic profile shown in Fig. 1-8, the elbow loss may differ considerably from the tabulated values. Elbow losses are particularly sensitive to flow disturbances in the region of the elbow throat. High approach velocities along the inner radius tend to increase the loss, whereas high velocities along the outer arc decrease it. In consequence, the arrangement of elbows directly connected to fan outlets has considerable bearing on the elbow losses. Air flows through the wheel and casing of a centrifugal exhauster in a manner which produces a distorted velocity pattern in the fan outlet. Exit velocities are highest along the scroll sheet of the casing and in the plane of the wheel backplate. Hence, when a discharge elbow is so oriented that its throat receives the high velocity flow from these regions, excessive loss may be expected. Thus, high losses—as much as twice normal—have been found when the elbows were arranged as in Fig. 5-9a and c. Losses less than normal may be expected from arrangements such as Fig. 5-9b and d.

Compound Elbows

Two elbows joined together in tandem or connected by a short length of pipe usually imposed a loss for the combination appreciably different from the sum of the expected losses of the individual elbows reported in Figs. 5-6 and 5-7. The loss in the two elbows of the offset, Fig. 5-10a, is greater than that in two elbows used singly. In contrast, the gooseneck, Fig. 5-10b, which is used to connect the bottom of a hood or hopper, to an overhead pipe imposes a pressure drop lower than that of two individual elbows.

Venturi Elbows

The flow lines through a short-radius, plain elbow are indicated schematically in Fig. 5-11a. The eddies formed downstream of the throat persist, in a

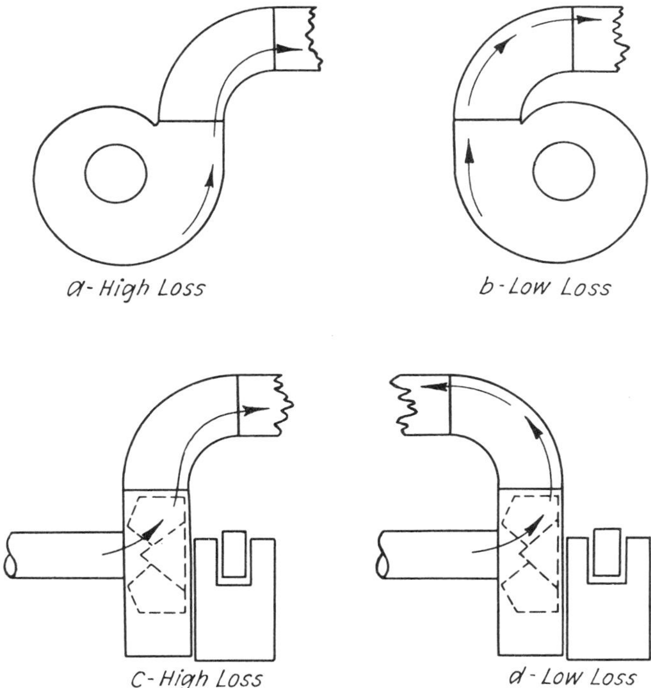

Fig. 5-9. Effect of fan discharge arrangement on elbow loss.

diminishing degree, for several pipe diameters from their source. They are responsible for no small part of the elbow loss. Shaping the pipe wall to conform to the natural flow lines of the accelerated stream discourages the formation of these eddies. An elbow so shaped, together with its downstream

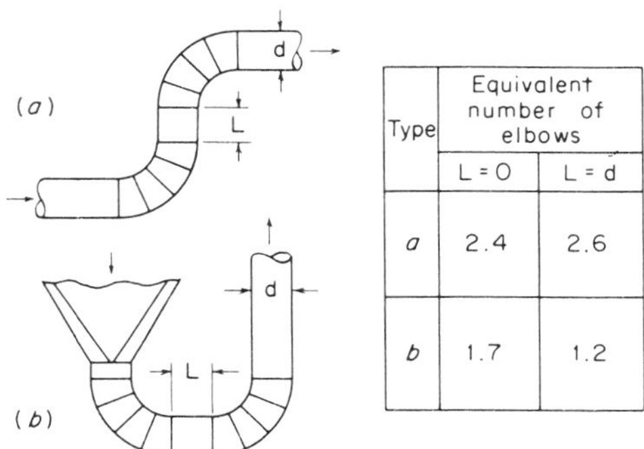

Type	Equivalent number of elbows	
	L = 0	L = d
a	2.4	2.6
b	1.7	1.2

Fig. 5-10. Losses in double elbows.

expansion piece, constitutes the venturi elbow, Fig. 5-11b. It will be observed from this figure that the duct area immediately following the bend is constricted to conform substantially to the vena contracta of the elbow. The table accompanying Fig. 5-12 gives suitable throat depths when the venturi elbow is substituted for plain elbows of various radii.

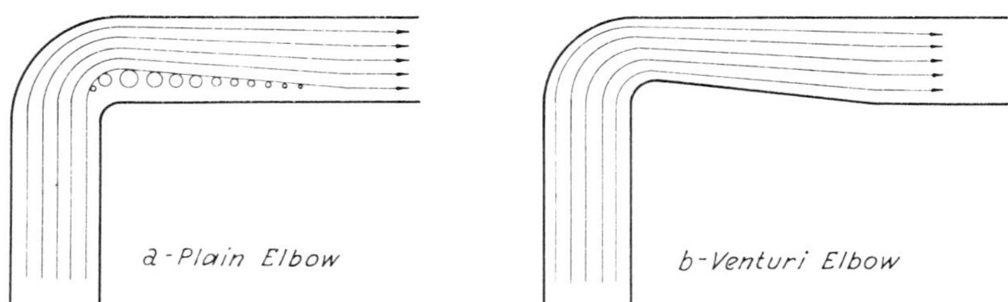

Fig. 5-11. Approximate flow lines through short radius elbows.

The reduction of pressure drop is greatest for very short radii. Thus, a reduction of 50 percent is attainable for a centerline radius of 0.5 diameters and 20 percent for 1.5 diameters. The venturi elbow is more costly than either round or rectangular plain elbows. However, its use sometimes can be justified when it can be designed to replace transformers, short pipes, or other details. Figure 5-13 is an example. This assembly of a fan and cyclone was built into a hammer mill. The piping consisted of a long, square-to-round connected to the fan outlet, a round elbow, and a

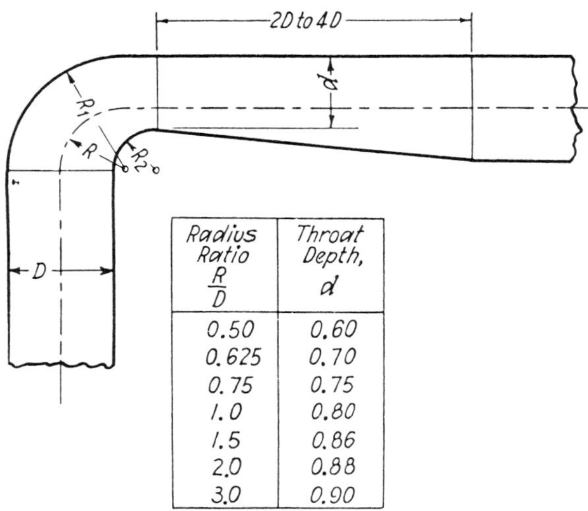

Radius Ratio $\frac{R}{D}$	Throat Depth, d
0.50	0.60
0.625	0.70
0.75	0.75
1.0	0.80
1.5	0.86
2.0	0.88
3.0	0.90

Fig. 5-12. Throat depth of venturi elbows of uniform width.

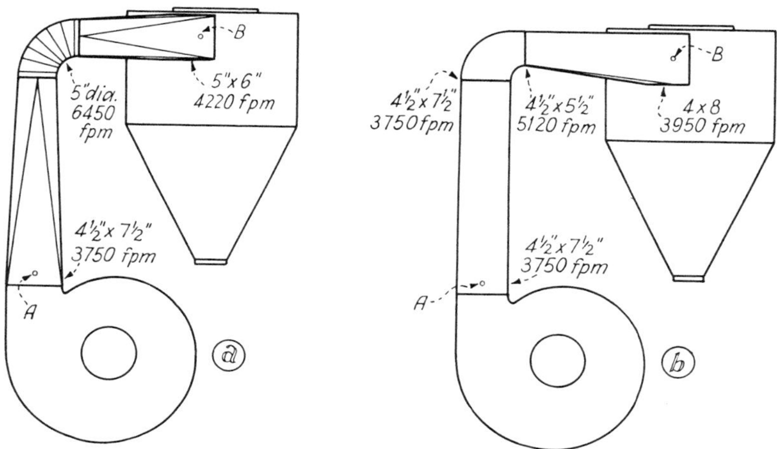

Fig. 5-13. Application of venturi elbow to small fan and cyclone.

transformer at the cyclone. It will be observed that the air was accelerated markedly between the fan and the elbow and decelerated between the elbow and the cyclone. The pressure loss from A to B was measured as 2.2 in. of water. When the construction shown in Fig. 5-13b was substituted and the pressure drop again measured, the loss from A to B was found to be 0.45 in. of water at the same rate of air flow as in Fig. 5-13a. Thus, the static pressure saving was about 80 percent. The venturi elbow was responsible for slightly less than one-half of the improvement, the remainder being due to lessened pipe friction and the absence of deceleration losses.

Enlargements

Bernoulli's theorem shows that the drop in velocity pressure resulting from an enlargement in a pipe is regained as static pressure if the velocity reduction can be made so gently as to permit complete conversion of kinetic to potential energy. The loss in an enlargement is the amount by which complete conversion fails of attainment. It may be expressed as a function of the difference in velocities in the original and enlarged sections of pipe. Thus,

$$H_L = k\left[\left(\frac{V_1}{4005}\right)^2 - \left(\frac{V_2}{4005}\right)^2\right]$$

H_L = pressure loss, in. wg
V_1 = upstream velocity, fpm
V_2 = downstream velocity, fpm
k = loss factor, Fig. 5-15

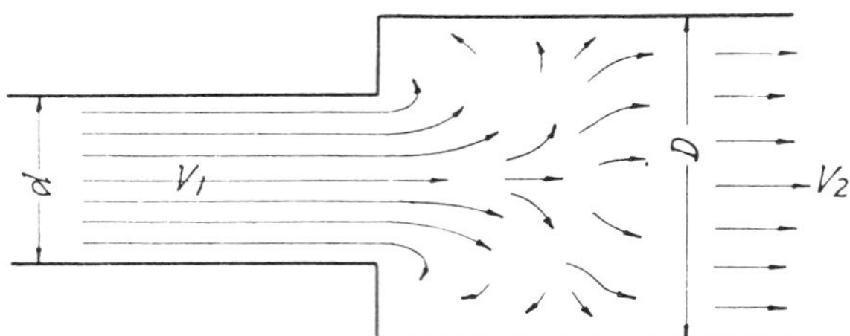

Fig. 5-14. Abrupt enlargement.

Losses in Abrupt Enlargements

The more abrupt the enlargement, the greater is the loss. Thus, the entire difference in velocity heads is lost in an enlargement similar to Fig. 5-14 wherein $k = 1.0$. No regain of static pressure takes place during the transition from the higher to the lower velocity. The ordinary box type of gravity trap is an example of sudden enlargement in which the terminal velocity is usually so low for the purpose of promoting settlement of solids that the entire initial velocity pressure is lost.

Losses in Tapers

When the enlargement is gradual, as in the common taper, k is a function of the included angle. In Fig. 5-15, k is plotted against the included

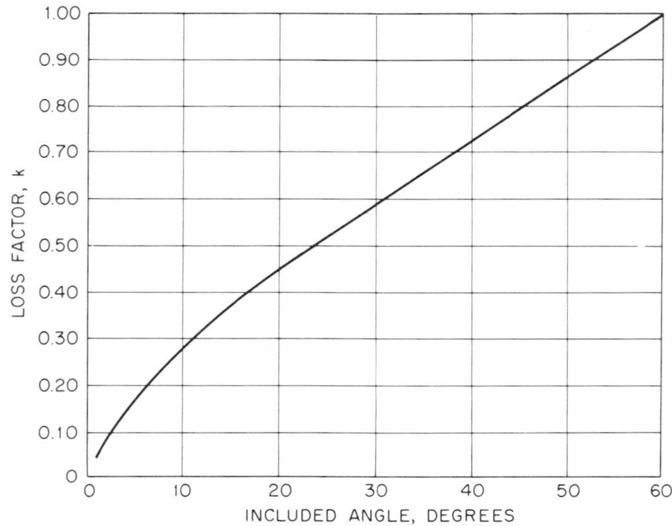

Fig. 5-15. Loss in tapered enlargements.

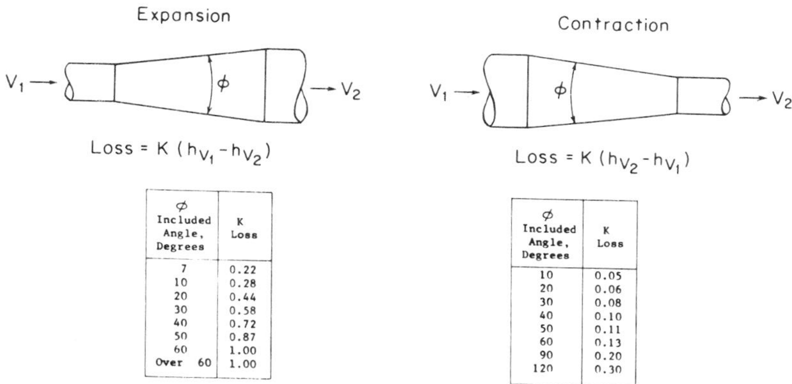

ϕ Included Angle, Degrees	K Loss
7	0.22
10	0.28
20	0.44
30	0.58
40	0.72
50	0.87
60	1.00
Over 60	1.00

ϕ Included Angle, Degrees	K Loss
10	0.05
20	0.06
30	0.08
40	0.10
50	0.11
60	0.13
90	0.20
120	0.30

Fig. 5-16. Losses in expansions and contractions.

angle of divergence. It will be observed that no regain of static pressure occurs when the included angle exceeds 60°. This angle, therefore, may be taken as the dividing line between abrupt and gradual enlargements. A condensed table of expansion loss-factors appears in Fig. 5-16.

No loss need be figured for tapers into which branch pipe tees enter. The velocity drop is small since the enlargement of the main is designed to accommodate the combined flows of the main and branch.

Losses in Contractions

The loss by reason of a gradual contraction is small. Abrupt contractions introduce vena contracta losses similar to those of the orifices shown in Fig. 4-5. Abrupt contractions are rare in well-designed exhaust systems except as outlets from chambers such as dust arresters, traps and booths in which the velocity of approach is low. Some approximate loss values appear in Fig. 5-16.

Losses in Tees

When two streams meet as in Fig. 5-17, eddies form at the interface and a transfer of momentum takes place between the streams. A pressure loss occurs both in the branch and in the main. The loss in the main generally is ignored because it is small, and only slightly affects the total main friction. The junction loss in the branch pipe is about 0.28 velocity heads for the common 45° tee, or the shoe tee, Fig. 11-2b. Numerically it is close to that of an elbow whose centerline radius is 2.0 diameters. Therefore, it is customary to simplify the friction calculations by adding an extra elbow to the length of the branch to allow for the loss at the tee. Figure 5-18 lists the factors by which the tee loss should be modified for entry angles other than 45°.

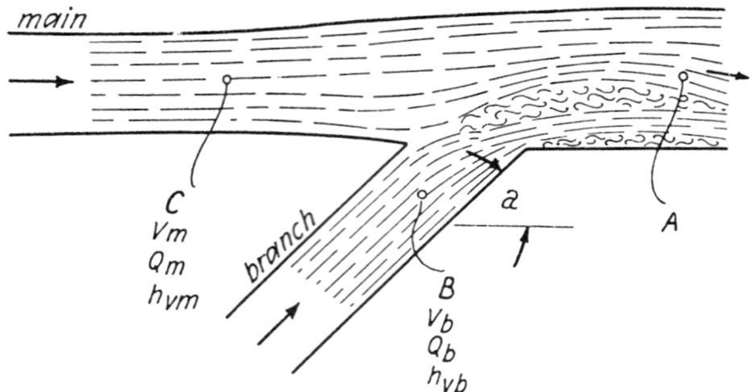

Fig. 5-17. Schematic representation of flow conditions at junction of branch pipe and main suction pipe.

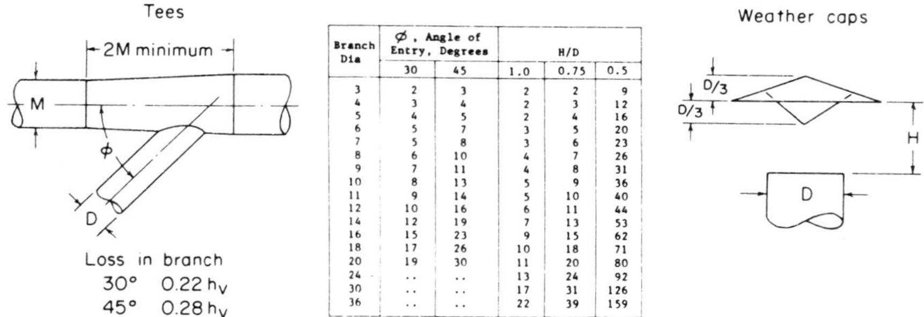

Branch Dia	φ, Angle of Entry, Degrees		H/D		
	30	45	1.0	0.75	0.5
3	2	3	2	2	9
4	3	4	2	3	12
5	4	5	2	4	16
6	5	7	3	5	20
7	5	8	3	6	23
8	6	10	4	7	26
9	7	11	4	8	31
10	8	13	5	9	36
11	9	14	5	10	40
12	10	16	6	11	44
14	12	19	7	13	53
16	15	23	9	15	62
18	17	26	10	18	71
20	19	30	11	20	80
24	..	..	13	24	92
30	..	..	17	31	126
36	..	..	22	39	159

Fig. 5-18. Resistance in equivalent feet of straight pipe.

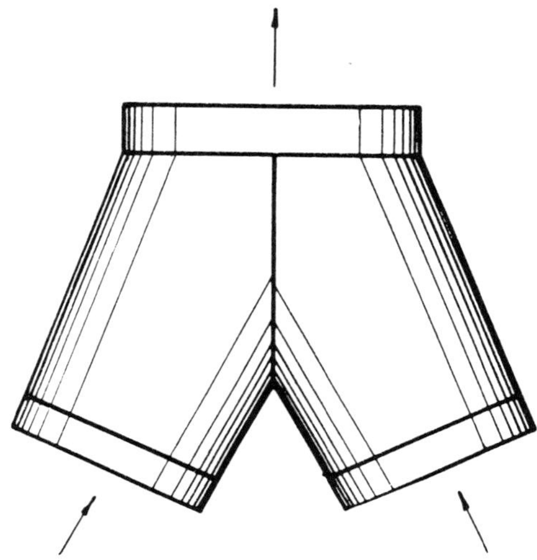

Fig. 5-19. Round breeching.

Losses in Breechings

The common round breeching or "pair of pants," Fig. 5-19, is a special form of tee in which both streams bend at the junction. The loss in each leg of this breeching is about 0.25 velocity head when the included angle is 60°. The rectangular breeching whose angle of junction is zero, as in Fig. 5-20, introduces no loss other than that of simple friction in the legs. Hence, it is the preferred construction for the outlets from double fans, for difficult offset breechings and for other situations in which it can compete in cost with the round breeching.

Vacuum Booster

A special form of tee known as the "vacuum booster" is used occasionally to produce a branch suction greater than that in the main. It consists of an extension of the branch pipe into the main, with the open end pointing downstream. The aspirating effect of the main stream raises the branch suction by an amount approaching the main-line velocity head. Figure 5-21 shows two representative types.

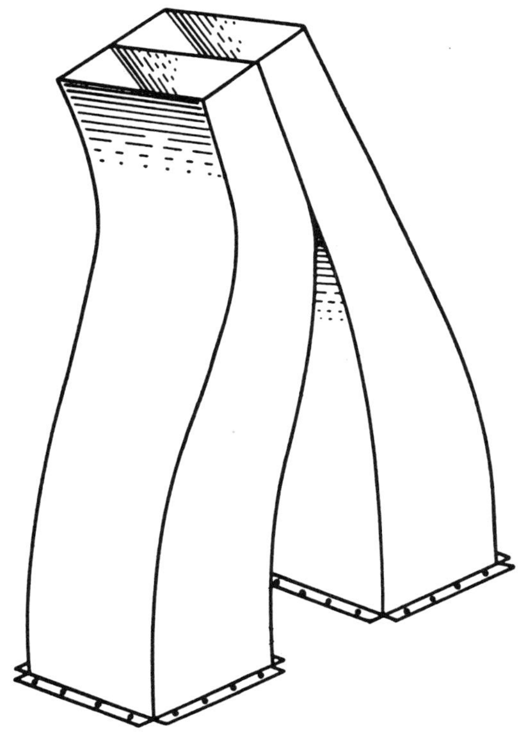

Fig. 5-20. Rectangular breeching.

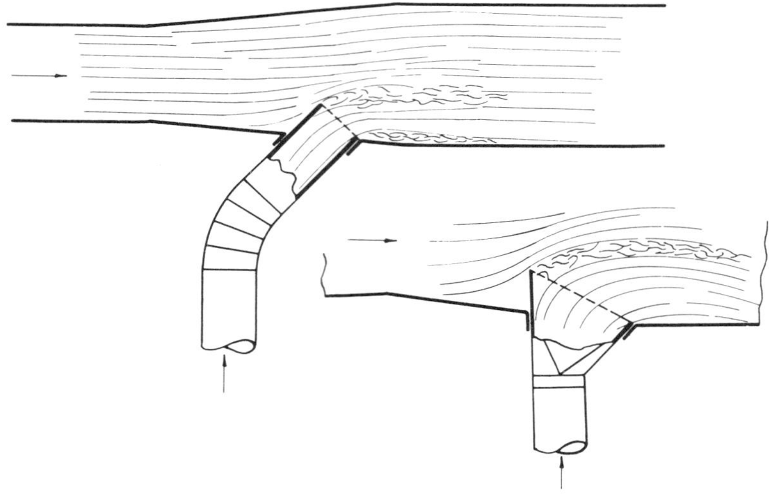

Fig. 5-21. Vacuum boosters.

The added energy in the branch stream is obtained at the expense of the flow in the suction main. From scattered field measurements it may be said that the pressure drop in the main, due to the presence of the booster, is in the neighborhood of 0.3 to 0.5 velocity heads. The vacuum booster is a useful device for correcting a low suction condition at one or two branches of an existing system. It cannot be used at the end of a main but must be installed at a location of substantial main-line flow.

Losses in Transformers

The section of duct forming the transition from a round to a rectangular pipe or vice versa, is usually called a "transformer." The loss in such ducts is close to the average of round and rectangular pipes of the same length. It is seldom worthwhile to compute transformer losses in detail. Ordinarily, the transformer is considered as an additional length of round pipe, reading the friction loss from Fig. 5-1. If a substantial velocity change takes place in the transformer or, if it is abnormally short and abrupt, it must be treated as an expansion piece or a convergent duct.

Weather Protection

The weather caps illustrated in Fig. 5-18 are suitable protection for pipes discharging out-of-doors and for the air outlets of cyclones when lateral diversion of the blast is not objectionable. They should be firmly supported by three or more legs bolted or welded to the outside of the pipe. The tabulated resistances are expressed in feet of equivalent pipe. Weather caps applied to cyclone outlets whose flow is vortical, will impose resistances which can be stated as a fraction of the velocity head in the outlet as in Table 5-3.

Where the optimum disposal of any residual contaminant is desired, the vertical discharge design, Fig. 7-1, is recommended. The use of that type of weather bond also minimizes any reentry potential through nearby air-supply intakes.

Table 5-3. Resistance of Weather Caps

H/D	Resistance, Velocity Heads
1.0	0.10
0.75	0.18
0.50	0.73

CHAPTER 6

Piping Design

From a pneumatic standpoint, the design of a system of exhaust piping embraces the determination of:

1. The air volume entering each hood
2. The static suction at each hood
3. The volume rate of flow in each length of pipe
4. The velocity in each length of pipe
5. The total air volume to be handled by the fan
6. The static suction and back pressure at the fan inlet and outlet, respectively.

Unless the designer can compute these values with reasonable accuracy, he has no assurance that a given piping system will meet the legal or other predetermined requirements. Neither can he predict the power requirements of the system within the limits of accuracy expected from sound engineering. Chapter 5 has supplied data and has described methods for establishing individual losses in hoods, pipes, elbows, and fittings. The following pages will develop an orderly procedure for applying these losses to the design of a complete piping system.

Outline of Piping Design Procedure

The preferred design sequence is as follows, although some latitude in the order of the various steps is permissible:

1. Sketch a floor plan, reasonably close to scale, of the equipment to be exhausted.
2. List the equipment, number and size of branch pipes, and the expected minimum suction, velocity, or volume at each hood.
3. Make enough freehand sketches of hoods to permit estimation of entry coefficients, listing the latter opposite the equipment descriptions in the preceding table.

4. Select the minimum allowable conveying velocity for each section of the system, dependent upon the nature of the material to be transported by that section.
5. Compute the approximate volume-rate of flow into each hood and add these values to the table.
6. Study the floor plan and sketch one or more possible piping arrangements. Unless operating factors such as accessibility, available supporting structures or location of utilities dictate, locate the exhauster so that duct runs are as short as possible and so that smaller branches with their higher friction losses can enter the main close to the fan inlet and with minimum distance from hood to main or sub-main.
7. Use the volume and velocity lines on the friction chart, Fig. 5-1, to arrive at approximate branch pipe and main sizes, marking these on the piping sketch, together with the air volume flowing in each pipe. (*Note:* Thus far, no friction computations need be made and all values have been approximate. The sketches need not be accurate as the purpose of the work to this point is to arrive as quickly as possible at a stage where broad overall judgment can be applied.)
8. Inspect the piping sketch to see whether branches originating at some distance from the main should be joined with others, forming sub-mains, to reduce friction; whether the arrangement should be changed to economize pipe sizes; whether building details, machinery or other obstructions interfere with pipe runs whose sizes are now known approximately; and to arrive at a final compromise arrangement.
9. Draw the piping scheme finally selected, usually a plan view only, leaving plenty of room for notes covering volumes, velocities, pressures, and similar items.
10. Calculate pressure losses, volumes, velocities, and pipe sizes as explained in previous chapters and illustrated in the examples which follow, recording values on the piping diagram.
11. Check all calculations.
12. Make shop and erecting drawings and prepare a bill of material.

Necessity for Systematic Calculation

Flow calculations start at the entrance end of the branch most remote from the fan and proceed step-by-step through the main and the remaining branches to the fan. The computations are progressive and the values cumulative. Hence, errors in assumptions, methods, or arithmetic may reach serious proportions at the fan. Of necessity, therefore, a systematic and orderly method of calculation and tabulation of results must be adopted and followed rigidly. Opportunities for error are so numerous that all computations should be set down in a manner which will facilitate checking. Careless calculations on loose scratch paper invite gross errors and omissions. Printed forms, on the other hand, reflecting the engineers' standard practice, will promote systematic work.

Data Sheets

The engineer will find it convenient to have all commonly used design information concentrated in one place. Tables and charts may be copied or cut from catalogs and periodicals and pasted on a single large sheet of stiff cardboard or on the slide of the desk. The exact arrangement is unimportant but the data must be instantly available and in such convenient form as to forestall any temptation to guess. The following tables and charts are essential:

1. Diameters of circles (in inches) and areas (in square feet)
2. Velocity pressures and corresponding velocities
3. Coefficients of entry of typical hoods
4. Exhaust requirements for various applications, air volume, velocity, hood suction, pipe size or other pertinent data
5. Minimum conveying velocities
6. Friction-loss charts for pipe, hose, and elbows
7. Weights of pipe and elbows.

Blast Gates and Floor Sweeps

The practice of cutting off idle branches by means of blast gates is not recommended. The amount of saving in heat and power is not great enough to offset the disadvantages. The suction main must be designed for unduly high velocities if settlement is to be avoided when some gates are closed. The resistance pattern of branch and main changes with each combination of open and closed gates so that it is virtually impossible to predict flow-rates and pressures. Moreover, blast gates seldom serve their purpose over a long period; workmen become careless and slides are lost or damaged so that the system eventually operates with wide-open branches. Blast gates are useful only for floor sweeps which are generally used for very short periods. Floor sweeps have limited value except in woodworking plants. In most industries power floor-sweepers and industrial vacuum-cleaners achieve better, and more economical, housekeeping.

Calculation of Typical Exhaust Systems

The design procedure for two small exhaust systems is carried out in the following pages. The first, Fig. 6-1, is a system for the removal of wood waste. Its purpose is to promote good housekeeping, and to reduce accident and fire hazard. Recovery and salvage of the collected material is of no consequence. Intelligent layout, careful flow calculations, and the correct selection of the fan and dust separator will nearly always insure satisfactory dust control without the need for adjustment and correction after installation. Errors, if any, should be on the liberal side since flow in excess of the design intent is beneficial and the cost increase is small.

The second example is one in which flow adjustment after installation is inevitable. This system, shown in Fig. 6-2, services a spray dryer and a bagging station in a process industry. The product is packed for delivery at the bagging station and every pound which is picked up by the exhaust system is a pound diverted from shipment. It is impossible to know without a trial exactly what air volume and hood-face velocity is necessary to control the dust without picking up salable product. Hence, the designer must plan in advance for some means of adjusting the hood-flow to the exact degree which will give good dust control, with a minimum loss of usable material. He usually provides a slide gate which may be made

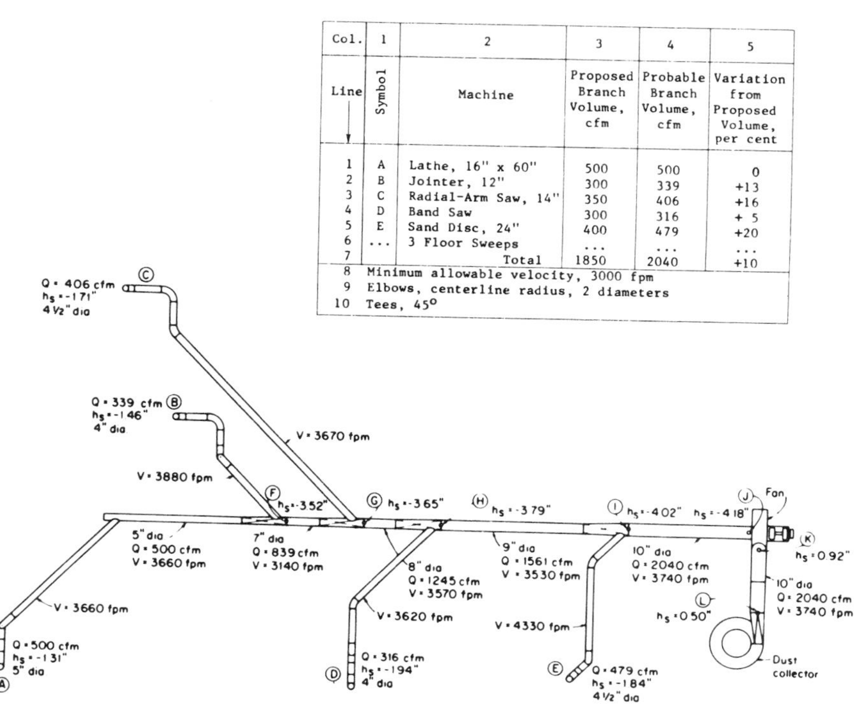

Col.	1	2	3	4	5
Line ↓	Symbol	Machine	Proposed Branch Volume, cfm	Probable Branch Volume, cfm	Variation from Proposed Volume, per cent
1	A	Lathe, 16" x 60"	500	500	0
2	B	Jointer, 12"	300	339	+13
3	C	Radial-Arm Saw, 14"	350	406	+16
4	D	Band Saw	300	316	+ 5
5	E	Sand Disc, 24"	400	479	+20
6	...	3 Floor Sweeps	...	...	...
7		Total	1850	2040	+10
8	Minimum allowable velocity, 3000 fpm				
9	Elbows, centerline radius, 2 diameters				
10	Tees, 45°				

Fig. 6-1. Pattern Shop exhaust system.

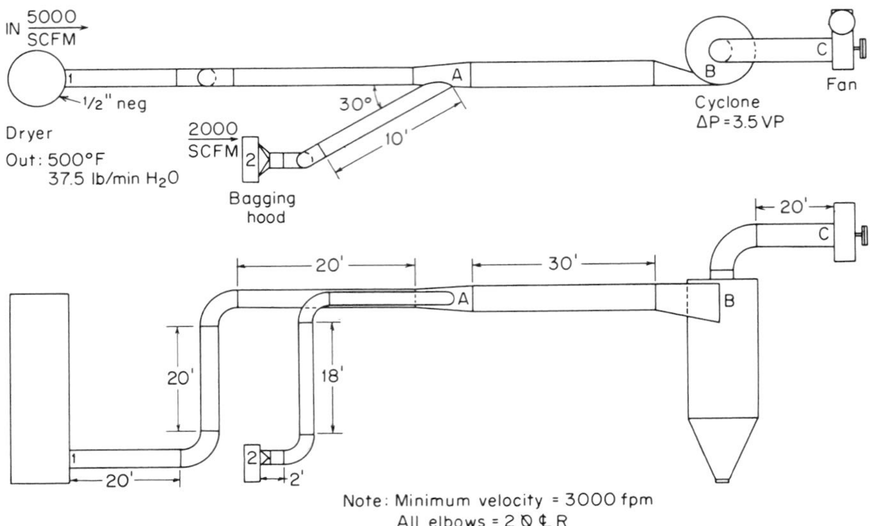

Fig. 6-2. The spray-dryer exhaust system.

tamper-proof by locking it after adjustment. As an alternative, he may arrange to bleed air into the system downstream from the hood.

Flow-regulating devices such as the gates and equalizers shown in Figs. 11-2c and 11-3, seldom are necessary or desirable in refuse-disposal systems where the material is of little or no value. On the other hand, in the process industries much of the collected matter is either a finished product or an intermediate, either of which can be reclaimed only at additional expense. For the refuse system the designer computes the flow in each branch, raising or lowering it to the desired value by reducing or increasing the branch resistance. This is accomplished by judicious selection of pipe sizes. When he designs a system handling a valuable product the designer follows the same steps to arrive at a computed flow which is amply large, but he also provides gates which can be adjusted by trial, to reduce the unwanted pick-up to an acceptable level.

In the following examples all elbows and tees have been translated into equivalent lengths of straight pipe, measured in feet. The resistances were then computed directly from these lengths using values taken from Fig. 5-1. Some engineers prefer to express the equivalent lengths in terms of pipe diameters and their resistances in velocity heads, taken from Figs. 5-3, 5-6, and 5-8. The choice is a matter of convenience and individual preference. The end results are the same, since both methods derive from the same basic data. The velocity-head method simplifies balanced branch calculations and is an excellent technique for field estimation should no reference be available.

Design of a Woodworking System

A small pattern shop exhaust system, illustrated in Fig. 6-1, has been chosen as an example of system computation. A large, and complex system, or one for a different industry is calculated in exactly the same way. Table 6-1a accompanying Fig. 6-1, lists in Col. 2, the machines to be exhausted, and in Col. 3, the desired air volumes. Floor sweeps are not included in the system load since they are closed off by blast gates except during their infrequent periods of use. In this example, items 1 through 8 of the procedural outline have been completed and the drawing represents the final piping arrangement.

The flow calculations take place in two steps. The first, represented by Table 6-1a, establishes the minimum pressure in the main suction pipe which will induce the desired rate-of-flow in each branch. This is the pressure at the junction of the branch and main and it includes both the hood suction and the pressure drop between the hood and the main. These computed pressures are trial figures only and seldom agree with the final values. They are merely the starting point for the second step which calculates the probable true pressures and flows which may be expected. Table 6-1b carries out this operation.

The following explanatory notes refer to the columns and line numbers of the tables:

Table 6-1a.

Cols. 1 and 2 are self-explanatory.

Col. 3 has been selected from Table 3-4, from state codes, or from experience.

Cols. 4 and 5 have been read from the friction chart, Fig. 5-1. (See Col. 10.) Any velocity over 3,000 fpm is acceptable.

Cols. 6 and 7 are obtained by scaling the layout and counting the elbows. As mentioned in Chapter 5, the tee is treated as an additional elbow since its pressure loss is approximately the same.

Col. 8 is taken from Fig. 5-7, for elbows.

Col. 9 is the sum of Cols. 6 and 8.

Col. 10 is read from the friction chart, Fig. 5-1, at the same time as the pipe size and velocity are obtained.

Col. 11 is the product of Cols. 9 and 10, divided by 100.

Col. 12 is estimated from freehand sketches of the hoods.

Col. 13 is the negative static pressure at the hood which will produce the flow of Col. 3 through the pipe connection of Col. 4, when the coefficient of entry is that of Col. 12.

Col. 14 is the sum of Cols. 11 and 13. This is the minimum negative pressure in the suction main which will produce the proposed flow in the branch.

The preceding computations are preliminary to the determination of the flows and pressures to be expected in the physical system. The conversion to the final figures takes place in Table 6-1b.

Table 6-1b.

Cols. 15 and 16 may be identified from the drawing, Fig. 6-1.

Col. 17 has been transferred from Col. 14, Table 6-1a.

Col. 18, line 1 is the pressure in the main for branch *AF*. Calculations start at the hood for which the expected pressure drop from hood to fan inlet is the greatest. This is generally, but not always, the most distant hood.

Col. 18, line 2 is the main line pressure for branch *BF* which joins branch *AF* at this point. Since the pressure-drop from the junction at *F*, to the atmosphere at *A* and *B* must be equal for both branches, the junction pressures must be the same.

Col. 19, line 2 computes the effect on the hood suction at *B* of the increased junction pressure at *F*. The hood suction increases in proportion to the increase in junction pressure.

Col. 20, line 2 gives the effect of the higher pressure on the branch volume.

Col. 21, line 2 is the product of the tentative volume, Col. 3, and the factor in Col. 20.

Col. 22, line 2 is the expected hood-suction obtained by multiplying the tentative suction, Col. 13, by the pressure ratio, Col. 19.

This completes the first stage of the adjustment of the proposed branch flows and hood pressures to the levels expected in the actual system. Thus far, the numerical work has been confined to lines 1 and 2. It will be seen from line 1, that the original conditions assumed for branch *AF* have remained unchanged. Line 2 shows that both the volume and hood pressure of branch *BF* have been raised because the junction pressure at *F* has been increased from 2.76 to 3.52 in. wg. We next examine the flow through the section of main *FG* to establish the pipe size and friction loss. The pressure at the next junction, *G*, will be the sum of the friction loss and the pressure at *F*.

Col. 23, line 3 is the sum of the branch volumes; Col. 21, lines 1 and 2.

Cols. 24, 25, and 30 are picked off the friction chart Fig. 5-1.

Cols. 26 to 29 inclusive, are taken from the piping layout.

Col. 31 is the product of Cols. 29 and 30, divided by 100, and is the pressure drop in section *FG*. This figure is added to that in Col. 18, line 2, and entered in Col. 18, line 4.

The process advances step-by-step; first, correcting the junction pres-

Table 6-1a. Computations for Pattern Shop Exhaust System *

Col.	1	2	3	4	5	6	7	8	9	10	11	12	13	14
			Proposed Branch Conditions							Friction, in. wg			Tentative Pressure, in. wg	
Line →	Branch Symbol	Machine	Volume Q, cfm	Velocity, V, fpm	Diameter, inches	Length, Straight Pipe, feet	Number Elbows plus One Tee	Straight Pipe Equivalent to Elbows, feet	Total Length, Pipe & Elbows, feet Col. 6 + Col. 8	Per 100 Feet	In Branch Col. 9 × Col. 10	Hood Entry Coefficient, C_e	At Hood $\left(\frac{V}{4005\ C_e}\right)^2 = \left(\frac{\text{Col. 4}}{4005\ \text{Col. 12}}\right)^2$	At Junction of Branch and Main
1	AF	Lathe – 16″ x 60″	500	3660	5	28	4	20	48	4.6	2.21	0.80	1.31	3.52
2	BF	Jointer – 12″	300	3440	4	13	4½	18	31	5.2	1.61	0.80	1.15	2.76
3	CG	Radial-arm Saw – 14″	350	3160	4½	22	3½	16	38	3.8	1.44	0.70	1.27	2.71
4	DH	Band Saw – 30″	300	3440	4	16	4	16	32	5.2	1.66	0.65	1.75	3.41
5	EI	Sand Disc – 24″	400	3620	4½	15	3½	16	31	4.9	1.52	0.80	1.28	2.80
6	—	3 Floor Sweeps	—	—	6	—	—	—	—	—	—	—	—	—
7	Proposed System Volume		1850	—	—	—	—	—	—	—	—	—	—	—

* All pressures are negative.

Table 6-1b. Computations for Pattern Shop Exhaust System *

Col.	15	16	17	18	19	20	21	22	23	24	25	26	27	28	29	30	31
		Junction Pressure, in. wg					Expected					In Section of Main				Friction, in. wg	
Line ⟶	Junction of Branch and Main	Section of Main	Tentative, From Col. 14	Expected, Col. 18 + Col. 31	Col. 18 ÷ Col. 17	$\sqrt{\text{Col. 18} \div \text{Col. 17}}$	Branch Volume, cfm Col. 3 × Col. 20	Hood Static Pressure, in. wg Col. 13 × Col. 19	Volume in Main, cfm Sum of Col. 21	Velocity in Main, fpm	Diameter of Main, inches	Straight Pipe, feet	Number of Elbows	Straight Pipe Equiv. to Elbows, feet	Total Length of Pipe & Elbows, feet	Per 100 Feet	In Section of Main, in. wg
1	AF		3.52	3.52	1.0	1.0	500	1.31									
2	BF		2.76	3.52	1.27	1.13	339	1.46									
3		FG							839	3140	7	6	—	—	6	2.20	0.13
4	CG		2.71	3.65	1.35	1.16	406	1.71									
5		GH							1245	3570	8	6	—	—	6	2.35	0.14
6	DH		3.41	3.79	1.11	1.05	316	1.94									
7		HI							1561	3530	9	12	—	—	12	1.95	0.23
8	EI		2.80	4.02	1.43	1.20	479	1.84									
9		IJ							2040	3740	10	8	—	—	8	2.00	0.16
10	J	Fan Inlet		4.18													
11		KL		0.42					2040	3740	10	9	1	12	21	2.00	0.42
12	L	Cyclone		0.50													
13	Fan, Total Pressure			5.10													

* Lines 1 to 10, inclusive: All pressures are negative.
Lines 11 to 13, inclusive: All pressures are positive.

sure; next, recomputing the branch volume; and finally, obtaining the pressure loss in the main to the next junction point. We arrive finally at the fan inlet, *J*, where we find the negative pressure to be 4.18 in. wg. In line 11 the friction loss of the discharge pipe is figured and recorded in Col. 18. A suitable cyclone has been selected and its probable back-pressure entered in Col. 18, line 12.

The arithmetic sum of lines 10, 11, and 12 in Col. 18, disregarding signs is the total pressure, line 13, to be developed by the fan. This is not the static pressure quoted in fan-rating tables. For a discussion of fan ratings and the fan-static pressure, see Chapter 9.

If a test of the completed system should show the arithmetic sum of the static pressures at the fan to fall between 4.8 and 5.4 in. wg, and the volume to be between 1990 and 2090 cfm, the design requirements would be considered to have been met within the normal range of uncertainty.

Balancing the System

In each instance the computed flow through the hoods equaled or exceeded the proposed values. In a small system such as in Fig. 6-1, most designers would make no effort to reduce the excess flow to conform more closely with the preliminary estimate. The reduction of power would be negligible, about 1/8 hp, and would be insufficient to justify the engineering effort. In a large system, or one with heavy flow through certain branches, the economic balance might be different. Also, if there were a deficiency of flow, rather than an excess in one or more branches, further treatment would be in order.

Perhaps the most common method for correcting deficient volume through one or more hoods is to raise the system pressure by increasing the fan speed. Generally, this is the least desirable procedure because it increases the flow through branches which are already adequately supplied. The power demand increases as the cube of the speed, often requiring a larger motor. The preferred practice is to regulate the flow by raising or lowering the resistance of individual branches. This operation is known as "balancing," or "equalizing." It is simply the process of selecting a pipe size for the offending branch, the computed resistance of which will exactly absorb the difference between the hood suction and the suction in the main when passing the desired flow. When so adjusting the branch size, the designer must be certain that the resulting velocity is sufficient to maintain the conveyed solids in suspension. Another cure is to insert equalizers, such as in Fig. 11-2c, in all branches with excess volume, with the expectation that the flow through the deficient branch will be raised to a satisfactory level. This remedy usually is applied when the deficiency is discovered after installation.

Restrictions of this type are sometimes useful as a means for reducing pick-up of valuable product caused by excessive hood-face velocity. The conveying velocity must not be reduced to a point where settlement in the pipe can occur. Equalizers must be made tamper-proof by riveting, soldering, or welding. They must be rugged enough to resist abrasive wear which might destroy their effectiveness.

A vacuum booster, Fig. 5-21, will improve the performance of a branch which is close to the fan or where there is substantial flow through the main; perhaps 5 to 10 times that in the branch. In summary, it is best to balance the system while it is still on the drawing board, but when through error or unforeseen circumstances the completed system is deficient in some respect, field remedies are still available.

Influence of Density Changes

The pattern shop example is typical of many exhaust systems where the air density needs no correction for slight changes in temperature, humidity, or altitude. For locations above 2000 feet, for temperatures above 150F, and for systems releasing quantities of water vapor or gases, other than air, density corrections are indicated. Correction factors for temperature and altitude are shown in Table 6-2, or can be calculated from:

1. For altitude—Air density varies with barometric pressure.
2. For temperature—Air density varies directly in proportion to absolute temperature (absolute zero is —460F).
3. The density for water vapor can be obtained from high temperature psychrometric charts, steam tables, or from the gas constant where:

   cfm water vapor at standard air conditions (70F, 29.92 in. Hg) =

   $$\frac{387 \text{ (gas constant)}}{18 \text{ (mol. weight water)}} \times \text{pounds water.}$$

   (Water vapor, standard conditions, equals 21.5 cu ft/pound or 0.62 density of air.)

In turbulent flow, viscosity has little influence on friction factor for air, although in laminar flow its effect substantially offsets the reduction of density.

Design of System for Process Material

The spray-dryer exhaust system, Fig 6-2, demonstrates the effect of change in density on system calculations. It involves high-temperature air and substantial water vapor from the dryer which then mixes with

Table 6-2. Density Factors for Change in Temperature and Elevation

Temperature—Density			Altitude—Density		
Temp., F	Density Factor	Wt. per cu ft	Elev., ft	Density Factor	Wt. per cu ft
0	1.152	.0864	0	1.000	.0749
70	1.000	.0749	500	.981	.0735
100	.946	.0709	1000	.962	.0721
150	.869	.0651	1500	.944	.0707
200	.803	.0602	2000	.926	.0694
250	.747	.0560	2500	.909	.0681
300	.697	.0522	3000	.891	.0668
350	.654	.0490	3500	.874	.0655
400	.616	.0462	4000	.858	.0643
450	.582	.0436	4500	.842	.0631
500	.552	.0414	5000	.826	.0619
550	.525	.0393	5500	.810	.0607
600	.500	.0375	6000	.795	.0596
650	.477	.0358	6500	.780	.0585
700	.457	.0342	7000	.766	.0574
750	.438	.0328	7500	.751	.0563
800	.421	.0315	8000	.737	.0552
850	.404	.0303	8500	.723	.0542
900	.390	.0292	9000	.710	.0532
950	.376	.0282	9500	.697	.0522
1000	.363	.0272	10000	.685	.0514

ambient air from the bagging hood branch. Before design of the system can start, the volume and density of 500F gas to be handled must be calculated:

5,000 scfm (375 pounds) heated to 500F =

$$\frac{5{,}000}{0.55 \text{ density factor}} = 9{,}100 \text{ cfm @ 500F}$$

37.5 pounds per minute water vapor =

$$37.5 \times \frac{387^1}{18} = \text{cfm @ 70F}$$

$$37.5 \times \frac{387}{18} \times \frac{1}{.55} = 1{,}455 \text{ cfm @ 500F}$$

Total exhaust volume from dryer =
9,100 + 1,455 = 10,555 cfm @ 500F

[1] Refer to item 3, in equation, preceding paragraph.

$$\text{with density of } \frac{375 \text{ pounds air} + 37.5 \text{ pounds water}}{10{,}555 \text{ cfm of mixture}} =$$

$$0.039 \text{ pounds/cu ft}$$

$$\text{Density factor} = \frac{\text{density of mixture}}{\text{density of standard 70F air}} = \frac{.039}{.075} = 0.52$$

Inspection of the layout will indicate that the bagging hood branch will have the governing resistance. The branch diameter is small and the air density is greater. The dryer branch calculations, Table 6-3, have been complicated by the 0.50 inch loss through the dryer. This loss includes such slight entrance or acceleration loss that it can be ignored when entry loss to the branch duct is calculated.

Calculations of the *SP* losses for Branch 1 and 2 indicate that Branch 1 must be restricted to introduce 1.52″ − 1.11″ = 0.41″ added resistance. Using the Equal Branch Resistance method, it means the 25 in. pipe diameter must be decreased so the velocity pressure, entrance or acceleration loss, and pipe resistance must equal the 1.52 in. less the dryer loss, or 1.02 in. at design conditions, or $\frac{1.02}{0.52} \doteq 1.95$ in. at standard air.

Entrance and acceleration loss	= 1.25 *VP*
60 ft (Approx. 30 diameters of new main) @ 65 diameters per *VP*	= 0.46 *VP*
2 elbows @ 0.27 *VP*	= 0.54 *VP*
	2.25 *VP*

$1\,VP = \frac{1.95''}{2.25} = 0.87''$ for 3,730 fpm. Reducing 25″ pipe to 23″ produces the balanced losses between Branch 1 and 2.

The junction of the two branches at *A* results in a mixture of:

Branch 1 — 5,000 *scfm* =
375 pounds dry air = 9,100 cfm @ 500F
37.5 pounds water vapor = 1,455 cfm @ 500F

Branch 2 — 2,000 *scfm* =
150 pounds dry air = 2,000 cfm @ 70F

To find temperature *T* of the mixture in the Main *A-C*:

Btu of the mixture in excess of 0F equals:

375 pounds × .24 specific heat × 500 =	45,000
37.5 pounds × .44 specific heat × 500 =	8,250
150 pounds × .24 specific heat × 70 =	2,520
562.5 pounds	55,770 Btu

Specific heat of the mixture equals:

$$\frac{.24\ (375 + 150) + .44 \times 37.5}{562.5 \text{ pounds}} = 0.26$$

Temperature of the mixture equals:

$$562.5 \text{ pounds} \times 0.26 \times T = 55{,}770 \text{ Btu}$$
$$T = 380F$$

Density factor for the mixture:

$$5{,}000 + 2{,}000 \text{ scfm Air} \times \frac{460 + 380}{460 + 70} = 11{,}100 \text{ cfm @ } 380F$$

$$800 \text{ cfm water vapor} \times \frac{460 + 380}{460 + 70} = \underline{1{,}270} \text{ cfm @ } 380F$$

$$12{,}370 \text{ cfm @ } 380F$$

$$\frac{562.5 \text{ pounds}}{12{,}250 \text{ cfm}} = .046 \text{ pounds per cubic foot}$$

$$\text{Density factor} = \frac{.046}{.075} = 0.615$$

Note the ease with which the density factor can be calculated from the absolute temperature ratio instead of consulting the temperature-density factor data from Table 6-2.

From the computation sheet, Table 6-3, the fan selected must have capacity for 12,370 cfm. As discussed in Chapter 9, to develop 3.06 in. *TP* at design conditions, speed required would be that for 5.00 in. *TP* at standard conditions although the horsepower indicated for 12,370 cfm at 5.00 in. would be reduced by the density factor.

A blast gate should be specified for Branch 2, for field adjustment, to provide good dust control without excessive product pick-up.

The System Characteristic Curve

When the pressure necessary to force a given air volume through a certain resistance is known the volume at any other pressure is easily computed from the expressions $V = 4{,}005\sqrt{H}$ or $H = \left(\frac{V}{4{,}005}\right)^2$. A system consisting of an aggregation of hoods, fittings, and piping may be treated as a single resistance. Therefore, knowing the computed pressure and volume at the fan, a curve can be drawn which describes the performance of the system under all conditions of flow. Figure 6-3 shows this curve for the system in Fig. 6-1. Crossing this curve is another showing the pressure-volume characteristics of a fan selected from a manu-

Table 6-3. Computations for Spray Dryer Exhaust System

Plant name ________ Refer to ________ Elevation ________ Factor ________ Remarks ________

Location ________ Temperature ________

Department ________

1	2	3	4	5	6	7	8		9	10	11	12	13	14	15	16	17	18	19
										Col. 7 plus Col. 9		Col. 10 x Col. 11 / 100	From Col. 6		1.00 plus Col. 14	Col. 13 times Col. 15	Col. 12 plus Col. 16	At junction	
No. of Br. or Main	Dia duct, in in.	Area duct, sq ft	Air volume, cfm		Vel, fpm	Length of duct, feet					Resistance in inches water gauge					Resistance in inches of water			corrected, cfm
			in Branch	in Main		straight runs	Number of elbows	Number of entries	equiv. length	total length	per 100	of run	one VP	entry loss (VP)	hood suct (VP)	hood suct.	static press.	gov. SP	
2	11	0.66	2000		3000	30	2	1	38	68	1.2	0.82	0.56	0.25	1.25	0.70	1.52	1.52	←
2		LOSS	THROUGH		DRYER @	500 F											0.50	0.50	
1	25	3.41	10,555		3100	60	2		76	136	0.44	0.60	0.60	0.25	1.25	0.75	1.19		IN BALANCE
										1.19"	FOR	STANDARD	AIR ×	0.52	DENSITY	FACTOR =		0.61	
																		1.11	
			LOSS	THROUGH	DRYER	@ 500 F											0.50	0.50	
1	23	2.89	10,555		3660	60	2		76	136	0.62	0.84	0.83	0.25	1.25	1.03	1.87"		←
										1.87"	FOR	STANDARD	AIR ×	0.52	DENSITY	FACTOR =		0.97	
																		~~1.41~~	
																		1.52	
AB	27	3.98		12,370	3120	30				30	0.4	0.12 ×	DENSITY	FACTOR		0.615	0.07	1.59	
B	27	3.98		12,370	3120								0.61	× 3.5	VP =	2.14"			
													× DENSITY		FACTOR	0.615	0.15	3.06	
BC	27	3.98		12,370	3120	20	1		40	60	0.4	0.24 ×	DENSITY		FACTOR	0.615	0.15	3.06	

Calculated fan characteristics for standard conditions — Corrected for temperature and density

Capacity (   ) 12.370 cfm — Fan, type and size ________ — ________ rpm 12.370 cfm — Motor ________

Fan TP $\frac{3.06}{.615}$ = 5.0 in. wg — ________ — ________ bhp 3.06 TP — V Belt ________

________ — ________ rpm ________ bhp — ________ SP — ________

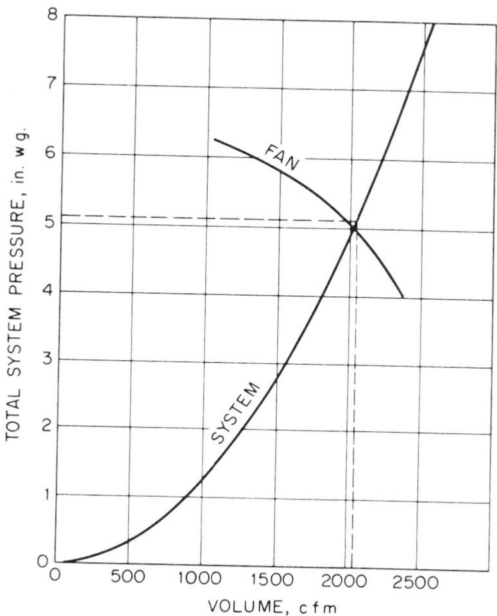

Fig. 6-3. Operating point of system established by fan and system characteristic curves.

facturer's catalog. Since the operating characteristics of the fan will always lie on this line and the characteristics of the system will lie on the system line, the point of intersection will be the operating condition of the combination. By chance, the fan selected matches the system requirements very closely. Usually the fan curve crosses either above or slightly below the desired operating point. In either instance the point of intersection is the probable operating condition.

This relationship requires pressure losses through each element of the system to vary as the square of the flow-rate. Certain types of collectors do not have this pressure-volume relationship. For example, the losses of fabric arresters increase as a first power function; some wet type collectors have almost a fixed pressure-loss regardless of volume change.

Reduction of Fire and Explosion Hazard

The following rules for the design of exhaust systems will minimize the likelihood of disastrous fires or explosions:

1. Do not connect spark-producing processes such as grinding, to exhaust systems handling combustibles.

2. Install adequate traps to take out heavy metallic objects near the source.
3. Do not run pipes through fire walls unless absolutely unavoidable.
4. Install automatic fire dampers on both sides of each wall through which an exhaust pipe passes.
5. Do not depend on solder for structural strength of any joint.
6. Allow at least 6-in. clearance between exhaust pipes and floors, ceilings, or combustible materials.
7. Electrically ground all fans, piping, dust arresters, and motors.
8. Treat as explosive all airborne finely-divided solids having considerable calorific value.[2]
9. When handling explosive substances, locate collectors on the roof or otherwise safely isolated.
10. Nonferrous fans are an added safety precaution against fire or explosion.

For more specific design information, including explosion venting for dusts noted in Item 8, the engineer is referred to the publications of the National Board of Fire Underwriters and the Associated Factory Mutual Fire Insurance Companies.

Make-up Air

No exhaust system design is complete until the method is resolved by which the exhausted air will be replaced. See Chapter 12.

Checking Design of Purchased Systems

The buyer of an exhaust system will find it advantageous to check the piping design by the same methods as shown in Table 6-1. By so doing he will determine whether the predicted pressures can actually be attained; whether the velocities in the various sections are adequate to prevent clogging; and whether the pipe sizes and arrangements are the most economical. To make such a check possible, the contractor should furnish hood sketches and estimated entry coefficients, a table of expected suctions and air quantities and a piping diagram similar to that in Fig. 6-1, with the proposed dimensions and lengths. Pressures and volumes should check within 10% and 5%, respectively.

[2]This includes flour, starch, grain, dust, sugar, milk powder, ground spices, phenolic molding powder, pulverized fuel, wood flour, aluminum buffings, magnesium dust and chips, hard rubber dust, and sulfur dust.

CHAPTER 7

Collectors

The preceding chapters have shown how to entrap the contaminant at the source and how to convey it, economically, through the system. There remains the problem of separating the contaminant from the air with which it is intimately intermingled.

Devices are available which will remove solid contaminants to any degree of cleanliness which the situation demands. Their characteristics and limitations are well-understood and the selection of the separating medium is dictated by the purpose for which the system is designed.

Removal of the highest fraction of dust at reasonable cost and reasonable maintenance should be the objective of all collector selections. For most applications the technology is sufficient to meet such objectives. The area of greatest difficulty is that of high-temperature gas systems where the temperature, and frequently corrosive nature of the gas-stream limits equipment types and demands expensive materials of construction and other complications.

The Collector as an Air-pollution Control Tool

Under the authority granted the Environmental Protection Agency under the Clean Air Acts, relatively uniform emission standards throughout the United States prescribe permissible quantities discharged from exhaust stacks against criteria based on Process Weight, Opacity, and the BAT (Best Available Technology) concept.

Process Weight Standards prescribe the maximum allowable solids-by-weight that can be discharged from industrial operations, incinerators, and indirect heat exchangers. Early efforts were based on concentrations in the exhaust stream defining limits in grains per standard cubic foot, or pounds of particulates per 1000 pounds of gas. Current trend follows the process weight concept—the larger operation with its heavier total process weight must provide a higher order of cleaning than the smaller process with its fewer pounds of generated contaminant.

Opacity Standards prescribe limits on the visibility of the particles in the stack discharge plume. Submicroscopic particles, especially smokes and fumes, contribute little to the particulate deposit at ground level or to the weight of the escaping particulates. However, they contribute to objectionable smog formation and to discoloration of interior and exterior surfaces as well to the esthetic quality of the atmosphere.

While opacity is a function of particle size, color, concentration, gas volume, location of emission point, and atmospheric conditions, visual measurements by trained observers have become an accepted monitoring technique. Its development represents an extension of the Ringelmann Smoke Chart evaluation of visual emissions from fossil-fuel-burning equipment.

BAT Standards postulate that those standards based on Process Weight or Opacity should be minimum values and that emissions should be reduced as much further as available collection equipment will permit. This approach has practically ruled out the use of dry centrifugal or inertial collection mechanisms except as primary elements preceding more efficient final collector designs. The increased capital and maintenance costs represented by this upgrading of collector performance has been practically ignored since the major area of investigations concerns the application feasibility of the more efficient designs.

Ironically, this emphasis has increased the use of fabric-type collectors with their very high collection efficiency, but has placed inplant environment into greater jeopardy, because a malfunction with fabric-type collectors usually results in reduced exhaust volume handled by the connected exhaust system.

The Collector as a Product Salvage Device

Particulate collectors not only assist pollution control but also are a means for recovery of usable solid particulate material carried in the gas stream. Collectors intended for either purpose are substantially identical. The type of collector selected will depend on the product or process. For example, the dry centrifugal or gravity trap design will separate larger particulates allowing the smaller fraction to be segregated by the final collector. Wet collectors will be used where the slurry can be returned to a liquid or wet phase of the process. Dry collectors will be used where the collected material is an end product or where return to process in a dry state is desired.

Preferred Characteristics of Air Cleaning Plants

Although no single type of dust separator embodies all virtues, the following characteristics are desirable:

1. The dust concentration in the cleaned air stream should be below the predetermined permissible limit.
2. It should retain its cleaning efficiency throughout its life.

3. Its cleaning efficiency should be substantially constant throughout its daily operating cycle.
4. Its cleaning efficiency should be nearly independent of the rate of airflow and the entering dust concentration.
5. It should require no shut-downs for cleaning or routine maintenance during normal working hours.
6. Normal maintenance and periodic disposal of collected dust should introduce no new hazard.
7. It should embody the usual elements of low cost, durability, minimum maintenance, minimum space, and the other factors which purchasers expect of all factory equipment.

Cleaning Efficiency

No great significance can be attached to the usual expression of cleaning efficiency wherein the weight of dust collected is compared with the weight of dust fed to the separator. The true criterion of separator quality is more nearly the degree of contamination of the cleaned air either by particle count, by opacity, or by weight of solids-per-unit air volume. To illustrate, a small cyclone received ground corn from a hammer mill at the rate of 16,000 lb per hr. The separating efficiency exceeded 99.5%, yet the quantity of dust was intolerable. More than a pound per minute of flour-like powder was discharged from the air outlet at a concentration of 8 grains per cu ft. This dust loading *after* cleaning is greater than that in most factory exhaust systems *before* cleaning. It is evident that if the usual cleaning efficiency figures are to be used, they must be weighted in accordance with the dust concentration of the entering air. Thus, high dust loadings require greater separating efficiency to reach a given discharge-cleanliness-level than do lower loadings. The larger the air volume at a given entering dust-loading the higher must be the cleaning efficiency, if the weight of emitted dust is to be kept within acceptable limits.

The effectiveness of an exhaust system often is measured by the presence or absence of visible dust in the stack discharge. If this is the criterion by which it is to be judged, high separating efficiency on a weight basis gives no assurance of a satisfactory system. In fact, it is possible to have 99 percent efficiency with no noticeable improvement in the appearance of the effluent. Visibility is a function of the light-reflecting characteristics of the contaminant. A factor of importance is the combined reflecting area of all of the particles in the discharge. The area of a small particle is very great with respect to its weight. Therefore, the escape of a multitude of low-micron particles may create a dirty discharge even though their total weight is only a small fraction of the initial dust load. With such submicroscopic materials as metallurgical fumes, air cleanliness in the order of 0.03 to 0.05 grains per cubic foot is necessary to remove the bulk of the visible plume.

Location of Collector and Cleaned-air Discharge

The locations of dry-type collectors should be selected to minimize the potential for fugitive dust escapement to their neighborhood or to employee property during the emptying of collector hoppers and the transfer and transport to a disposal site. A preferred location would be within a courtyard or enclosed area sheltered from prevailing winds.

For wet-type collectors where sludge is collected in tote boxes and transported by lift truck, spillage of entrained water is a housekeeping problem. A collector location that permits outdoor transfer rather than movement along plant aisles has a distinct advantage.

Likewise, the location of the cleaned air discharge and its height can minimize the potential for reentry through air intakes and the problems arising from collector malfunction. In general, stacks should extend 10–15 feet above the roof or nearby higher ones. An upward discharge velocity of 2,500–3,500 fpm will produce good dispersion if not suppressed by weather caps or elbows. The preferable method of weather protection is illustrated in Fig. 7-1. Alternatively, a drain can be installed in the housing of a vertical up-discharge fan or in an elbow discharging into a vertical stack.

The stack location should be coordinated with intake air inlets, and the two separated as far as practical. The air intake openings should be kept close to the roof. The rapid diffusion of escaping contaminants from the taller collector stacks will keep reentry to a minimum in spite of downwash or eddies created by wind patterns.

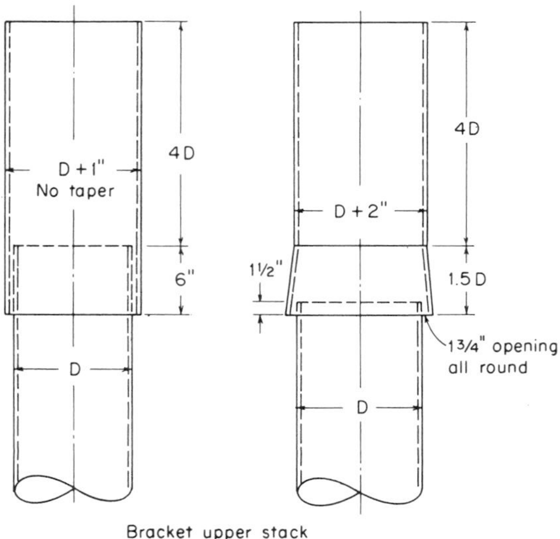

Fig. 7-1. Vertical discharge caps. By permission from ACGIH, *Industrial Ventilation Manual* (January 1968), and "Estimating Length Limits for Drain Type Stacks," by J.S. McKarns; R.G. Confer; and R.S. Brief, *Heating, Piping, and Air Conditioning*, Vol. 37, No. 7 (July 1965).

Size Properties and Settling Rates of Dusts

Particles smaller than 0.1 micron are commonly termed smokes. They are in active Brownian movement. Gravity separation is theoretically and practically impossible in this range. Larger particles, falling in still air, attain velocities at which the air resistance exactly balances the force of gravity. Known as the *terminal velocity*, this is the maximum speed of free-fall which the particle can attain. Finely divided dusts reach their terminal velocities almost instantly. Table 7-1 gives the calculated settling rates of spherical particles in still air at 70F for material of specific gravity of 1.0. Since actual dust particles are far from spherical, and since true, still-air conditions do not exist in practice, the rate of fall as determined by experiment is not far from one-half the values in Table 7-1. Table 7-2 lists the approximate median size of a number of airborne dusts. In order to compare the micron dimensions of particles with the more familiar standard screen-mesh numbers, Table 7-3 is presented.

Table 7-1. Approximate Settling Rate of Spheres (sp gr 1.0) in Still Air at 70F

Diameter, Microns	Rate of Fall	
	Ft per min	In. per hr
5000	1750	. . .
1000	790	. . .
500	555	. . .
100	59.2	. . .
50	14.8	. . .
10	0.592	. . .
5	0.148	. . .
1	0.007	5
0.5	0.002	1.4
0.1	0.00007	0.05
Smaller	0 Brownian movement	0

Mechanics of Separation

One characteristic is common to all types of dust separator. Each particle must be acted upon by some force which does not act upon the entraining air or acts upon it in a different, or lesser, degree so that the particle will move from the conveying air stream to a region where the conveying forces are less effective or non-existent or counteracted by more powerful forces of retention. In all separators the particle must move through some distance laterally across the air stream. At its destination it must be entrapped in

Table 7-2. Approximate Median Size of Airborne Dusts*

Kind of Dust	Median Size, Microns
Outdoor dust	0.5
Sand blasting	1.4
Granite cutting	1.4
Trap rock milling	
Crusher house	1.4
Screen house	1.3
Disc crusher	0.9
Foundry parting compound	1.4
General foundry air	1.2
Talc milling	1.5
Slate milling	1.7
Marble cutting	1.5
Soapstone	2.4
Aluminum dust	2.2
Bronze dust	1.5
Anthracite coal mining	
Breaker air	1.0
Mine air	0.9
Coal drilling	1.0
Coal loading	0.8
Rock drilling	1.0

*The Determination and Control of Industrial Dust — Public Health Bulletin No. 217, U. S. Public Health Service, 1935.

some manner so that it cannot again enter the cleaned air. Six mechanisms[1] can be considered to be available to cause collection: gravity, centrifugal force, inertial impaction, direct interception, diffusion, and electrostatic effects. The magnitude of the collection effect of each mechanism is generally related to particle size; smaller particles requiring more effort and cost to remove.

Gravitational Force is usually restricted to applications in settling chambers.

Centrifugal Force is utilized in cyclonic dust collectors where a gas is caused to rotate in vortex flow.

[1] American Industrial Hygiene Association, *Air Pollution Manual*, 1968.

Table 7-3. Micron Dimensions of Standard Sieves

Sieve Designation*		Open-ing, In.	Sieve Designation*		Open-ing, In.	Microns	Approx. Sub Mesh
Microns	U. S. Std. Sieve No.		Microns	U. S. Std. Sieve No.			
4760	4	0.187	420	40	0.0165	35	450
4000	5	0.157	350	45	0.0138	30	500
3360	6	0.132	297	50	0.0117	20	625
2830	7	0.111	250	60	0.0098	10	1250
2380	8	0.0937	210	70	0.0083	5	2500
2000	10	0.0787	177	80	0.0070	2	6250
1680	12	0.0661	149	100	0.0059	1	12500
1410	14	0.0555	125	120	0.0049	. . .	. . .
1190	16	0.0469	105	140	0.0041	. . .	. . .
1000	18	0.0394	88	170	0.0035	. . .	. . .
840	20	0.0331	74	200	0.0029	. . .	. . .
710	25	0.0280	62	230	0.0024	. . .	. . .
590	30	0.0232	53	270	0.0021	. . .	. . .
500	35	0.0197	44	325	0.0017	. . .	. . .

*ASTM Standard Specifications for Sieves for Testing Purposes, E 11-26.

Inertial Impaction occurs as a flowing fluid diverges to pass around an object in the stream. The inertia of particles carried in the fluid causes them to continue forward in a more nearly straight path. They are deflected less than the conveying fluid and may impact on the object.

Direct Interception arises from the finite dimensions of the small particles and is essentially a correction factor. It takes into consideration the possibility that while the center of the particle, whose trajectory has been calculated, may pass by the object placed in the gas, the particle may still come in contact with the object due to its finite width. Particle impaction and direct interception occur on spray water droplets in scrubbers of all types, and on filter fibers and granules. The larger the particle or the smaller the obstruction, the greater the chances for impaction. Direct interception is independent of velocity, while impaction increases with velocity. Both forces increase approximately as the square of the particulate diameter.

Diffusion occurs when particles become small enough (less than 0.5 micron) to have reasonable motion under the action of molecular impacts. Gas containing small particles must remain in the collector for a reasonable period because diffusion is a relatively slow process. This limits practical gas cleaning applications of diffusion to low velocity, high efficiency, fibrous or granular filters, which operate almost entirely through mechanisms of diffusion and direct interception. Diffusion rate is independent of particle density, and increases as velocity decreases.

Electrostatic mechanisms operate when either the collecting object or the particle—or both—carry an electrostatic charge or when the particle distorts an externally applied electric field.

Utilization of Collection Mechanisms

It is evident that for effective separation, the differential force acting upon the particle must be as great as possible and that the distance through which the particle moves must be a minimum. Since the particle must traverse the air stream laterally, the stream must be as narrow as possible or must be broken into a number of streams of small dimensions. Practically, some of the effect of the forces tending to separate the particle from the gas stream is nullified by reentrainment during either the separation cycle or during its removal to a storage receptacle. Reentrainment is especially significant in the dry type of collectors. In wet collectors, particulates are trapped and held in the liquid scrubbing media except for those reentrained during evaporation of the liquid droplet while suspended in the air stream.

Types of Particulate Collectors

The principal types of industrial particulate-arresting devices are:

1. Gravity chambers
2. Centrifugal, or inertial separators
3. Fabric collectors
4. Wet scrubbers
5. Electrostatic precipitators.

Intermediate types may employ a combination of operating principles as illustrated by gravity-inertial settling chambers or centrifugal air washers. The cleaning plant may consist of a single dust-removing device or of two or more cleaners in sequence. The two cleaners of a tandem pair are selected for their ability to perform complementary functions. The first cleaner, usually a cyclone or gravity separator, removes the larger and heavier constituents comprising the major dust-loading by weight, whereas the second takes out the finer particles which constitute the majority by count of particles.

It is interesting to note that the above types of collectors are the same as those available a generation or more ago. This is in spite of the promise of technological breakthroughs anticipated with the national emphasis on improved air quality, both external and inplant. Except for design modifications that improve reliability and reduce capital or maintenance cost, the period produced the following major introductions:

1. Fabrics that withstand high gas temperatures, extending the application of fabric arresters into hot gas cleaning fields.
2. Introduction of the pulse-jet type of fabric collector cleaning action which permits higher air to cloth ratios, relatively constant pressure loss, and the ability to operate continuously without shutting down compartments for dust cake removal.
3. Introduction of the high-energy wet scrubber, which extended the cleaning efficiency of wet collectors on fine particulates to that of fabric arresters and electrostatic precipitators.

Characteristics of Particulate Collectors

Relative range of minimum particle sizes removed with substantial efficiency is shown by collector groups in Table 7-4. Data must be treated as relative since collector performance will vary with particle shape, density, concentration, characteristics of the gas stream and, in some cases, the size of the collection device.

In general, for a given category, the design requiring the greater energy input will be the more efficient. As collectors are not classifiers, there will be a substantial overlapping of size range in both the collected fraction and the effluent. Most collectors have a built-in performance characteristic and there

Table 7-4. Approximate, Minimum-particle Size for which Various Collector Types are Suitable

Collector Type	Minimum Particle Size, in Microns
Gravity	200
Inertial (Chamber type)	50 to 150
Centrifugal	
Large-diameter cyclone	40 to 60
Intermediate-diameter cyclone	20 to 30
Small-diameter cyclone	10 to 15
Fan type	15 to 30
Scrubber	
Pressure drop 3 in. to 6 in.	2.0 to 3.0
High energy	0.25 to 1.0
Fabric Filter	0.25
Electrostatic precipitator	0.25 to 1.0

Table 7-5. Collector Types used in Industry

Operation	Concentration	Particle Sizes	Cyclone	High Eff. Centrifugal	Wet Collectors		Fabric Arrester	Hi-Volt. Electrostatic	See Remark No.
					Medium Pressure	High Energy			
CERAMICS									
a. Raw product handling	light	fine	rare	seldom	frequent	no	frequent	no	1
b. Fettling	light	fine to medium	rare	occasional	frequent	no	frequent	no	2
c. Refractory sizing	heavy	coarse	seldom	occasional	frequent	rare	frequent	no	3
d. Glaze & vitr. enamel spray	moderate	medium	no	no	usual	no	occasional	no	
CHEMICALS									
a. Material handling	light to moderate	fine to medium	occasional	frequent	frequent	frequent	frequent	rare	4
b. Crushing, grinding	moderate to heavy	fine to coarse	often	frequent	frequent	occasional	frequent	no	5
c. Pneumatic conveying	very heavy	fine to coarse	usual	occasional	rare	rare	usual	no	6
d. Roasters, kilns, coolers	heavy	med-coarse	occasional	usual	usual	frequent	rare	often	7
COAL MINING AND POWER PLANT									
a. Material handling	moderate	medium	rare	occasional	frequent	no	frequent	no	8
b. Bunker ventilation	moderate	fine	occasional	frequent	occasional	no	frequent	no	9
c. Dedusting, air cleaning	heavy	med-coarse	frequent	frequent	occasional	no	often	no	10
d. Drying	moderate	fine	rare	occasional	frequent	occasional	no	no	11
FLY ASH									
a. Coal burning—chain grate	light	fine	no	occasional	no	no	no	no	12
b. Coal burning—spreader stoker	moderate	fine to coarse	no	usual	no	no	occasional	occasional	
c. Coal burning—pulverized fuel	heavy	fine	no	frequent	no	no	occasional	usual	13
d. Wood burning	varies	coarse	occasional	occasional	no	no	no	no	14
FOUNDRY									
a. Shakeout	light to moderate	fine	rare	rare	usual	seldom	occasional	no	15
b. Sand handling	moderate	fine to medium	rare	rare	usual	no	occasional	no	16
c. Tumbling mills	heavy	med-coarse	no	no	frequent	no	usual	no	17
d. Abrasive cleaning	moderate to heavy	fine to medium	no	no	frequent	no	usual	no	18
GRAIN ELEVATOR, FLOUR AND FEED MILLS									
a. Grain handling	light	medium	frequent	occasional	rare	no	usual	no	19
b. Grain dryers	light	coarse	?	?	no	no	no	no	20
c. Flour dust	moderate	medium	often	often	rare	no	usual	no	21
d. Feed mill	moderate	medium	often	often	occasional	no	frequent	no	22

Table 7-5 (Continued). Collector Types used in Industry

Operation	Concen-tration	Particle Sizes	Cyclone	High Eff. Centrifugal	Wet Collectors: Medium Pressure	Wet Collectors: High Energy	Fabric Arrester	Hi-Volt. Electro-static	See Remark No.
METAL MELTING									
a. Steel blast furnace	heavy	varied	frequent	rare	rare	frequent	no	frequent	23
b. Steel open hearth, basic oxygen	moderate	fine to coarse	no	no	no	often	rare	frequent	24
c. Steel electric furnace	light	fine	no	no	no	occasional	usual	rare	25
d. Ferrous cupola	moderate	varied	no	no	rare	frequent	frequent	rare	26
e. Non-ferrous reverberatory	varied	fine	no	no	rare	occasional	usual	?	27
f. Non-ferrous crucible	light	fine	no	no	rare	rare	occasional	no	28
METAL MINING AND ROCK PRODUCTS									
a. Material handling	moderate	fine to medium	rare	occasional	usual	no	considerable	no	29
b. Dryers, kilns	moderate	med-coarse	frequent	frequent	frequent	occasional	rare	occasional	30
c. Cement rock dryer	moderate	fine to medium	rare	frequent	occasional	rare	rare	occasional	31
d. Cement kiln	heavy	fine to medium	rare	frequent	no	no	usual	usual	32
e. Cement grinding	moderate	fine	rare	rare	no	no	usual	rare	33
f. Cement clinker cooler	moderate	coarse	occasional	occasional	?	no	occasional	no	34
METAL WORKING									
a. Production grinding, scratch brushing, abrasive cut off	light	coarse	occasional	occasional	considerable	no	considerable	no	35
b. Portable and swing frame	light	medium	rare	frequent	frequent	no	usual	no	
c. Buffing	light	varied	frequent	rare	frequent	no	rare	no	36
d. Tool room	light	fine	frequent	frequent	frequent	no	frequent	no	37
e. Cast iron machining	moderate	varied	rare	occasional	considerable	no	considerable	no	38
PHARMACEUTICAL AND FOOD PRODUCTS									
a. Mixers, grinders, weighing, blending, bagging, packaging	light	medium	rare	frequent	frequent	no	usual	?	39
b. Coating pans	varied	fine to medium	rare	rare	frequent	no	frequent	no	40
PLASTICS									
a. Raw material processing	(See comments under Chemicals)								41
b. Plastic finishing	light to moderate	varied	rare	occasional	frequent	?	frequent	no	42
RUBBER PRODUCTS									
a. Mixers	moderate	fine	no	no	frequent	no	usual	no	43
b. Batchout rolls	light	fine	no	no	usual	no	frequent	no	44
c. Talc dusting and dedusting	moderate	medium	no	no	frequent	no	usual	no	45
d. Grinding	moderate	coarse	often	often	frequent	no	often	no	46
WOODWORKING									
a. Woodworking machines	moderate	varied	usual	occasional	rare	no	frequent	no	47
b. Sanding	moderate	fine	rare	occasional	occasional	no	usual	no	48
c. Waste conveying, hogs	heavy	varied	usual	rare	occasional	no	usual	no	49

is little that can be done to improve or to scale down its efficiency through modifications in the field. For most installations, performance will not be adjusted to permissible emission standards, but will be selected from a design that has a high, built-in collection ability for the operation to be controlled. Table 7-5[2] reviews a number of typical industrial operations and their appropriate types of collectors.

Remarks Referred to in Table 7-5

1. Dust released from bin filling, conveying, weighing, mixing, pressing, forming. Refractory products, dry pan, and screening operations more severe.
2. Operations found in vitreous enameling, wall and floor tile, pottery.
3. Grinding wheel or abrasive cut-off operation. Dust abrasive.
4. Operations include conveying, elevating, mixing, screening, weighing, packaging. Category covers so many different materials that recommendation will vary widely.
5. Cyclone and high efficiency centrifugals often act as primary collectors followed by fabric or wet type.
6. Usual set up uses cyclone as product collector followed by fabric arrester for high overall collection efficiency.
7. Dust concentration determines need for dry centrifugal precleaners. High temperatures are usual and corrosive gases not unusual.
8. Conveying, screening, crushing, unloading.
9. Remote from other dust producing points. Separate collector usual.
10. Heavy loading suggests final high efficiency collector for all locations.
11. Loadings and particle sizes vary with the different drying methods.
12. Public nuisance from boiler blow-down can be a problem.
13. Higher efficiency of electrostatic or fabric indicated. Occasionally used in conjunction with dry centrifugal.
14. Public nuisance from settled wood char indicates collectors are needed.
15. Hot gases and steam usually involved.
16. Steam from hot sand, adhesive clay bond involved.
17. Concentration very heavy at start of cycle.
18. Heaviest load from airless blasting due to higher cleaning speed. Abrasive shattering greater with sand than with grit or shot. Amounts removed greater with sand castings, less with forging scale removal, least when welding scale is removed.
19. Operations such as car unloading, conveying, weighing, storing.
20. Collection equipment expensive but public nuisance complaints are more frequent.
21. In addition to grain handling, cleaning rolls, sifters, purifiers, conveyors, as well as storing, packaging operations are involved.
22. In addition to grain handling, bins, hammer mills, mixers, feeders, conveyors, bagging operations need control.
23. Primary dry trap and high efficiency Wet Scrubbing or Electrostatic is required.
24. Air-pollution control expensive for open hearth, accelerating the use of substitute melting equipment such as Basic Oxygen and Electric-Arc.
25. Fabric collectors have found extensive application for this air pollution problem.
26. High energy Wet Scrubbing or Fabric Collectors are the usual selections. Fabric requires controlled cooling through cooling towers or heat exchangers.
27. Corrosive gases can be a problem, especially in secondary aluminum.
28. Zinc oxide plume can be troublesome in certain plant locations.
29. Crushing, screening, conveying, storing involved. Wet ores often introduce water vapor in exhaust air stream.
30. Dry centrifugals used as primary collectors, followed by final cleaner.
31. Collection equipment installed primarily to prevent public nuisance.
32. Collectors usually permit salvage of material in addition to air pollution prevention.
33. Salvage value of collected material high. Same equipment used on raw grinding before calcining.
34. Coarse abrasive particles readily removed in primary collector types, temperature surges during upset conditions a problem, especially with Fabric Collectors.
35. Roof discoloration, deposition on autos can occur with cyclones and with dry centrifugal.
36. Linty particles and sticky buffing compounds can cause trouble in high efficiency centrifugals and fabric arresters. Fire hazard is also often present.
37. Unit collectors extensively used, especially for isolated machine tools.
38. Dust ranges from chips to fine floats including graphitic carbon.

[2] "Guideposts To Dust Collection Equipment," by J. M. Kane, *Plant Engineering*, November 1954. Revised by the author for this Fifth Edition.

39. Materials involved vary widely. Collector selection may depend on salvage value, toxicity, sanitation yardsticks.
40. Controlled temperature and humidity of supply air to coating pans makes recirculation from coating pans desirable.
41. Manufacture of plastic compounds involves operations allied to many in chemical field and varies with the basic process employed.
42. Operations are similar to woodworking and collector selection involves similar considerations.
43. Concentration is heavy during feed operation. Carbon black and other fine additions make collection and dust-free disposal difficult.
44. Often, no collection equipment is required. Contaminant is mainly fumes.
45. Salvage of collected material often dictates type of high efficiency collector.
46. Fire hazard from some operations must be considered.
47. Bulky material. Storage for collected material is considerable, bridging from splinters and chips can be a problem.
48. Production sanding produces heavy concentration of particles too fine to be effectively caught by cyclones or dry centrifugals.
49. Primary collector invariably indicated with concentration and partial size range involved, wet or fabric collectors when used are employed as final collectors.

GRAVITY CHAMBERS

Gravity separators are seldom used except as traps associated with local exhaust hoods. They are wasteful when applied as primary separators in large central systems. Their separating efficiency is limited to particles of 200 microns and larger such as saw edgings, blocks, tramp metal and similar large and heavy objects. They must be large in cross section so that the suspension velocity is 300 fpm or less, and must be long enough to provide adequate settlement time. Usually, they are more costly than a conventional cyclone of equal capacity, their pressure drop is no lower, and their cleaning efficiency is inferior.

Miscellaneous Traps

All traps in which a change of direction of flow takes place utilize inertia or centrifugal force in some degree. Thus, while the trap in Fig. 7-2a is essentially a gravity trap, some inertial separation takes place. Likewise, some gravity separation occurs in the inertial trap in Fig. 7-2b. Figure 7-3 illustrates an effective trap for the removal of stray metal from cotton. Were the bottom of the vertical pipe to be blanked off by a solid cap, the pipe would soon fill with matted cotton. Enough air is admitted through the perforations to float the cotton but not the metal. The difference in specific gravity of metal and cotton is so great that the area of the secondary-air inlet is not critical. However, sufficient air must be admitted through the perforations to maintain adequate conveying velocity in the vertical pipe even though the air supply through the hopper is cut off by excessive quantities of cotton.

Hood Traps

Buffing hoods may be designed to incorporate traps to catch and retain small work pieces twisted out of the operator's grasp. These parts often are salvageable and, in any event, should be kept out of the fan and separator.

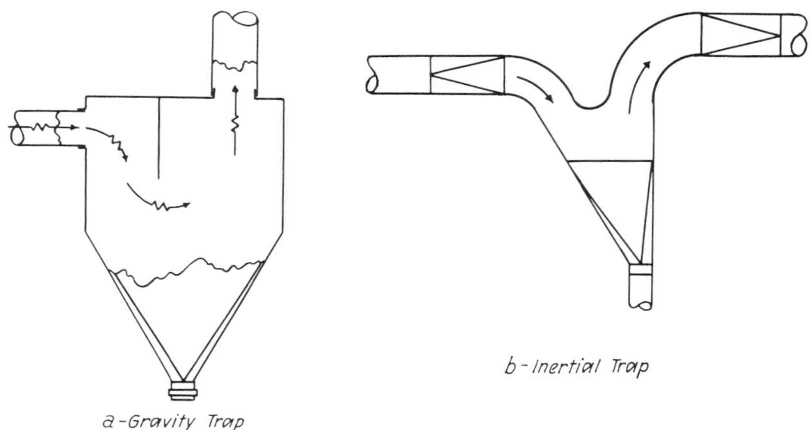

Fig. 7-2. Gravity and inertial traps.

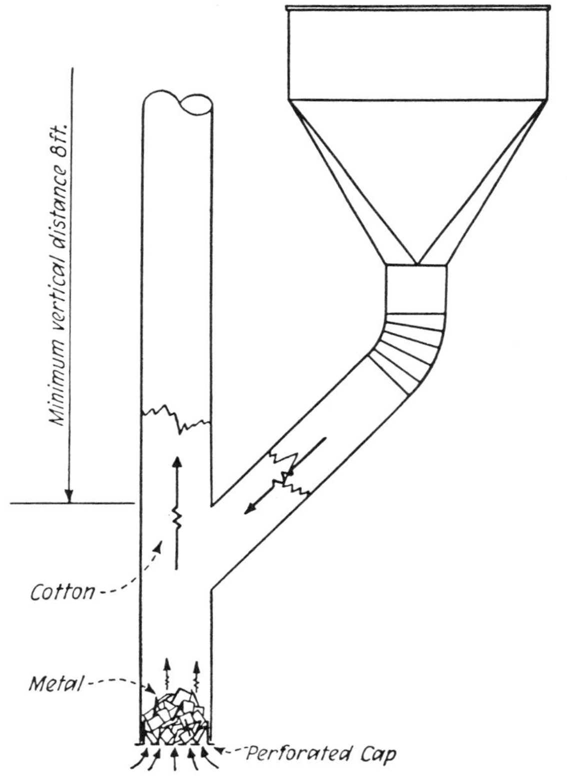

Fig. 7-3. Tramp iron trap.

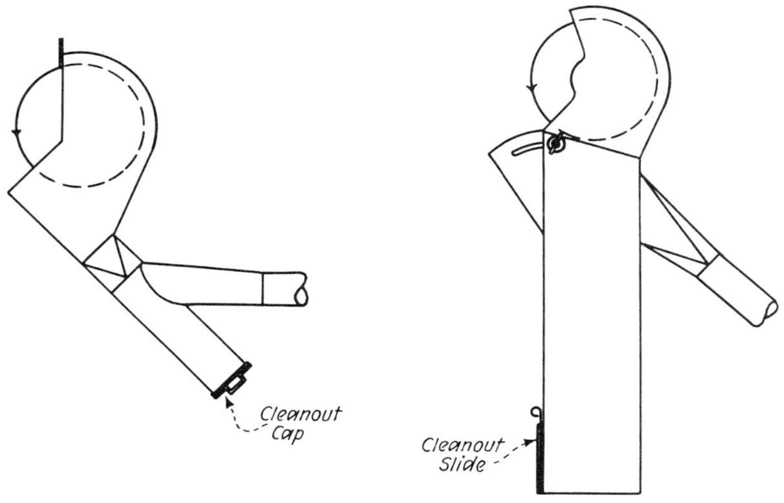

a. Buffing hood

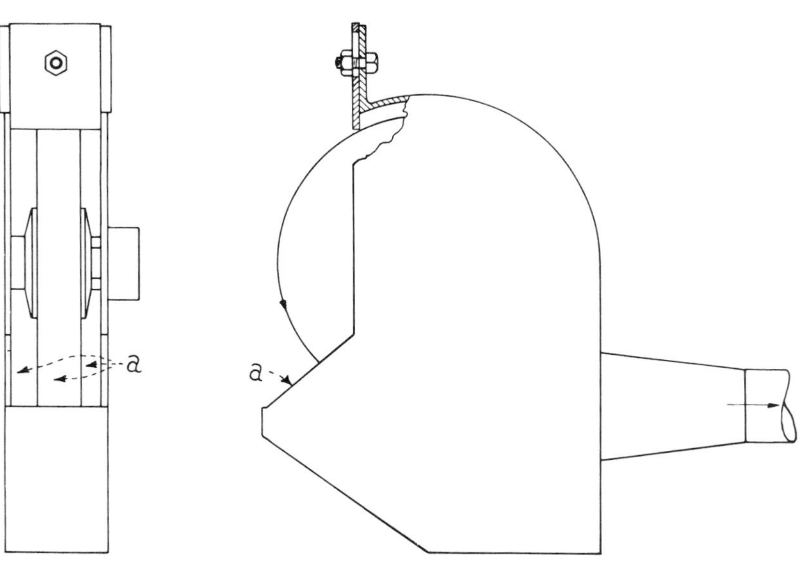

b. Grinding hood

Fig. 7-4 Hood traps.

Figure 7-4a illustrates common constructions. The grinder hood, Fig. 7-4b, can be made to serve the same purpose by extending the forward lip and by deepening the portion below the pipe connection. A successful variant of this hood replaces the metal pan below the wheel with a sheet rubber, basket-like extension which not only catches lost parts but also prevents bruises and scratches on the operator's arms and hands.

CYCLONES

Vortical Flow Through Cyclone

An ordinary cyclone appears in Fig. 7-5. Dusty air enters the tangential inlet, whirls through several revolutions in the body and cone, depositing its dust load, and departs, still whirling, through the axial cylindrical air-outlet. Under the influence of centrifugal force, the dust particles which have been dispersed throughout the entering stream tend to concentrate in the thin layer of air next to the cyclone wall. The downward helical motion of the main air-stream and the discharge of a small quantity of air through the dust outlet tend to project the separated solids into the dust bin.

Two distinct vortices are present in a cyclone. One is the large-diameter, descending helical current in the body and cone, and the other, an ascending helix of small diameter which extends upward from the region of the dust outlet, through the inner cylinder, to the atmosphere. As soon as the lower end of the inner cylinder is reached, the inner layers of the larger, vortical current detach themselves in an effort to escape into the low-pressure region along the cyclone axis. Separation of more and more of the air from the outer vortical stream occurs as the latter approaches the apex of the cone until, finally, all of the descending current has joined the rising inner vortex.

In its passage from the inlet to the apex of the cone, a dust particle has been subjected to tangential, axial, and radial forces. The latter are the inward drag of the air escaping into the inner vortex and the opposing centrifugal force of rotation. If the downward airflow has been smooth and unbroken, the dust which is now coasting spirally downward will pass out of the dust outlet with minimum reentrainment. Exploratory studies of vortical flow in cyclones indicate that the rising inner vortex, or core, has a diameter equal to approximately ⅔ that of the air outlet or inner cylinder. It is at the boundary between the inner and outer vortices that the highest tangential velocity and, therefore, the highest separating force exists. For this reason it is believed that some of the dust which may have been reentrained at the dust outlet is re-precipitated into the outer vortex as it passes upward toward the mouth of the inner cyliner. The probability of re-precipitation suggests that a relatively long cyclone is advantageous.

Factors Affecting Separation

Separation is best when the cyclone diameter is small, the inlet velocity high, the radial thickness of the air-stream a minimum, and the number of convolutions of the vortices relatively great. The centrifugal force of separation is proportional to the square of the velocity and inversely proportional to the radius of rotation. Resistance to separation is a function of the radial distance the dust particle must travel to reach the cyclone wall, its gravitational settling-rate in still air, and the length of time it is acted upon by centrifugal separating forces. The time of exposure to these forces is

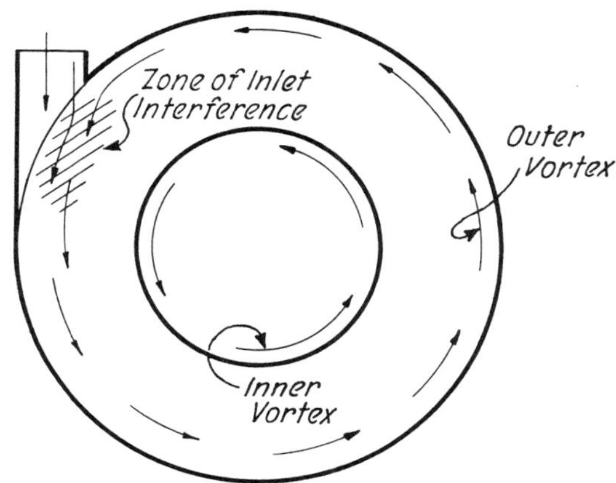

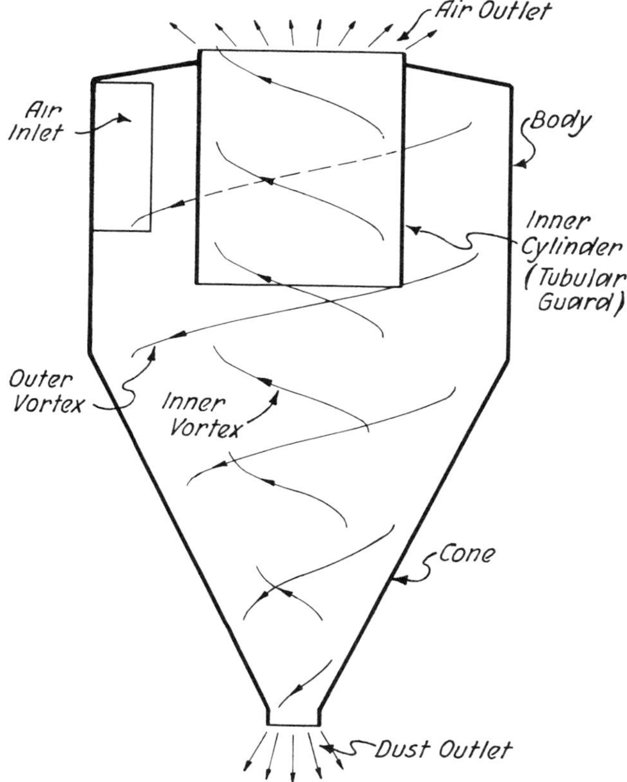

Fig. 7-5. Common cyclone.

a matter of rotational speed and the number of convolutions of the dust path from the inlet to dust outlet.

Separation Coefficient of Cyclones

The centrifugal force acting on a particle is:

$$F = \frac{wv^2}{gr}$$

where:

w = weight of particle, lb,
v = tangential velocity, ft per sec,
g = gravitational acceleration, ft per sec^2
r = radius of rotation, ft.

Since the weight, w, is the force of gravity acting on the particle, the sepa rating effect of a centrifugal cleaner as compared to gravity separation is: is:

$$S = \frac{v^2}{gr}$$

where S may be termed the "separation coefficient." The separation coefficient of a gravity chamber is, of course, 1.0. The separation coefficient has been plotted in Fig. 7-6, for various diameters of rotation and the more common tangential velocities.

A high separation coefficient generally is beneficial. There are exceptions, however. Experience has demonstrated that long ropy fibers and fluffy cotton are separated more effectively at lower rotational speeds and larger diameters. Also, coarse but light particles which tend to bounce on the cyclone walls sometimes escape into the inner vortex of very small cyclones of 2- or 3-inches diameter. Therefore, a high separation coefficient by itself is no guarantee of high collection efficiency. Nevertheless, it is an index to a cyclone's potential.

Note from the above that the larger the diameter the lower the angular acceleration and the lower the collection efficiency as a family of cyclones increases in size. With the separation coefficient a function of the tangential velocities, likewise, collection may drop off with a reduction of exhaust volume below design values.

Angular Travel During Separation

The angular distance through which a particle must travel during its radial movement across the entraining air stream is indicated in Fig. 7-7. A heavy particle entering the cyclone at a is shown to reach the wall of the cyclone at b, with comparatively small angular movement. A lighter particle entering at the same place must travel through a much greater angle to reach the wall at c. The smaller the particle size, the greater must be the angle of rotation. Consequently, the greater the number of convolutions of the separating vortex, the smaller will be the particles which can be separated effectively.

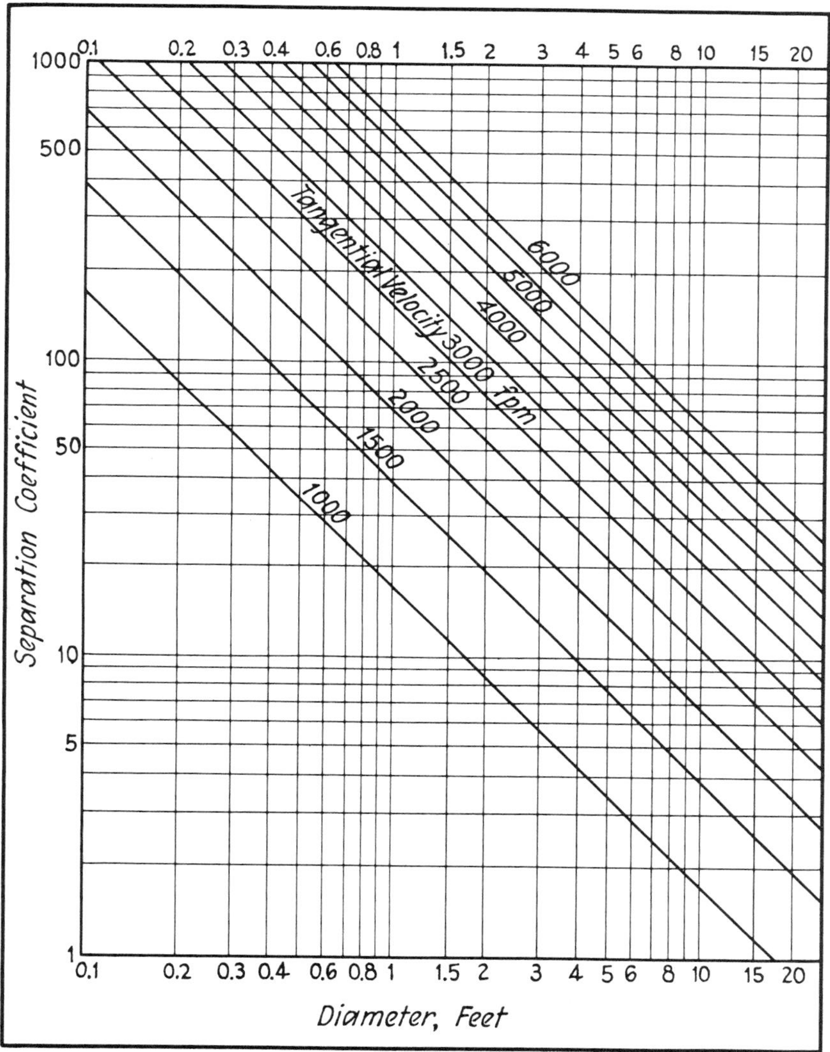

Fig. 7-6. Separation coefficient of centrifugal separation.

Field of Application of Large Diameter Cyclone

In this category falls the common cyclone whose body diameter is from 3-½ to 6 times the diameter of the inlet pipe. It is useful in situations where large air-handling capacity is required and where moderate separating efficiency is adequate. It handles a larger volume of air per dollar of first cost than any other cleaning device. Hence, its applications include the separation of wood wastes, grinding and buffing dusts, textile fibers, and similar

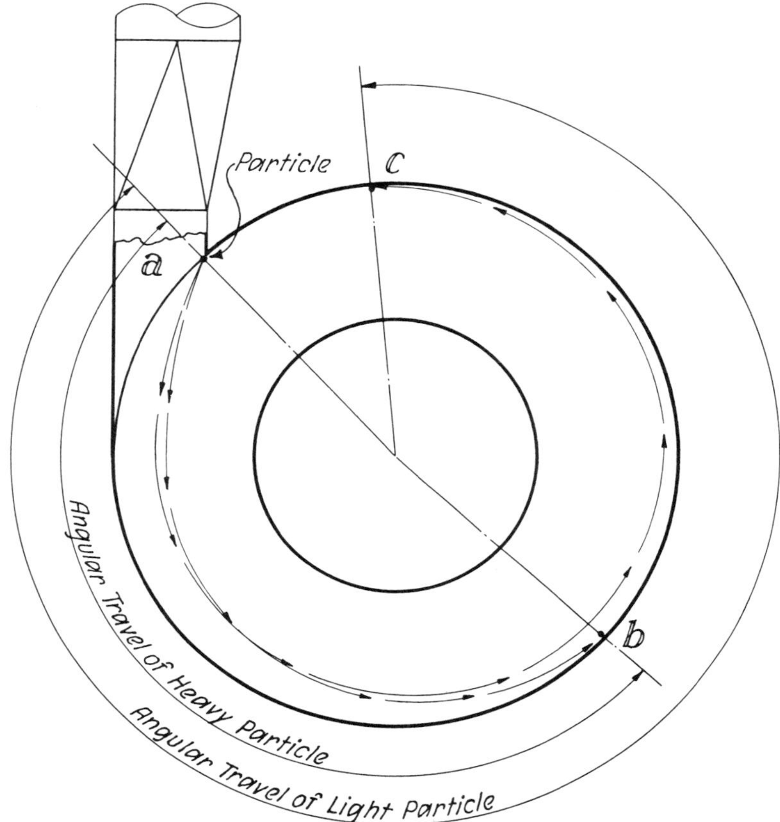

Fig. 7-7. Angular travel of dust particle during centrifugal separation.

materials whose particle size is not less than 50 microns. In present day practice, the design finds many uses as a primary collector especially when preceding a wet type final collector where removal of the coarse particulates in a dry state aids the handling and disposal of the collected material. When used ahead of a fabric type collector, its function can be that of a spark arrester or of a separator to remove coarse pieces that could cause bridging within the collector elements or jamming of rotary locks or screw conveyors used for collected material transfer from collector hoppers. (Note that a cyclone will not relieve a high pressure loss of an undersized final collector by reducing the concentration reaching it. See discussion under the Fabric Collector section of this chapter.)

The low pressure drop of the common cyclone, its large dust outlet size, and its relatively maintenance-free performance make it a more usual precleaner selection than the higher pressure loss, more efficient designs.

Pressure Drop Through Cyclones

It is regrettable that the literature usually dismisses the pressure drop through the cyclone with such casual statements as "the resistance of a well-designed cyclone should not exceed 1.0 velocity head in the inlet pipe." The reader is left with the problem of recognizing a "well-designed cyclone" and of reconciling actual measurements of resistance ranging from 0.25 velocity heads to 6 or 7 velocity heads.

Most of the formulas for cyclone resistance may be resolved to the form:

$$h = C\,h_v$$

where:

h_v = velocity pressure in cyclone inlet pipe,
C = constant.

Figure 7-8 lists several published values for C. It is evident that not all of them can be right. Furthermore, their extraordinary disagreement casts discredit upon the entire list. To illustrate in a practical way the shortcomings of these formulas, they have been used to compute the resistances of two cyclones shown in Fig. 7-8. These are identical except for the addition of the inlet deflector in Fig. 7-8b. The inlet velocity of each was 6430 fpm, the inlet velocity pressure 2.59 in. of water, and the measured resistances of Fig. 7-8a

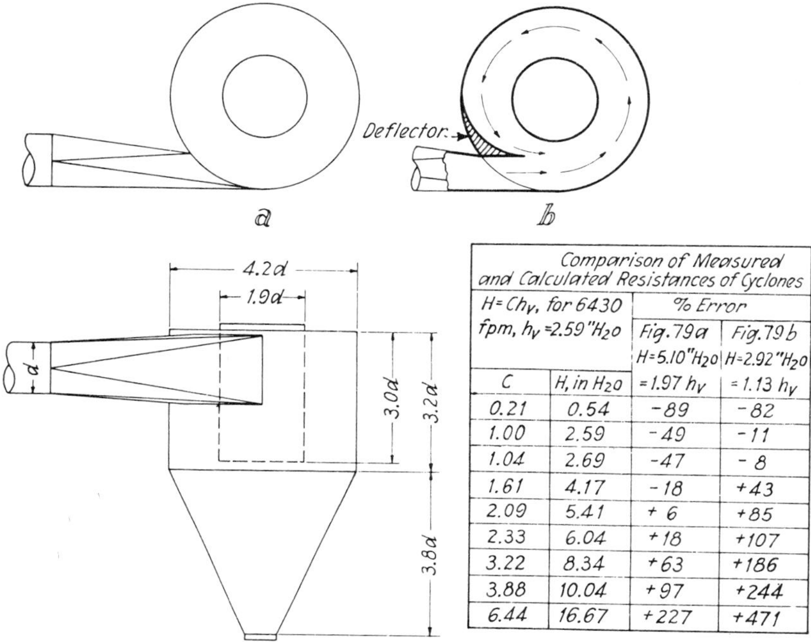

Comparison of Measured and Calculated Resistances of Cyclones

$H = Ch_v$, for 6430 fpm, h_v = 2.59" H_2O		% Error	
		Fig. 79a H = 5.10" H_2O = 1.97 h_v	Fig. 79b H = 2.92" H_2O = 1.13 h_v
C	H, in H_2O		
0.21	0.54	−89	−82
1.00	2.59	−49	−11
1.04	2.69	−47	−8
1.61	4.17	−18	+43
2.09	5.41	+6	+85
2.33	6.04	+18	+107
3.22	8.34	+63	+186
3.88	10.04	+97	+244
6.44	16.67	+227	+471

Fig. 7-8. Two cyclones whose resistances are calculated by formulas tabulated above.

and b were 5.10 and 2.92 in, of water, respectively. Since the inlet velocities were identical, the resistance formulas assign equal pressure drops to the two cyclones. The extent to which these expressions give misleading results is shown in the comparison of computed values tabulated in Fig. 7-8, together with their percentage of departure from the measured resistance. Except for space limitations, the comparison could be extended to many other cyclones for which records are available with no closer agreement between calculated and measured pressure drops. No satisfactory method for predicting pressure drops from cyclone dimensions alone has yet been achieved. To be meaningful, pressure drop must be determined experimentally from dimensionally similar prototypes.

Low-Loss Cyclones

While we have too few data to predict cyclone pressure drop in general terms, two types of cyclone can be described which definitely eliminate the major avoidable loss. Referring again to Fig. 7-5, it will be observed that the entering stream is deflected and partially shut off by the impingement of the whirling stream that has completed one revolution within the cyclone body. The impact of the whirling mass on the inlet stream introduces resistance to entry in much the same way as do two streams uniting in a breeching, or tee.

An important contributor to the cyclone pressure-drop is the region labeled "Zone of Inlet Interference" in Fig. 7-5. In this region occurs what some investigators have termed the "squeeze." Acceleration of the combined streams takes place in this zone and other energy-absorbing factors undoubtedly are present. The loss can be minimized by bringing the streams into substantial parallelism. The involute inlets of Fig. 7-13b and c accomplish this as does the helical top shown in Figs. 7-9 and 7-11. An inlet deflector as in Figs. 7-8b and 7-10, which may be merely an extension of the inner wall of the inlet transformer either with or without the fairing shown, accomplishes much the same purpose. Each of these expedients reduces the pressure drop substantially, usually in the range of 40 to 50 percent.[3]

Table 7-6 gives the dimensions and capacities of helical-top cyclones whose pressure drop will usually be less than 0.6 velocity head. The dimensional symbols refer to Fig. 7-9.

High Efficiency Cyclones

Efficiencies higher than those of the large low-loss cyclone are developed at the expense of increased pressure drop by:

1. Intermediate types ranging in diameter from 10 in. to 48 in.,
2. Small diameter types in the 4-in. to 9-in. range.

[3] "Flow Pattern and Pressure Drop in Cyclone Dust Collectors," by C. B. Shepherd and C. E. Lapple, *Industrial & Engineering Chemistry*, Vol. 32, No. 9, (Sept. 1940), 1245-1248. Compare reduction of 44% reported there with 43% reduction recorded in Fig. 7-8.

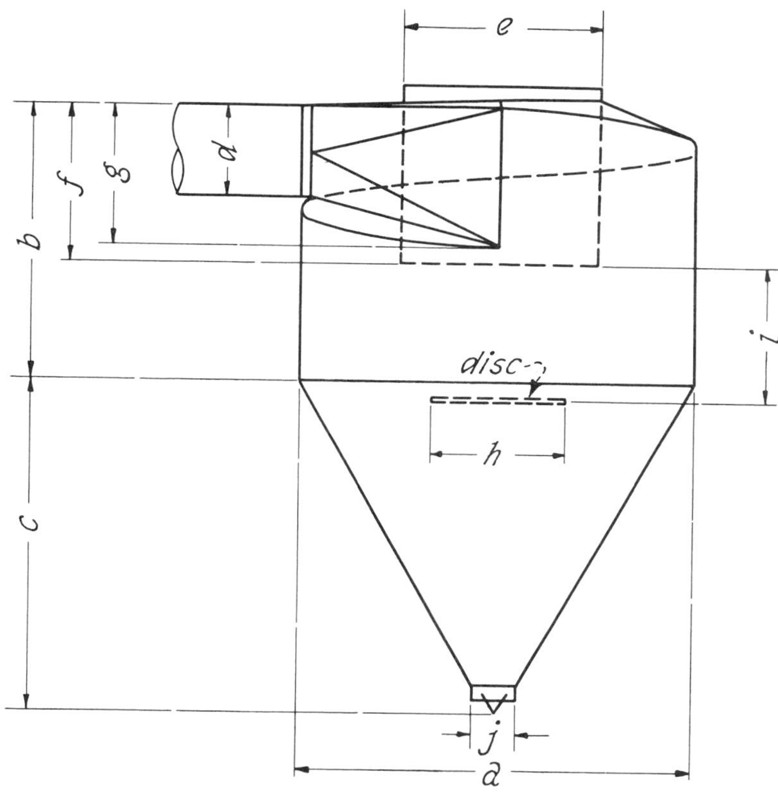

Fig. 7-9. Low resistance cyclone with helical roof.

Intermediate Diameter Cyclones

Because of the smaller diameter and relatively great length of the intermediate group, the separating efficiency is high for particles as small as 20 microns. They seldom exceed 4 ft in diameter and, in consequence, are limited in air-handling capacity. For greater air loads than a single cyclone can handle, they are used in pairs as in Fig. 7-14a, in multiple as in Fig. 7-14b, or in clusters of 4 or more over a common bin and served by a plenum inlet or a manifold. The proportions of a typical cyclone of this character are shown in Fig. 7-11 and the pressure drop for various sizes and capacities is plotted in Fig. 7-12. Reentrainment is reduced by the addition of a throw-out cone such as is shown attached to the dust outlet of Fig. 7-11. Other cyclone forms are shown in Fig. 7-13.

Small Diameter Cyclones

Several forms of small diameter cyclones are available in body diameters of from 4 in. to 9 in. Typical individual units appear in Fig. 7-15 a and b.

Table 7-6. Dimensions of Helical-Top Cyclones

Capacity, cfm	Inches									
	a	b	c	d[1]	e	f	g	h	i[2]	j[3]
500	37	15	33	5	10	12	8	7	8	3
1,000	44	21	40	7	14	16	11	10	11	5
2,000	54	30	49	10	20	19	15	14	15	6
3,000	63	36	57	12	25	22	18	18	19	7
5,000	75	48	68	16	32	28	24	22	24	10
7,500	87	60	78	20	39	34	30	27	30	10
10,000	97	68	87	23	45	38	34	32	34	12
12,500	105	75	95	25	50	42	38	35	38	12
15,000	114	82	103	27	55	45	41	38	42	12
20,000	127	94	114	32	63	51	47	44	48	13
25,000	139	105	125	35	70	57	53	49	54	13
30,000	151	116	136	39	77	62	58	54	59	14
35,000	163	126	147	42	84	67	63	59	64	14
40,000	173	135	156	45	90	72	68	63	69	15

[1]Nominal inlet pipe diameter.
[2]Adjustable.
[3]Optional—May be reduced if connected to relief fan.

Because of the limited capacity per tube they are installed in clusters within a casing which embodies the inlet and outlet ducts as well as the dust bin. Figure 7-16a illustrates a cluster of cyclones with vane-type inlets similar to Fig. 7-15a. Figure 7-16b represents a typical assemblage of tubes having tangential inlets.

Two methods are employed for generating high tangential velocities within the tubes. One utilizes a series of inclined vanes in the top of the cyclone extending from the inner cylinder to the outer wall. Dusty air enters from above and spins helically downward. The other style is equipped with one or more tagential inlets similar to those of conventional cyclones. Figure 7-15a and 7-15b are illustrative.

Many factors affect the efficiency of small cyclones. Among these are the inlet velocity, gas temperature, distribution of particle sizes and the characteristics of the dust such as specific gravity, its electrostatic charge, and its tendency to agglomerate. In practice, there is little difference in the performance of small cyclones of equal diameter and similar proportions, regardless of type. In general, the smaller the diameter the higher the efficiency but because of the multiplicity of elements and the restriction at the scaled-down dust outlet, diameters less than 4 inches find use only in a narrow range of light dust-loading applications.

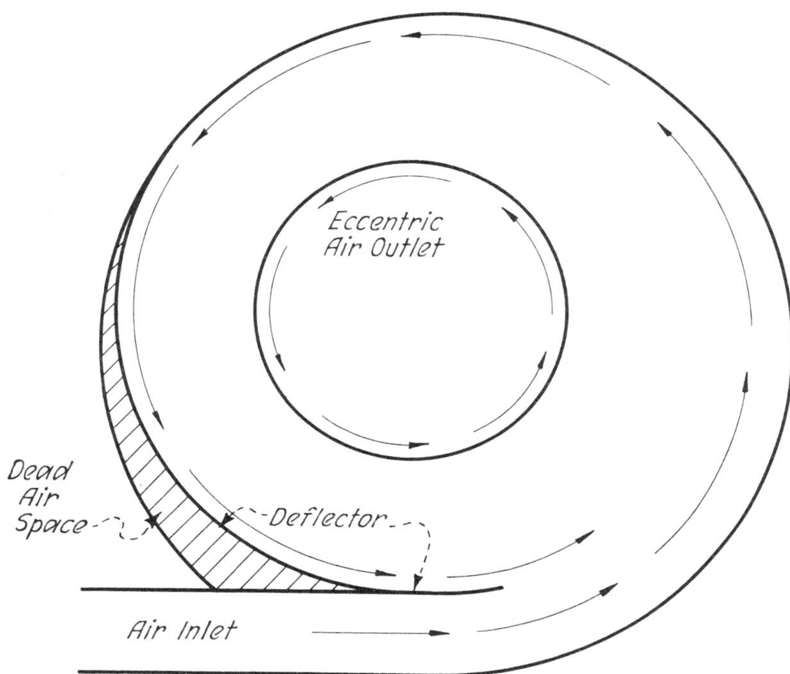

Fig. 7-10. Low resistance cyclone with inlet deflector.

The cyclone is a poor classifier and cannot make a sharp size-cut between particles accepted and particles rejected. Therefore, no cyclone has a single value of efficiency. From the chart in Fig. 7-17, it is evident that a cyclone will collect a fraction, however small, of each size of particle present in the dust load. This curve is typical as to shape only; the numerical values must be taken as approximations.

Cyclone Air Outlets

The flow through a cyclone air outlet is strongly vortical with an upward axial component near the periphery of the outlet pipe and often a downward component near the center. The presence or absence of this downward flow seems to depend upon some combination of cyclone proportions and tangential velocity. It has been observed in cyclones as small as 3.6-inches diameter and as large as 12 feet.

Tangential air outlets similar to that shown in Fig. 7-13c are designed to take advantage of the vortex in the air outlet tube. The latter is usually capped by an involute chamber similar to a centrifugal fan housing. This design is particularly adapted to cyclones operating under suction. When

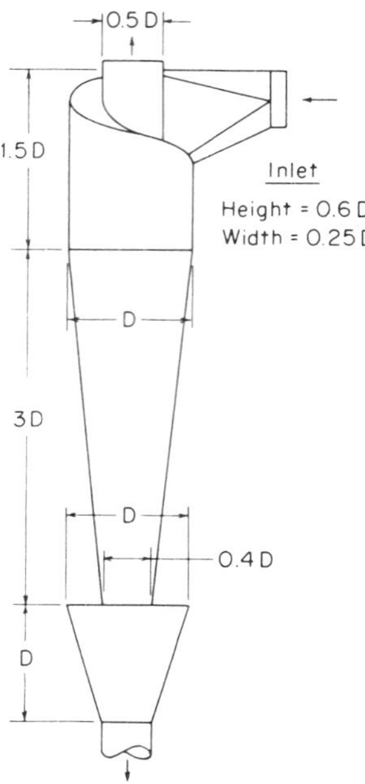

Fig. 7-11. Intermediate diameter cyclone with helical roof.

operating under positive pressure the outlet sometimes takes the form of an expanding nozzle to recover some of the velocity pressure.

Factors Affecting Separation Efficiency

Air should be fed to the cyclone in a radially thin sheet to minimize the distance through which a particle must travel to reach the wall. Therefore, it is desirable to limit the inlet width to one-half or less of the inlet height. Exact tangency of the inlet also promotes smooth entry of the air stream.

Elbows in the inlet pipe immediately preceding the cyclone can help or hinder separation. Thus, an elbow such as Fig. 7-18c encourages centrifugal separation because the elbow concentrates the dust on the outside of the bend. When the direction of rotation of the bend is opposed to that of the cyclone, as in Fig. 7-18d, the dust load is introduced into the cyclone at the maximum distance from the cyclone wall.

Two identical cyclones connected in series offer little advantage over a single cyclone. Since the collecting efficiency of the second cyclone is no higher than the first it can precipitate only a very small fraction of the dust passed by the first cyclone. This is confirmed by a test wherein a single cyclone captured 94% of a certain dust and two in series raised the collecting efficiency to only 96%.

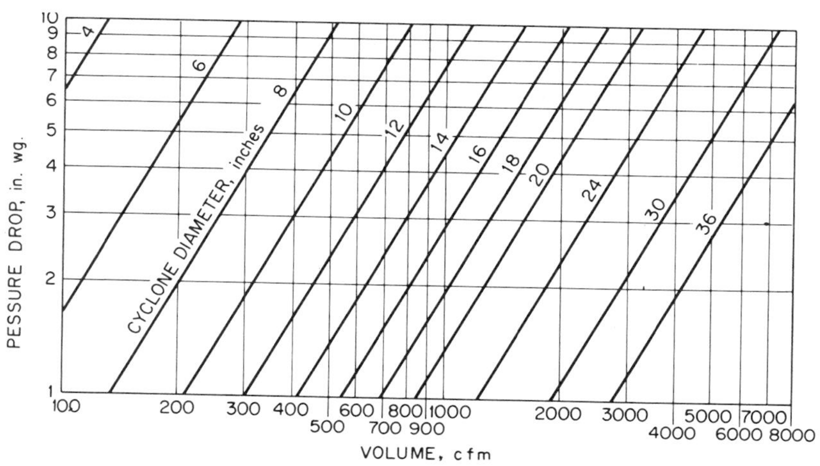

Fig. 7-12. Pressure drop through cyclones similar to Fig. 7-11.

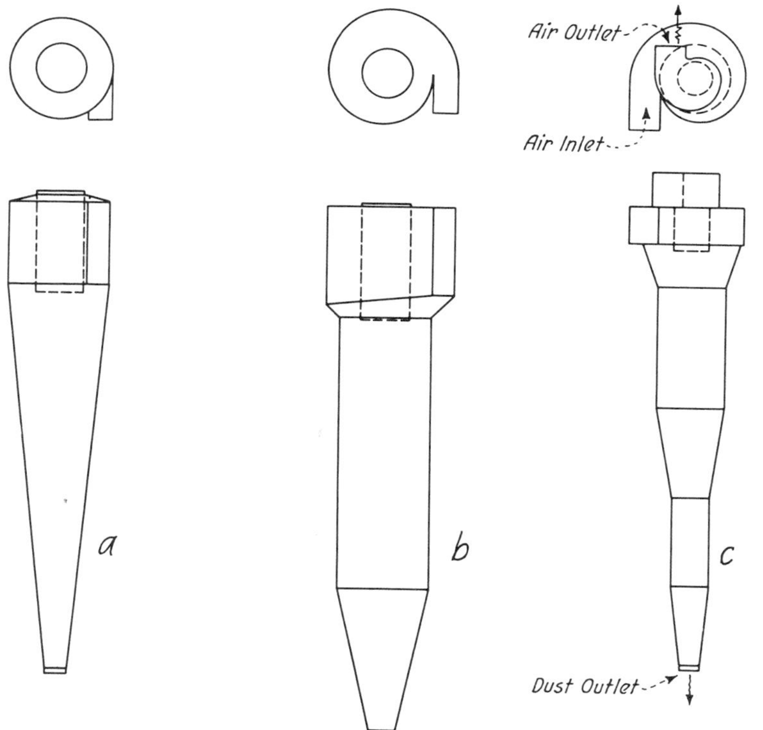

Fig. 7-13. High efficiency, intermediate diameter cyclones.

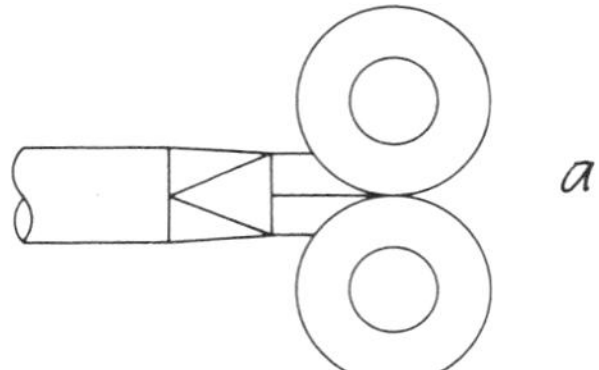

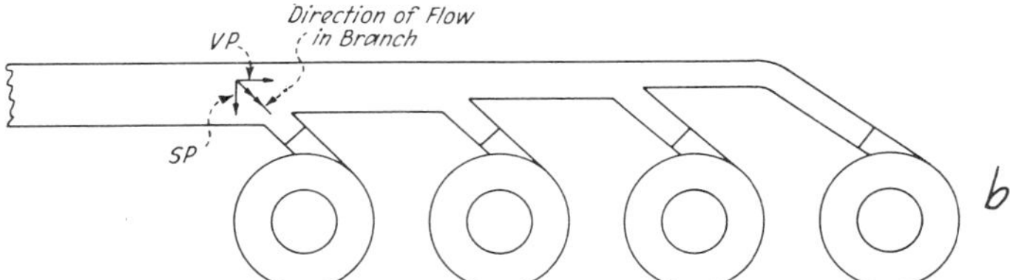

Fig. 7-14. Multiple cyclones.

Dust Bins

The dust hopper can contribute to a dirty stack discharge through reentrainment of dust already deposited. The hopper must be air- and dust-tight and must be free from excessive cross currents. A single cyclone discharging into its own tight bin rarely is guilty of excessive pick-up of deposited dust. Multiple cyclones and multiple section precipitators, however, are sensitive to dust bin conditions. Back flow through one or more units is not uncommon and if pronounced may produce bin currents which will sweep suspended dust from the bin to the clean air outlet. Some materials, notably carbon black, respond readily to low entrainment velocities and are difficult to retain in a hopper.

To minimize reentrainment, uniform distribution of air between units is helpful; pressures at the dust outlets of the units should be equal; the bin should be deep and its cross section large enough to minimize crossflow velocities. Above all, it must be airtight, and the level of the collected material must be kept well below the dust outlets. The bin may be connected to a small, secondary fan and collector which need handle only the air entering from the dust outlet of the cyclone. A purge rate of 10% of the main flow has been reported to reduce the dust emission from an 8-inch cyclone by 20%. The same effect is attained when a cyclone is served by a relief or relay fan, as in Fig. 8-8, b and c, and in Fig. 11-9 f.

Axial Flow Separators

The axial flow separator is a device of the skimming type employing an annular opening at the periphery of the whirling dust column. In the form

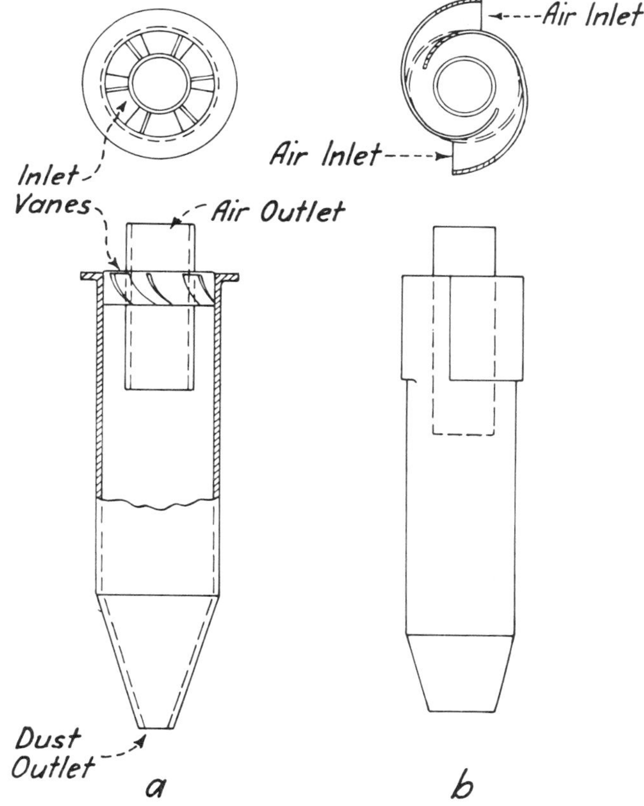

Fig. 7-15. High efficiency, small-diameter cyclones.

shown in Fig. 7-19, the whirl is induced by the impingement of the high-speed air stream on helical vanes. This design also has been modified by the insertion of a venturi throat at the skimming section to accelerate the air stream and thereby increase the separating action.

Particles of 150 microns, and larger, can be extracted satisfactorily when the skimming outlet opens into the dead air space of a bin. Smaller particles, however, can be removed only by the influence of airflow through the skimmer. This can be accomplished by putting the dust bin under suction and discharging the air drawn from the bin into a secondary cleaning device. Best separation at the skimming annulus takes place when the bleed-off velocity is as high as or higher than that of the main stream. Extraction of from 10% to 30% of the primary air takes place under these conditions and the separator then becomes merely a dust concentrator.

The critical zone in all skimming separators and inertial devices is the

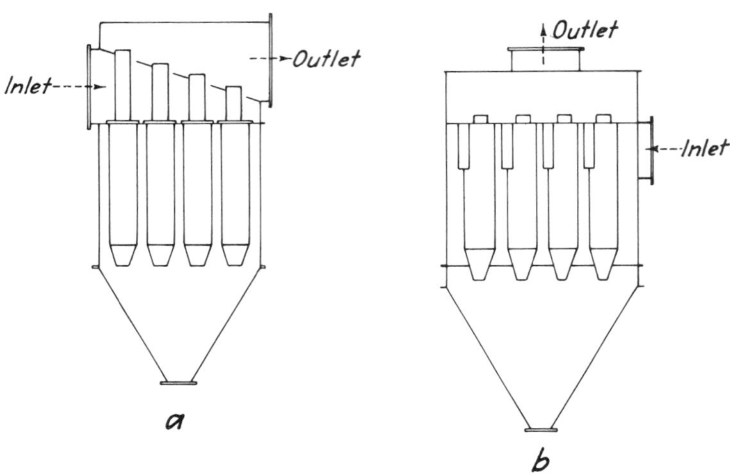

Fig. 7-16. Clusters of small-diameter cyclones.

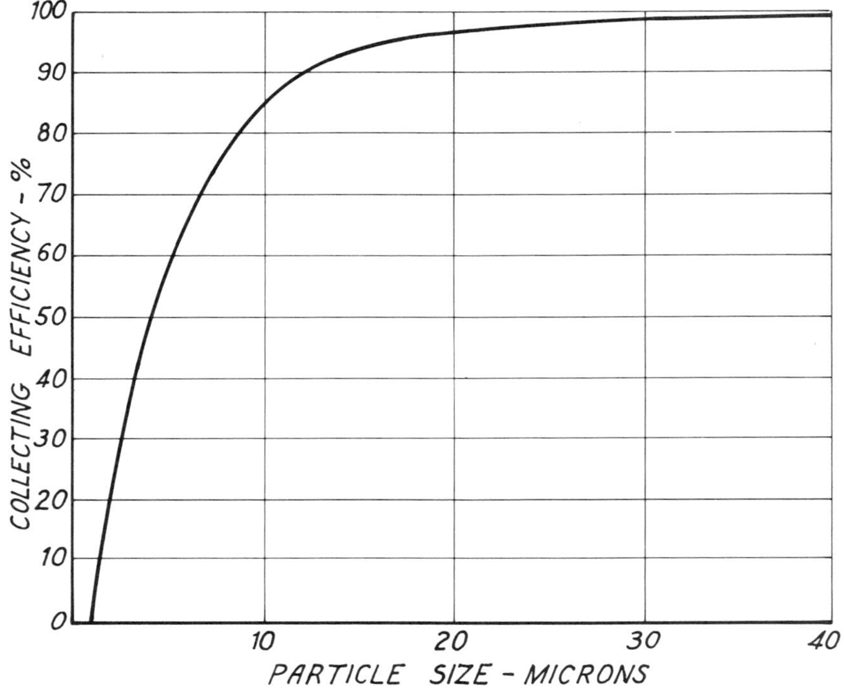

Fig. 7-17. Small-diameter cyclone efficiency.

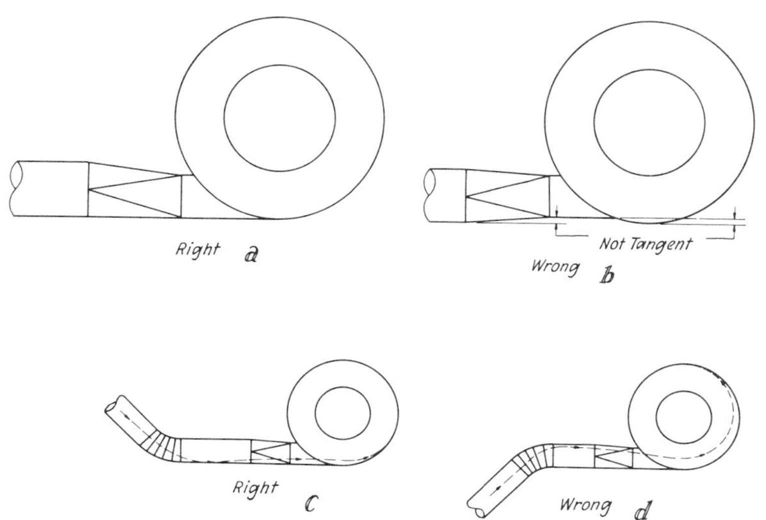

Fig. 7-18. Cyclone inlet arrangements.

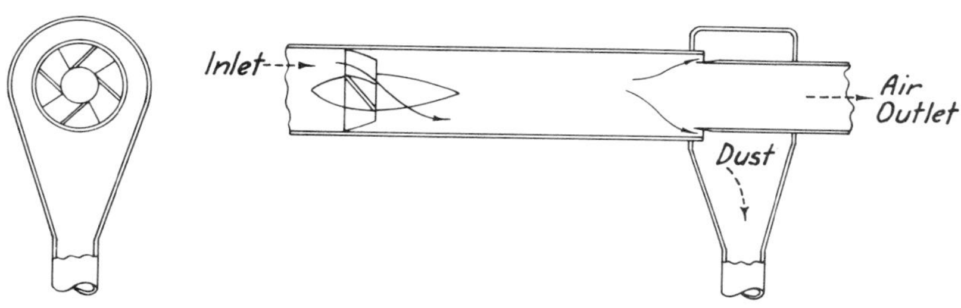

Fig. 7-19. Axial flow separator.

region surrounding the skimmer blade or tongue. Trailing eddies and minute swirls encourage reentrainment.

Experiments with an axial flow separator have shown a drop in efficiency as the velocity increased.[4] This was attributed to the rebound of large particles. A reduction in rebound was achieved by replacing the helical inlet vanes by a single tangential inlet. A significant improvement down to 10-micron size was also attained by wetting the separator walls with a film of water.

Inertial Separators

A form of inertial separator or, more correctly, dust concentrator, appears in Fig. 7-20. The separating element consists of a cone whose sides converge

[4] "Investigation of a Vortex Air Cleaner," by T. C. Daniels, *The Engineer*, Vol. 203, No. 5276 (Mar. 8, 1957), 358-362.

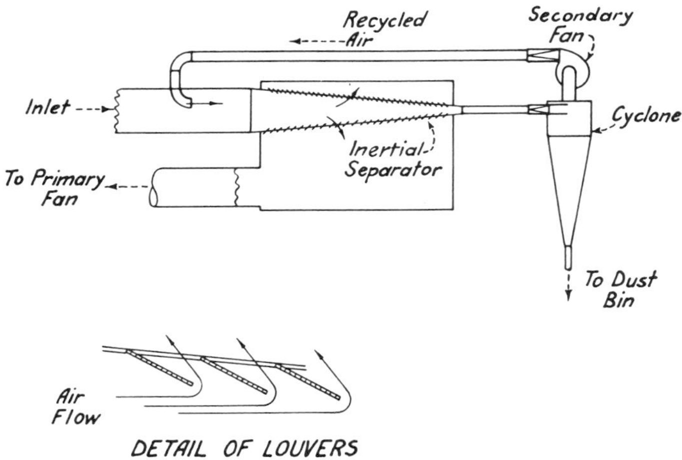

Fig. 7-20. Inertial separator.

at an included angle of about 10°. Embossed in the sheet metal cone are louvers, so shaped as to cause the escaping air to reverse its direction through an angle of at least 120°. The usual inlet velocity lies between 3,000 and 5,000 fpm. While the air is deflected sharply the dust particles tend to continue their flight toward the apex of the cone.

Roughly 5 to 10 percent of the incoming air is drawn off by the secondary fan and re-injected into the separator inlet after being relieved of its dust load by the cyclone. The chief virtue of the inertial separator is its ability to handle large volumes of air heavily contaminated with coarse dust. Pressure drops are moderate, ranging from about 1 in. of water at an inlet velocity of 3,000 fpm to about 3 in. at 5,000 fpm.

Commercial separators of this type are available in diameters from 9 in. to 25 in. with capacities from 1,500 to 15,000 cfm per cone. They may be installed singly or in banks of as many as 30. The collecting efficiency of a single-pass cone seldom exceeds 80% for 10-micron particles. When cones are installed in tandem the efficiency may be raised to 90 percent.

Accumulation on the louvers and sensitivity to abrasion are major problems for certain applications.

WET PARTICULATE COLLECTORS

Wet particulate collectors find a wide range of applications because of advantages such as:

a. Ability to handle moist gas and, often, sticky or adhesive particles without plugging.
b. Elimination of fire or explosion hazards.

c. Ease and economy of handling high temperature gases. Hot gas volume is easily flash cooled at the entrance or within the collector so that the collector can be sized for the contracted gas volume.
d. Attractive space and first cost considerations.
e. Dust-free disposal of collected material.

Disadvantages include:

a. Need to recycle water, unless water can be diverted to process or settling pond. Water pollution regulations prevent discharge of water clarified by the usual primary settling tank to sewer systems or streams. Continuous recycling of 100% of the water can introduce water quality problems requiring flocculent and/or neutralizing chemicals.
b. Corrosion can be a problem where combustion gases are involved.
c. Material disposal can introduce housekeeping problems because of free water trapped with the dewatered particulates.
d. High energy designs use substantially more horsepower than alternate collector types.
e. Freezing protection can be required in cold climates.

The principal requirements of an effective wet particulate collector are:

1. To bring liquid and particulates into intimate contact to promote high separation efficiency.
2. To prevent damp zones at the inlet area which can accumulate material.
3. To provide means to prevent carry-over of droplets into the cleaned gas.
4. To provide suitable arrangements for disposal of collected material.

Satisfactory solutions to these problems have resulted in a number of typical structures including, among others: towers, orifice types, and venturi scrubbers. Impaction and direct interception forces are employed, supplemented in some designs with centrifugal force. The impact between particle and water droplet increases the mass of the wetted particle making it more easy to remove from the conveying gas stream. Its entrapment in a liquid disposal system eliminates, or greatly reduces the reentrainment losses which account for much of the inefficiencies of the dry cyclones and inertials.

Designs are plentiful and the omission of any particular design should not be interpreted as an indication of marginal performance. Interesting configurations include the wet dynamic precipitator, the centrifugal tower with an intermediate wet centrifugal-exhauster stage, the rotating water distributors in orifice or tower, wet centrifugal and high water volume, induced-air venturi.

Table 7-7. Wet Collector Performance

Collector	In. wg	Collectance, Micron 1/4	1	2	5
Spray tower	½–1½	—	—	poor	poor
Medium pressure	4–8	poor	fair	good	excellent
	8–15	poor	good	excellent	excellent
High energy	30	fair	excellent	excellent	excellent
	45	good	excellent	excellent	excellent
	60	excellent	excellent	excellent	excellent

Wet particulate collectors may be divided into three groups by the pressure-loss ranges employed—medium pressure in the 4-in. to 8-in. wg range; intermediate in the 8-in. to 15-in. wg range; and high pressure in the 25-in. to 60-in wg range, occasionally with even higher pressures. The influence of pressure drop on collection of smaller size particulates has been indicated in Table 7-7.

Medium-pressure collectors are extensively used for the collection of mechanically generated dusts, such as those from grinding, machining, crushing, screening, conveying, etc. Collection efficiency for most designs are high down to the 2- to 3-micron range, with effectiveness extending to the 1-micron range as the energy expended is increased.

Tower Designs, Figs. 7-21 and 7-22, are, generally, medium pressure-drop collectors. One group relies on centrifugal forces to aid the impingement of dust onto the wetted collector surfaces, while another uses impingement plates to accomplish the wetting. Flow is countercurrent, water volumes 3 to 5 gallons per 1,000 cubic feet of air cleaned; collected material usually is continually sluiced to a remote tailings pond or clarifier. In most cases, cleaned water is recycled.

Collectors should not be confused with the low pressure-drop spray tower (½″ to 1 ½″ wg), where horizontal banks of sprays in a vertical counterflow tower wash plus-10-micron particles out of the gas stream.

Orifice Designs, Fig. 7-23, are medium pressure-drop collectors which rely on a shaped separator or orifice between gas inlet and exit chambers. The self-contained arrangement, Fig. 7-23a, incorporates a modified venturi shape arranged so that the velocity of the gas stream in the orifice element is sufficient to induce flow from an internal storage tank.

The arrangement is especially attractive for an isolated system since remote clarifying tanks, recirculating pumps, and piping are eliminated. Normally operated at a pressure loss of 5 in. to 6 in., increased operating

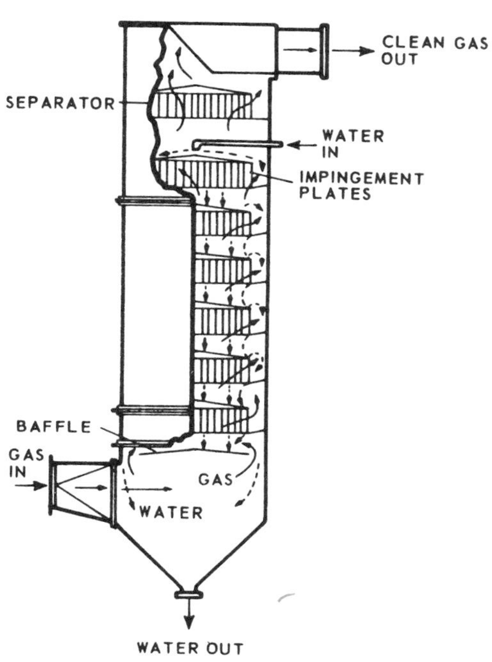

Fig. 7-21. Wet centrifugal collector.

water level height will produce a noticeable increase in collection efficiency on low micron sizes with accompanying pressure losses in the 10-in. to 12-in. range. The large water volume, 10 to 40 gallons per 1,000 cubic feet of gas cleaned, is handled in a closed circuit without need for recycling pumps. Collected material settles to the bottom of the collector and is usually removed with a drag conveyor.

Water levels may automatically compensate for exhaust volume variations, giving these designs a wide range of capacities at constant efficiency, and with minor changes in pressure loss. Liquid level is critical, and consequently, water-level control mechanism is important.

In the arrangement, Fig. 7-23b, orifices are formed by parallel rods. Normally designed for 5-in. to 8-in. wg, increased efficiency with increased pressure loss can be obtained by simple modifications of the orifice area. With another type of modification, the collection element can be converted into a high energy design of multiple parallel venturi slots.

Venturi Designs have found increasing use as alternatives to Electrostatic and Fabric Collectors for some of the more difficult air-pollution problems; especially those involved with high-temperature gases. The very high power input is often in the 40″ to 60″ wg range; water volumes, 5 to 15 gallons per 1,000 cubic feet of gas cleaned. The historic shape, Fig. 7-24, is still popular

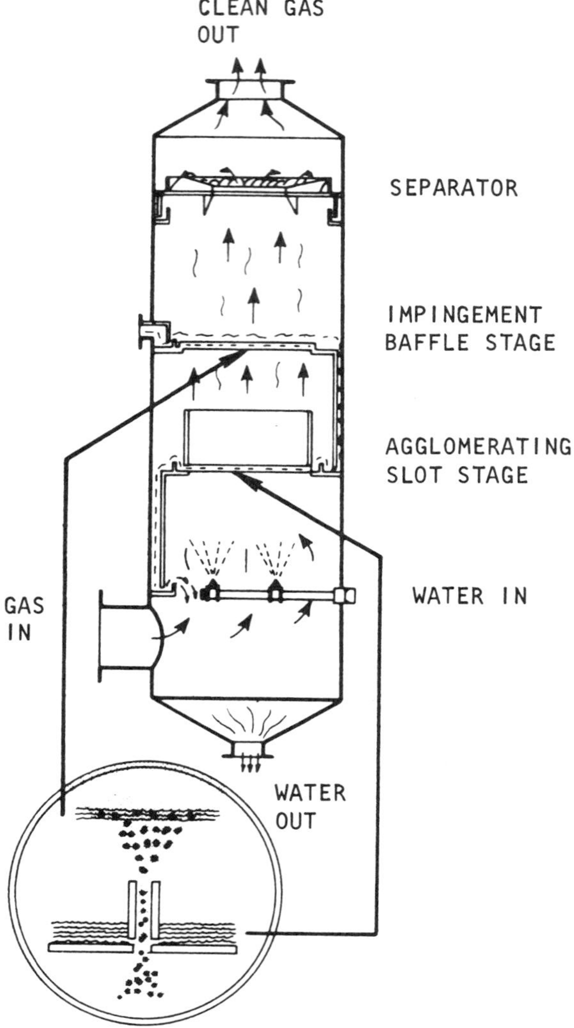

Fig. 7-22. Wet impingement collector.

although modifications, Figs. 7-25 and 7-26, are among the variations included in present-day designs.

The high throat-velocities of 20,000 to 30,000 fpm cause shear stresses which reduce water droplet sizes to close to the theoretical minimum. With the diffusion that takes place in the expanding downstream sections, increased contact between particulate and droplet occurs, and high collection of sub-micron particles results. Like the tower collectors, liquid and collected

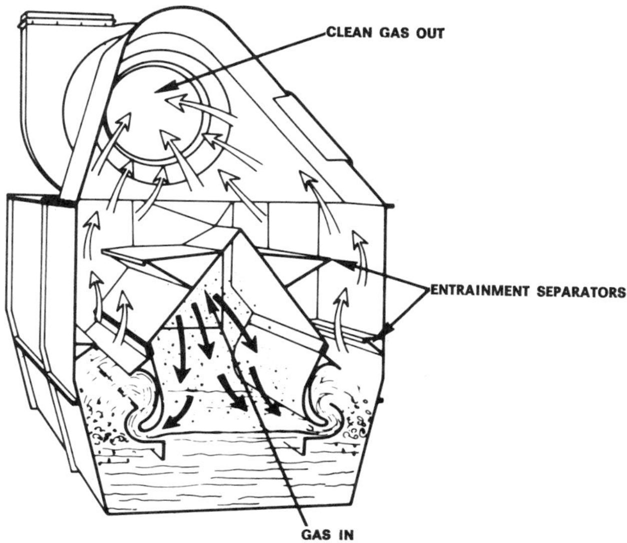

Fig. 7-23a. Wet orifice type collector.

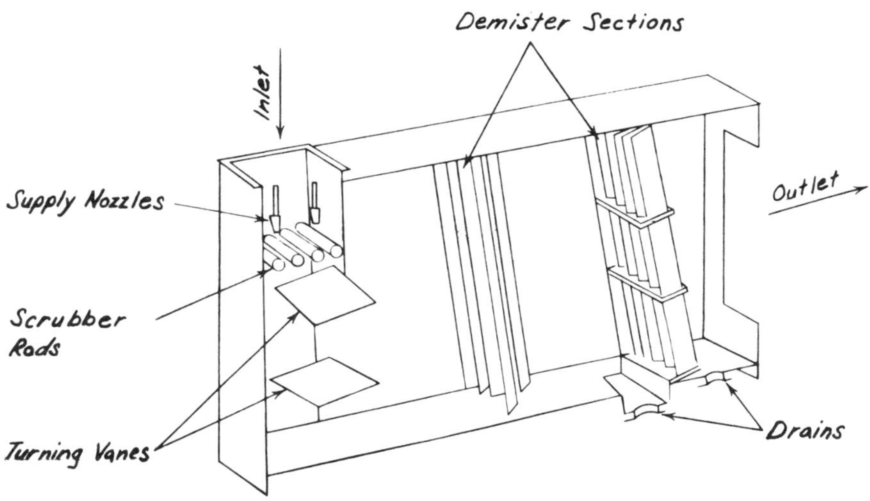

Fig. 7-23b. Parallel rod orifice type.

dust drains continuously to clarifying equipment and the cleansed water is usually recycled. High throat-velocities require erosion resistant construction and the tiny droplets require sophisticated entrainment separators.

Under variable gas density or flow rates, means must be included for adjustment of the venturi throat area to maintain the required pressure drop.

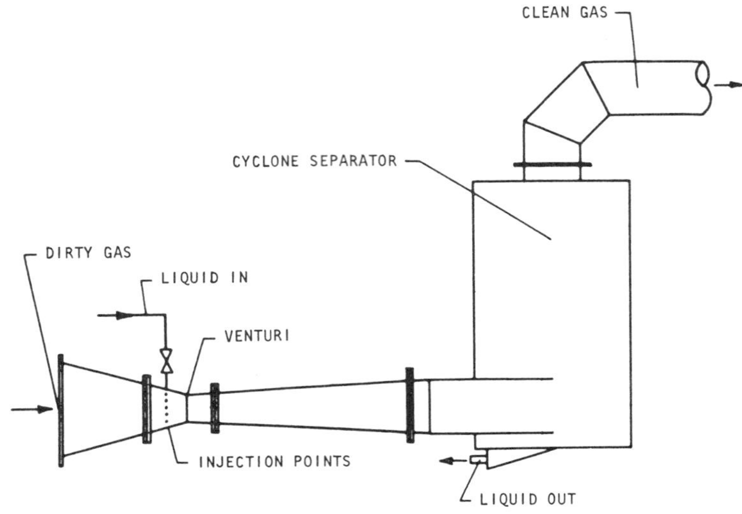

Fig. 7-24. Venturi scrubber.

The problem is especially critical in high temperature applications where gas temperatures vary within the process cycle. Such variations change the water vapor volume generated to cool the gases by direct evaporation and results in changes in gas volume and density at the collector and the fan inlet. With indirect heat exchangers the degree of cooling obtained also influences the gas volume and temperature that the collector and fan receive.

The flooded disc design, Fig. 7-25, controls the area of an annular throat by a vertical movement of the flooded disc within a conical section of the inlet housing. The vertical movement reportedly is readily adopted to automatic control devices for maintenance of the desired pressure drop.

With a rectangular throat, Figs. 7-24 and 7-26, adjustment to the throat area is accomplished by movement of an angular segment about a pivot paralleling the long dimension of the throat.

Probably the most sensitive element is the centrifugal fan which operates at such high tip-speeds that slight accumulation or wear can upset the balance and introduce vibration and the need for corrective maintenance. Water sprays are often added at the fan inlet to control accumulation, although water entrainment in the outlet gases, and added wheel erosion appear to be offsetting disadvantages. The use of two fans in series has certain attractions. Each fan runs at low tip-speed for reduced service factors; one fan can provide reasonable air pollution control in an emergency.

Chemical Additives

The search for higher efficiencies has led to exhaustive tests by manufacturers, suppliers, and users of chemical additives that would increase the

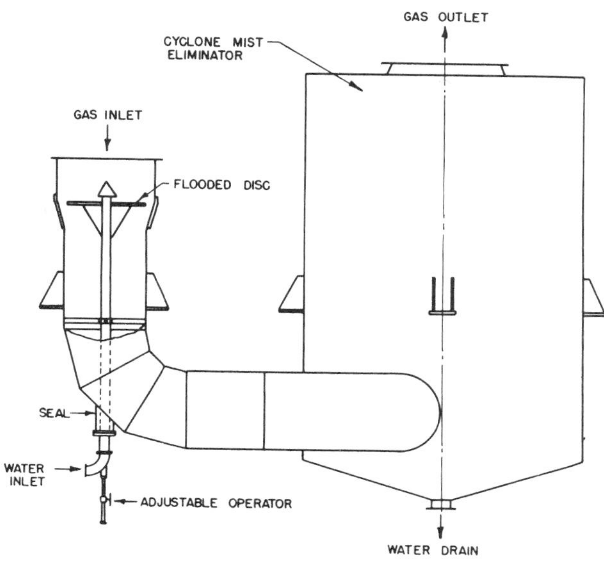

Fig. 7-25. Variable pressure, high-energy wet collector.

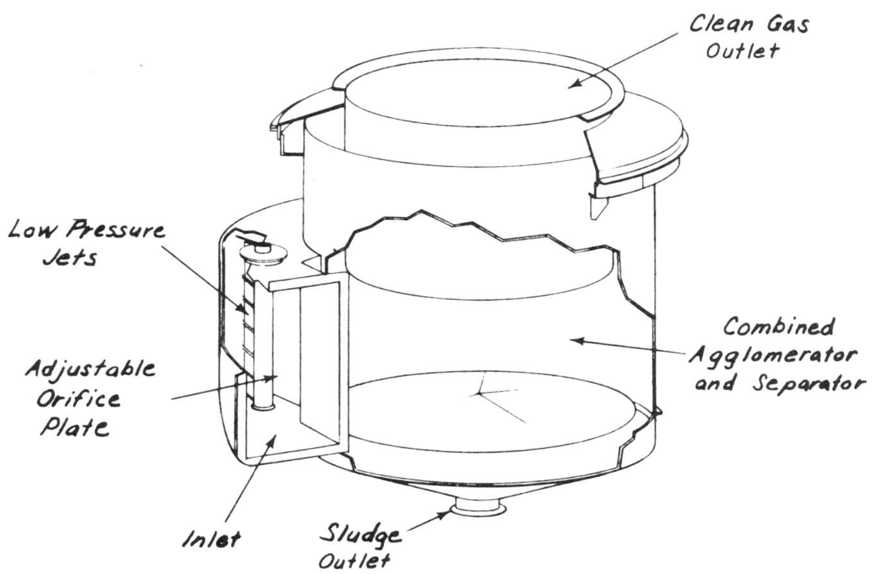

Fig. 7-26. Variable pressure, high-energy wet collector.

particulate-removal performance. While there could be exceptions to this observation, it is doubtful that the use of wetting agents will contribute materially to improved efficiency for any of the wet collector groups.

Chemical additives are successful, to a degree, in the clarification of effluent water to accelerate settling and to agglomerate flocculents and slurry-forming particulates. Drawbacks are often the cost and the availability of supervisory personnel to assure continuity of the treatment.

FABRIC COLLECTORS

The fabric collector is a filter which depends for its operation on the interception of suspended particulates by the fabric and the dust mat which collects thereon. Where fabric collectors can be applied, the separation efficiency, regardless of particle size, is the highest of all as long as the fabric is intact and the seal between the fabric and the supporting structure is airtight.

In addition to its excellent collection efficiency, other advantages include:

a. Material is collected dry, often permitting collected material to be returned to process or otherwise salvaged.
b. Collection efficiency is not affected by changes in gas volume or density.

Disadvantages include:

a. Cannot handle moist gas when condensation occurs on fabric.
b. Releasing sticky or linty materials during the cleaning cycle is difficult.
c. Introduces an added fire or explosion element where such hazards are present in the process exhausted.
d. Relatively bulky units requiring considerable headroom.
e. Secondary dust problems can occur during removal and transport of collected dust.

Principle of Operation

These collectors function by causing a dust cake to collect on the surface of a woven fabric or throughout the depth and the surface of a felted or nonwoven material. It is this filter cake that accomplishes the cleaning of the air-stream with an extremely high degree of particulate removal.

A new, clean medium usually has larger air passages than the size of particles which are eventually trapped. In the beginning some particles escape through the medium, but some collide with fiber surfaces, and others lodge on previously collected particles. The finer the fabric fiber, and the greater the surface area available for particle storage, the higher the initial efficiency and the shorter the time necessary to build the dust cake.

Within a short time, the air passages become smaller and smaller and longer and more tortuous as the filter cake increases in thickness, decreases in porosity, and the median size of the particles in the cake becomes smaller. The first layer of relatively coarse dust changes the porosity and permeability characteristics of the medium more than any subsequent layer of comparable weight. That layer of dust becomes a permanent companion of the fabric, operating as a single system. The medium must be "tight" enough to grow a suitable filter cake and "heal" fast enough after cleaning.

Mechanics involve impaction, direct interception, and diffusion.

Pressure-Drop Relationships

With the assured high collection efficiency of fabric collectors, the problem of reporting performance becomes not one of collection efficiency against a particle size-range, but rather, one of accurately forecasting the fabric pressure-drop which, in turn, determines whether required volume will be exhausted.

Theoretical analysis of the influencing factors is difficult to translate into specific yardsticks for any application, but does give a direction in which ratings can be established as an extrapolation on experience accumulated over the many years of fabric collector application. At the flow-rate through both the fabric and the dust cake layers, laminar flow prevails where:

$$\Delta P = \frac{Vu\,W}{K}$$

ΔP = Pressure drop between the air entering and the air leaving side of the fabric
V = Approach velocity to the collector fabric
u = Absolute viscosity of conveying air-stream
W = Mass of dust cake
K = Permeability of dust.

For a given dust and a specific concentration, the formula postulates that after the dust cake has been established: Resistance rise through an existing dust deposit would be directly proportional to the approach velocity.

The formula points up the importance of selecting a fabric collector of adequate size. Excessive flow-rates increase the pressure drop through normal resistance processes and, cumulatively, through the more rapid build up of the dust mat. To compensate for these additive effects the cleaning frequency must be increased drastically. A doubled flow-rate at constant dust loading requires four times the frequency.

The diagram, Fig. 7-27a, represents pressure relationships of a single compartment fabric-collector operating through its cycle at constant volume and with a uniform dust loading and a constant size distribution. In practice, neither of these conditions occur. Industrial dust-producing operations do

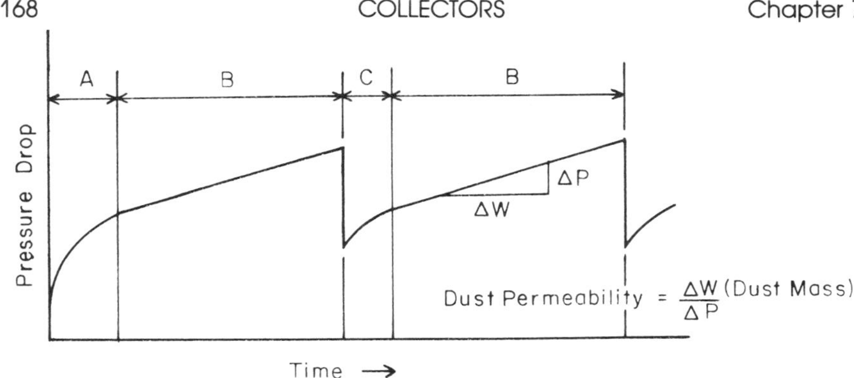

a. Basic Cycles

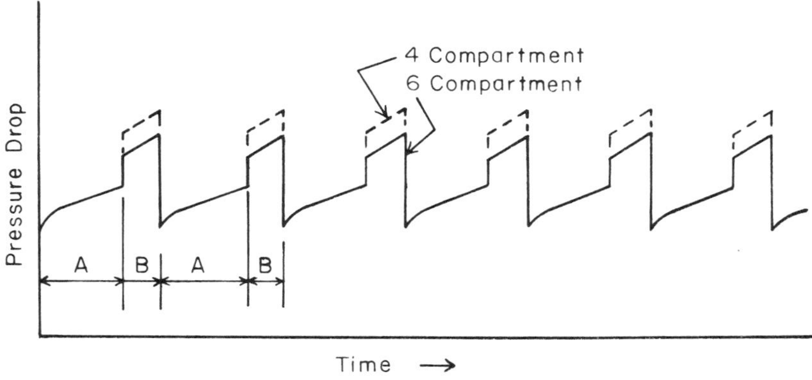

b. Compartmented Collector Cycles

Fig. 7-27. Pressure relationships—fabric collectors.

not release airborne contaminants at a uniform rate and the generated material will be of varying particle-size distribution. However, with the small increment of pressure rise that occurs where a cycle extends for 2 to 8 hours, these variations are insignificant for most systems, and a pressure-drop plot at constant volume would approach the linear slope of the illustration.

Exhaust volume through the usual single compartment fabric-collector will not be constant because of the increasing resistance to airflow as the dust cake accumulates. The reduction in flow rate will be a function of the system pressure-relationships and of the exhaust-fan characteristics and point of rating. Drop-off of exhaust volume is not severe in usual practice because:

1. Pressure losses for the system of ducts and hoods usually equal or exceed that of the fabric collector, so reduction in exhaust volume will cause a corresponding reduction in the pressure needs for that portion of the system.
2. Most fabric collectors have the centrifugal fan on the clean-air side of the collector where the more efficient backward-curved blade fan can be applied. This fan construction has a steeply rising pressure-volume characteristic, providing significant increase in available static pressure as exhaust volume is reduced.

This fan characteristic prevents overloading when collectors with new, clean media are first placed in service, and where, for a short time, the pressure loss through the clean fabric is low.

When fabric collectors are designed for continuous operation, pressure relationships become more complex. The smaller the fraction of the elements taken out of service at any one time for dust-cake removal, the more uniform the pressure-drop of the fabric collector. Typical pressure diagrams for four- and six-compartment, continuous fabric-collectors with mechanical shakers or reverse-flow cleaning are shown in Fig. 7-27b. For pulse jet types, the removal from service of only a few elements at a time and the almost instantaneous return to service reduce the amplitude of the pressure drop to insignificant variations.

Fabric Selection

For most ambient air applications, a woven cotton fabric is usual for shaker and reverse flow mechanisms and synthetic felted materials are usual for pulse-jet designs. The introduction of materials capable of withstanding high temperatures has permitted the application of fabric collectors to high temperature gas cleaning.

Characteristics of the more usual fabrics have been tabulated in Table 7-8, including upper temperature limits. Because high temperature applications often involve combustion gases or other corrosive materials, chemical attack to fabric or housing can be a problem if gases are cooled below their dew point.

Dust-Cake Removal

The accumulated dust loading must be removed from the filter surface with a frequency that will prevent gas-flow reduction below minimum

Table 7-8. Characteristics of Collector Fabrics

Fiber	Maximum Operating Temperature	Acid Resistance	Alkali Resistance	Flex Abrasion
Cotton	180°F	poor	very good	very good
Wool	200°F	very good	poor	fair to good
Nylon[a]	200°F	fair	excellent	excellent
Nomex[a]	425°F	fair to good	very good	very good
Acrylic (Orlon)[a]	260°F	excellent	fair to good	good
Polypropylene	200°F	excellent	excellent	excellent
Polyethylene	150°F	excellent	excellent	very good
Teflon[a]	500°F	excellent	excellent	good
Fiberglass	550°F	fair to good	fair to good	fair
Filtron[b]	270°F	good to excellent	good	good to very
Polyester (Dacron)[a]	275°F	good	good	good
Dynel[c]	160°F	excellent	excellent	very good
				fair to good

[a] Du Pont trademark.

[b] W.W.C. tradename.

[c] Union Carbide trademark.
By permission, W.W. Criswell Co., Bulletin 300.

acceptable volume. Filtering flow must be stopped while reconditioning of the fabric surface takes place. Reconditioning mechanisms include mechanical shaking, reverse flow, and pulse-jet devices.

Mechanical Shaker. For mechanical cleaning, the fabric, formed into envelopes or cylindrical tubes, is arranged as shown in Figs. 7-28 and 7-29. The tubes or envelopes are reconditioned by agitating the fabric with a shaking device to dislodge the accumulated material. The dislodged material settles in the storage hoppers before the collector compartment is placed back on stream. Where operations can be interrupted on a 4-hour frequency (usually lunch time or shift change), and where sufficient fabric is provided so that pressure-drop increase does not produce critical exhaust-volume variations, the single compartment unit is the usual arrangement. Where the system cannot be stopped for reconditioning, collectors can be compartmented into a number of separate sections, usually 4 to 6. Through a system of dampers and timers, compartments are taken out of service, in sequence, for reconditioning. Because it is difficult to maintain dampers airtight, relief dampers are often included which introduce a small volume of reverse air to keep pressure relationships at the fabric suitable for cake removal.

With shaker-cleaning mechanisms, flow rates through the fabric are usually in the 2- to 4-fpm range, and even lower where sub-micron particulates such as metallurgical fumes are collected. Use of compartments with their more frequent cleaning cycles does not permit substantial increase

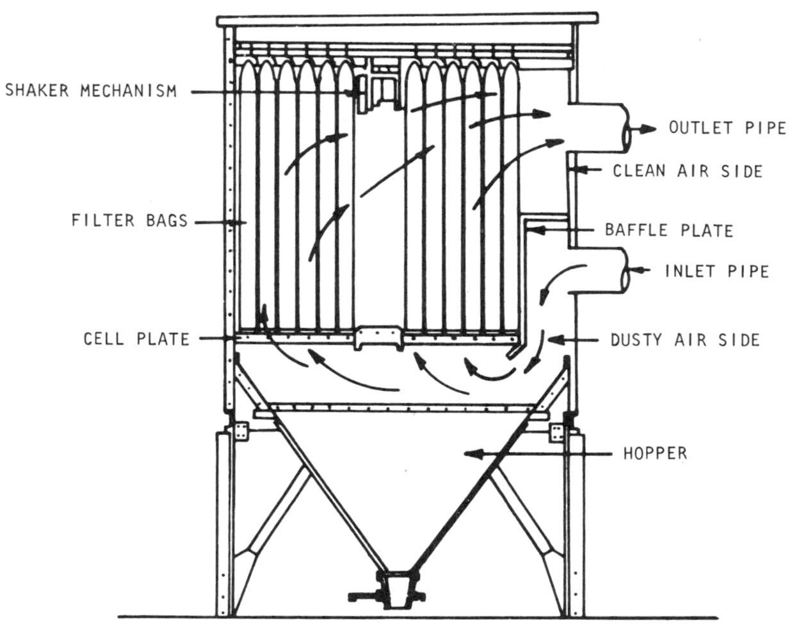

Fig. 7-28. Bag type fabric collector.

in flow rates over that of a single compartment unit cleaned every 4 hours. It appears that the best condition for fabric reconditioning occurs with the system stopped as it then assures ambient air conditions during the cleaning cycle.

Reverse-Flow. In this design the fabric is reconditioned by reversing the direction of flow through the fabric, assisted by the partial collapse of the bags. (See Fig. 7-30.) Reverse-flow cleaning is advantageous for fabrics which are damaged by the flexing and snapping action of shakers. Compartmented designs are standard because the substantial reverse-flow volumes entrain considerable collected material and must be directed to an on-stream compartment for cleaning. This reverse-flow circuit adds to the gross gas volume flowing through the collector's active filter surfaces and reduces the usual net-flow rate per square foot of filter media below that of shaker operated mechanisms on compartmented collectors. Flow rates through the fabric with all compartments in service are usually in the 1½ to 3 fpm range.

Pulse-Jet cleaning utilizes a compressed air jet operated for a fraction of a second to produce a rapid sound wave type of fabric flexing while maintaining an induced reverse air flow. Elements are usually cleaned one row at a time so that the total amount of fabric area removed from service is small and the removal from service is of short duration.

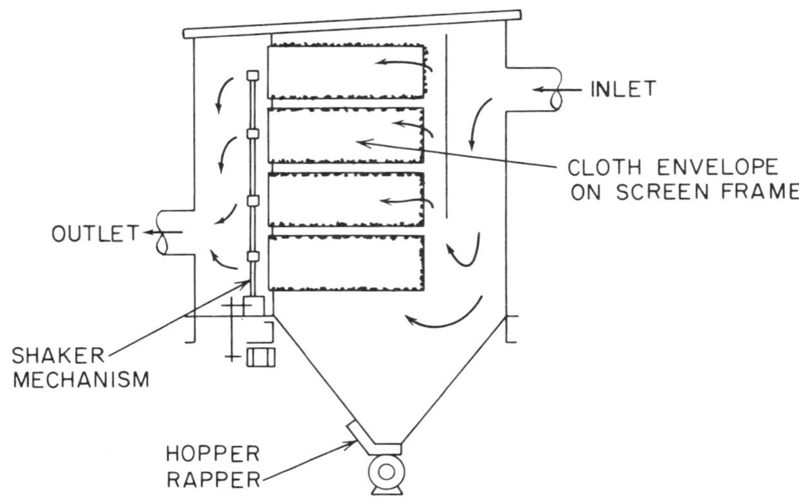

Fig. 7-29. . Envelope type fabric collector.

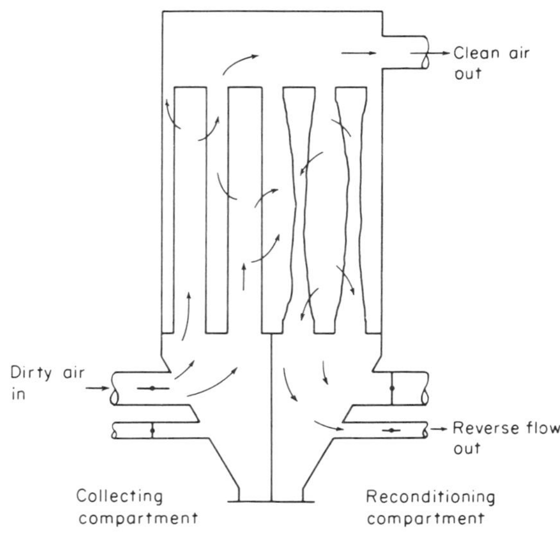

Fig. 7-30. Reverse flow collector.

Because of its ability to stay on stream during the cleaning cycle, to operate at high air flow rates, and to maintain a relative constant pressure drop, pulse-jet designs, Fig. 7-31, are the industry standard for most new installations. The filter medium is of felted texture to reduce migration through cleaned fabric surfaces; usual flow rates are in the 6 to 12 fpm range.

A modification of the conventional design, Fig. 7-31, is the cartridge

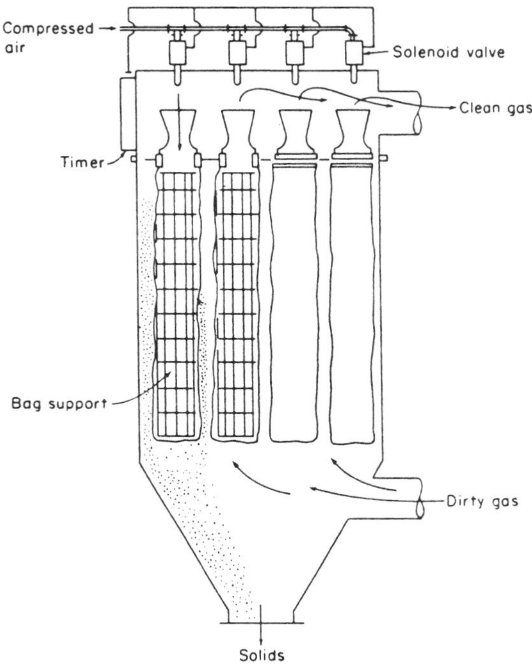

Fig. 7-31. Pulse-jet collector.

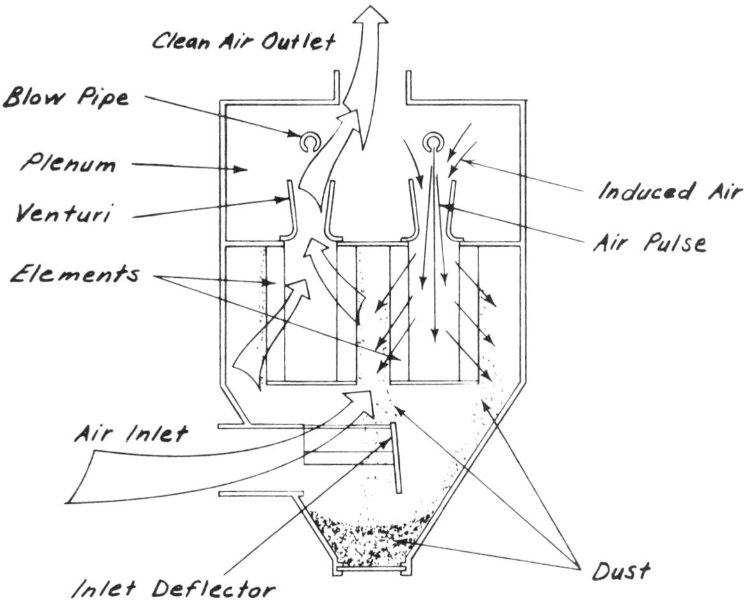

Fig. 7-32. Pulse-jet with cartridge elements.

arrangement, Fig. 7-32. The filter medium is a high efficiency pleated paper similar to that of a heavy duty engine intake filter. The pleated construction permits large filter surface area in a prefabricated replaceable cartridge. Flow rates are in the 1 to 2 fpm range, which permits operation at a lower pressure drop than the traditional design and with reduced headroom requirements.

Reverse-Jet. This design represents an earlier approach to high capacity, continuous cleaning construction. The concept used a moving manifold supplied by high pressure air to create a moving reverse flow zone. Maintenance problems are a major design weakness, and the pulse-jet construction has practically made the reverse-jet collector obsolete.

Maintenance

In addition to the usual attention to the cleaning mechanisms, maintenance efforts must also be directed toward locating bag failures. Detection is relatively simple for shaker bag or reverse flow designs because dust is deposited on the interior surfaces of the fabric elements. Ruptures, defective seals, or abraided surfaces will allow telltale leakage dust piles on the clean air side that are readily observed by examination from within the clean air side. For pulse-jet designs, detection is more difficult since dust is deposited on the outside of the fabric elements. Deposits on the inside of the bag are more difficult to see and in critical installations, photosensitive dyes are introduced into the entering air stream permitting leakage detection through the use of an ultraviolet fluorescent light.

Replacing bags in a pulse-jet design is a dirty chore because the dust is deposited on the outside surface. Top access removal designs, often with a walk-in weatherproof clean air manifold, are available to minimize this problem.

Where maintenance involves cutting or welding of any dry dust collector—and especially fabric collectors—precautions must be taken for fire or explosion prevention. All surfaces should be cleaned and access doors opened. For fabric filters, reconditioning mechanisms should be locked out to prevent dust cloud generation from released dust. Preferably, cloth filter elements should be removed.

ELECTROSTATIC PRECIPITATORS

An electrostatic precipitator, Fig. 7-33, consists of a number of high voltage, direct-current discharge electrodes placed between grounded collecting electrodes which form passages between which the contaminated gas flows. The suspended particles receive a charge as they pass through the ionized field between the electrodes. The interaction between the field and the charge causes the particles to migrate across the gas stream to the

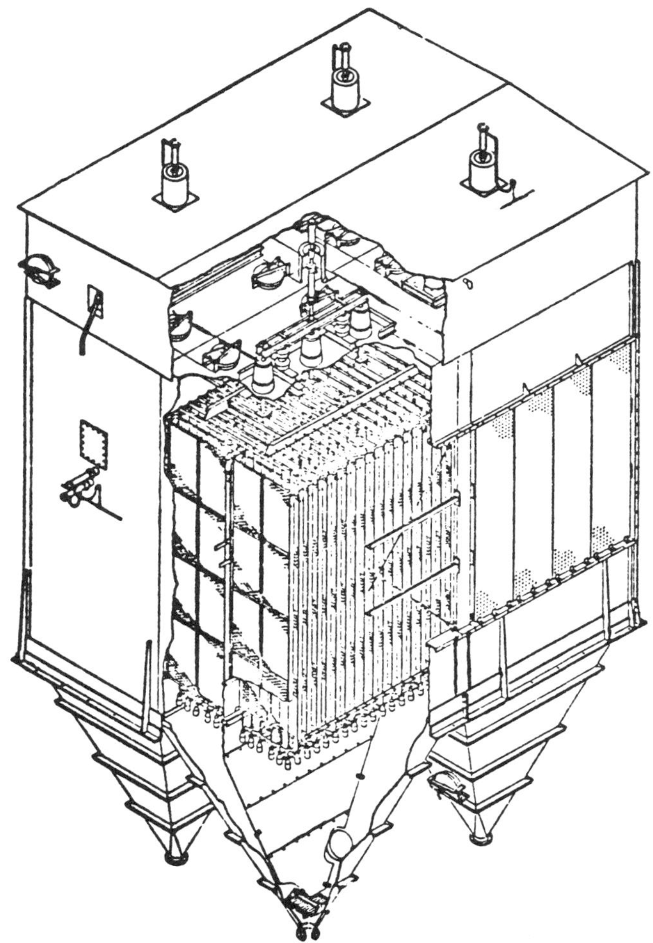

Fig. 7-33. Electrostatic precipitator.

collecting electrode and to adhere to it. The force causing migration depends on the intensity of the ionized field and the magnitude of the charge on the particle. Periodic rapping of the collector electrodes causes the dust to break away and fall toward the hopper.

Plate Type

Most precipitators are of this type, designed for gas velocities of 100- to 600-fpm. The collector plates are spaced about 8 to 10 inches apart and may be as high as 40 feet in very large precipitators. Dust dislodged from such heights is in grave danger of reentrainment and it is probable that much of it is entrained and re-deposited several times in its fall from plate to hopper. This points up the need for adequate retention time which, of course, is a function of gas velocity and precipitator length. Frequency and intensity of rapping depend on the dust concentration of the entering gas and on the properties of the dust cake.

The collecting efficiency of precipitators is sensitive to nonuniform distribution of the entering gas. Uniformity of flow often is difficult to attain because the entering velocity is low and the cross section large. Nonuniformity can be greatly aggravated by sharp bends in the inlet duct. When poor distribution is expected a transparent small-scale model in which the flow pattern can be studied may be the most economical guide to the best configuration of the full-sized installation.

Electrostatic precipitators are capable of cleaning very large volumes of gas at temperatures as high as 1,000F. The lower limit of economical use is about 50,000 cfm because of the cost of auxiliary equipment such as transformers, rectifiers, and control apparatus. These costs-per-unit-of-capacity increase rapidly with diminishing size.

Tube Type

The application of these precipitators usually is confined to special situations where the material is adhesive in nature, radioactive, extremely toxic, or where the gas must be processed at pressures demanding pressure-vessel construction. Usually, the volume treated is much smaller than that of plate type precipitators. The assembly consists of vertical tubes through which the gas flows in an upward direction. In the center of each is the discharge electrode. The entrained material is deposited on the inner wall of the tube and when the wall is washed by a thin film of liquid, very little of the captured material escapes.

UNIT COLLECTORS

Isolated dust sources often may be served to advantage by small self-contained units consisting of a fan and some form of dust collectors similar to those in Fig. 7-34. Fabric collector designs are the more usual providing high collection efficiency and, where conventional air to cloth ratios are employed, assuring that exhaust air flow between reconditioning cycle is maintained. The cyclone unit design has application where coarse dust is generated such as woodworking or metal grinding or machining and the cleaned air can be discharged to the atmosphere. Unit collectors using an air filter as the final collector element should be carefully evaluated before their selection. Air filters are designed for the light atmospheric loadings encountered in air supply and air conditioning service. Consequently, dust holding capacity is minimal and not suited to exhaust system concentration except in

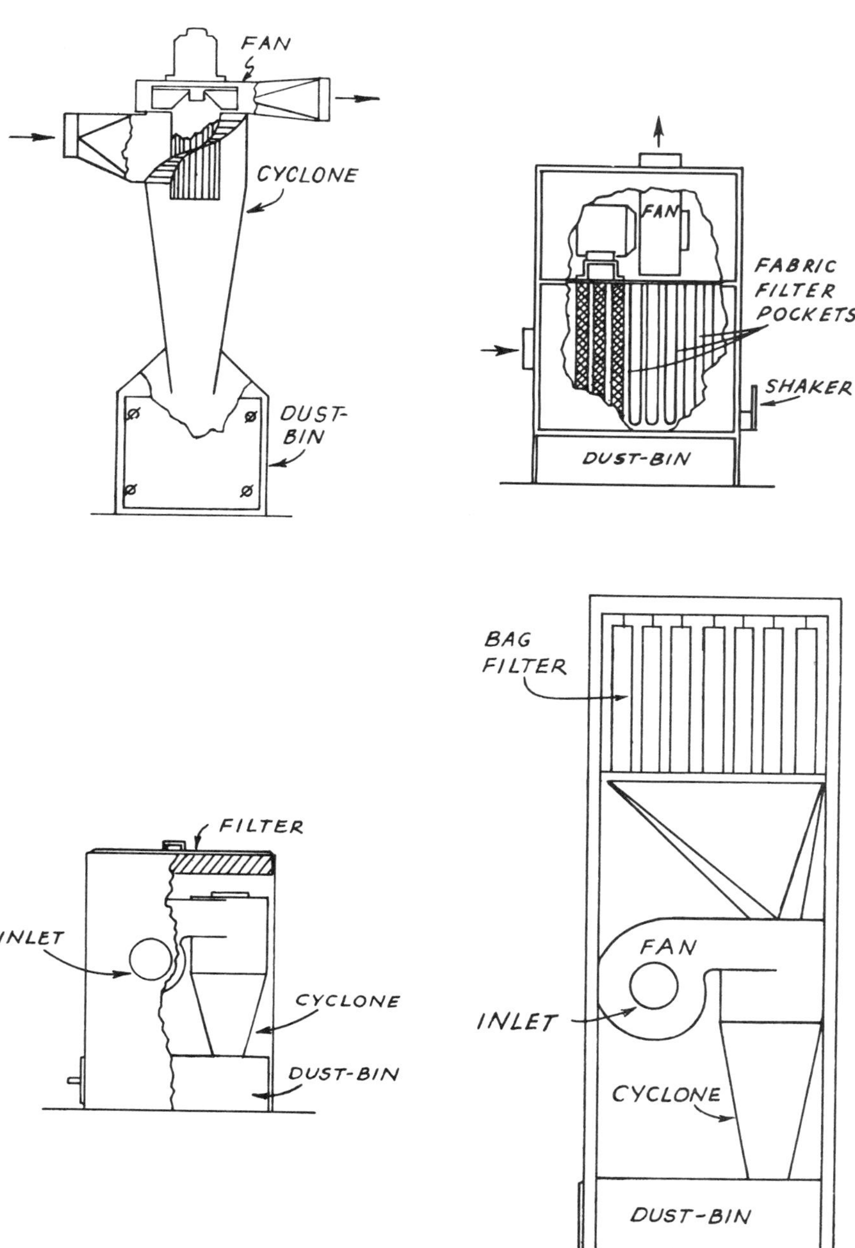

Fig. 7-34. Typical individual exhaust units.

the case of intermittent dust generation and the lowest of particulate quantities.

The pulse-jet design of fabric collectors has considerable unit collector application. Its ability to recondition the fabric elements while in operation makes it an ideal design for bin or silo venting where loading is either mechanical or pneumatic. For remote transfer points, the arrangement, Fig. 7-35, provides local exhaust ventilation to prevent dust dispersion and economically returns collected dust back to the main material flow.

The following list[5] of desired characteristics is a useful guide for the selection of recirculating units:

1. The cleaning efficiency should be such as to reduce the effluent dust content to acceptable values.
2. The unit should maintain its rated capacity expressed in cfm of air handled while accumulating large amounts of dust between cleanings.
3. The cleaning operation should be simple and should not increase the dust concentration in the room.
4. The unit should be capable of operating with no attention for 8 hours.
5. The dust storage space should be great enough to contain a full week's accumulation.
6. Renewable filters should not require replacement more frequently than once a month.
7. The unit should be rugged and substantial.
8. It should be quiet.

Individual recirculating units are not a satisfactory substitute for a central system where the latter can be applied. The maintenance of a multiplicity of small scattered units is unlikely to be as good as that of a single large collector and performance is more difficult to monitor. Moreover, the removal of dust from several small bins in the working area invites recontamination by careless handling. In general, such substitution is poor economy and can easily produce poor dust-control.

AIR FILTERS

Air filters, which are used extensively for removing particulates from outdoor and recirculated air ventilation systems, employ the same mechanisms as heavy duty industrial particulate collectors. Two major design parameters differ for the air filter group.

a. Dust Holding Capacity. Filters are designed for small particulate concentrations, normally not more than 0.1 grain per 1,000 cfm. Conse-

[5] "Characteristics of Unit Dust Collectors," by Stern, Baliff, Perina, Crowley, Feiner, and Urbano, *ASHVE Transactions*, Vol. 52 (1946), 237.

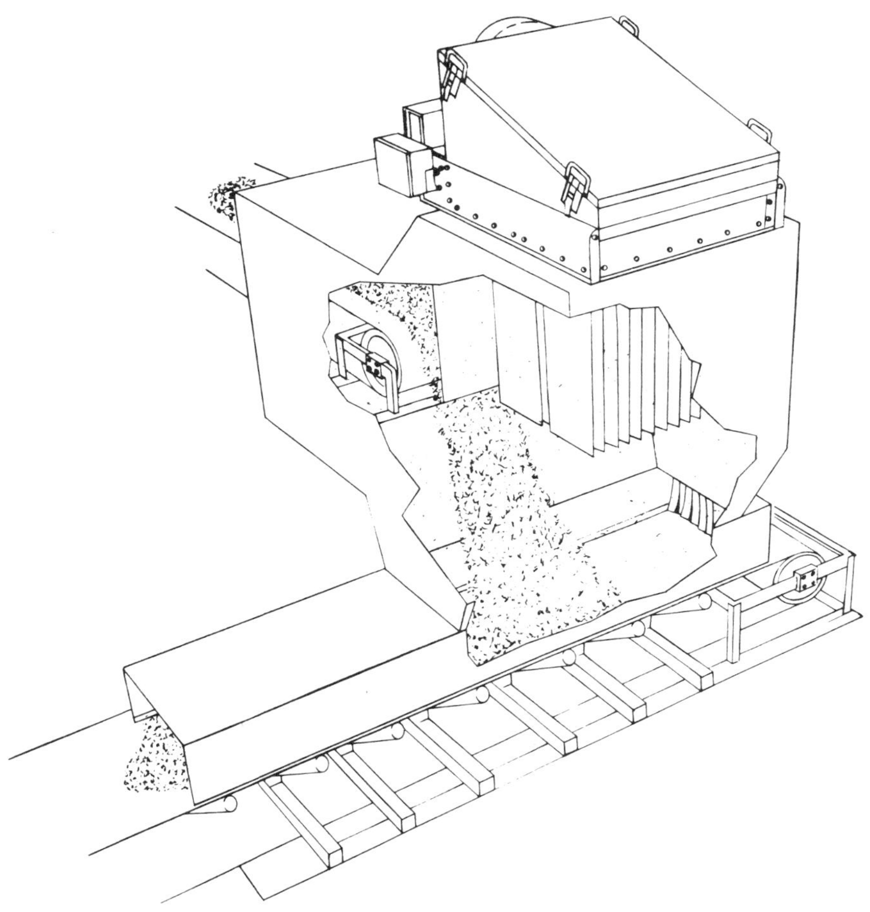

Fig. 7-35. Unit collector for isolated transfer point.

quently, particulate storage capacity is small and is seldom sufficient for industrial exhaust system service. (Industrial particulate collectors normally remove from 100 grains to 20,000 grains per 1,000 cfm.) However, there are a few contaminant producing operations where particulate loadings are light and generation is intermittent. Examples would be metal finishing from tool room machining; light duty paint spraying; and the collection of oil mists.

b. Efficiency. Filters must be designed for maintained efficiency from the time they are first placed in service. (The dust mat relied on by fabric collectors would take too long to develop in air filter service or an increased resistance to air flow would develop too rapidly for reasonable service life.)

CONTROL OF GASEOUS EMISSIONS

The principles of exhaust ventilation, including entrapment of contaminants and their movement through piping, apply equally to solid and gaseous contaminants. The methods for removal of solid contaminants from the gas stream have been treated in some detail in this chapter. The disposal of gaseous materials or the recovery of valuable gaseous products, on the other hand, will be described only briefly. In many instances, the solutions of these problems fall in the realm of chemistry and chemical engineering.[6] Usually, one or more of the elements of the problem are unique and not amenable to a generalized solution.

Dilution

The simplest means for disposing of gaseous contaminants is that of dilution and dispersion resulting from discharge into the atmosphere at sufficient elevation and exit velocity to keep ground level concentrations within the acceptable range.

Absorption

Wet scrubbing is a major mechanism for absorbing a contaminant into a scrubbing fluid, either water or a suitable chemical solution. With the possible exception of the high energy venturi scrubber, designs for gaseous contaminant removal differ from those for particulates. Particulate removal involves physical capture by impingement or impaction on a wetted surface; gas or vapor removal is more complex since the constituent is dissolved in the liquid and changes its properties.[7]

The usual collector is a packed scrubber with packings designed to present a large surface area over which the gas and liquid flow. The usual arrangement is for countercurrent vertical or crosscurrent horizontal flow of the gas stream.

Adsorption

Adsorbents are porous solids whose enormous internal surface area enables them to hold large numbers of captured molecules from the adjacent gas flow. Activated carbon is the most widely used for air pollution control where odors or organic vapors are involved.

[6] "Air Pollution Control—Part II: Gaseous Emission Control," *ASHRAE Symposium Bulletin Ch-73-2*, 1973.

[7] *Ibid.*

Incineration

High temperature oxidation is an effective way to destroy most odorous materials, to reduce opacity of organic aerosols, to reduce reactive hydrocarbon emissions, and to reduce explosion hazards from highly combustible organic materials. Contaminant concentrations in the carrier gas stream are seldom sufficient to support combustion and, consequently, disappointingly high energy consumption is required to maintain incineration temperatures even in those cases where the use of catalysts permits a substantial reduction in incineration temperature.

CHAPTER 8

Low Pressure Conveyors

Bulk materials which can be airborne may be transported for considerable distances, both horizontally and vertically, by pneumatic conveying systems which are similar to ordinary dust collecting systems. These systems are simple, cheap, and flexible. They will deliver material to almost any destination to which a pipe may be run. This characteristic favors the pneumatic conveyor for installation in existing buildings where plant arrangement and space limitations make other forms of material handling equipment difficult to apply. Pneumatic conveyors are dust-free and weather-proof and, therefore, may be run from building to building, across plant yards and public streets, without special protection and without causing public nuisance.

The mechanical efficiency of pneumatic conveyors is low. The resulting power consumption per ton of material sometimes offsets any advantages which pneumatic conveyors present. Moreover, the mile-a-minute velocities may shatter friable materials excessively by impact with pipe walls and elbows. For the same reason, abrasive substances may cause excessive wear of various parts of the system. While careful design and judicious selection of materials will minimize these effects, they are present, to some extent, in all pneumatic conveying systems.

The distinction between low- and high-pressure conveying systems is arbitrary. For the purposes of this chapter a low-pressure system is one in which the pressures—above or below atmospheric—do not exceed 5 percent of the barometric pressure, or about 20 in. wg. A low-pressure system employs centrifugal fans as air movers in contrast to positive pressure-blowers or exhausters.

Conveying Velocities

The principles of design of pneumatic conveyors are identical with those of exhaust systems. Velocities, air volumes, pipe sizes, and resistances must be determined. Economical velocities for pneumatic conveying are considerably higher than those employed in the dust-collecting field. High velocities mean high conveying capacities. For a given pipe diameter, the material handling capacity increases as the cube of the velocity when the solids are completely airborne. The air volume, itself, increases directly with the velocity, whereas the weight of conveyed material per cubic foot of air varies with the square of the velocity. The combined effect, therefore, is strongly favorable to high air-speeds.

Velocities must be selected with consideration for the nature and subsequent use of the conveyed material. Coffee beans, for example, must not be broken. Granulated sugar also is depreciated in value by shattering and dusting, while salt is benefited thereby. Therefore, a nice balance must be struck between conveying economy and damage to the material. Cement, salt, and bulk chemicals may be enhanced in value by the further attrition induced by the conveyor. No special consideration need be given to most refuse materials such as wood waste or ashes, since they neither improve nor deteriorate with pneumatic handling.

The lower limits of air-speed are not far from those listed in Table 5-1, for dust collecting. These, of course, are suitable only for systems in which the weight of solids per cubic foot of air is relatively low. In Table 8-1 a similar group of materials and corresponding velocity ranges are listed. The designer may use considerable discretion in the selection of velocities, preferably in the upward direction. The velocities in Table 8-1 are workable but, as mentioned in connection with Table 5-1, they are not necessarily the most economical nor the most suitable for a given set of conditions. Often, it is profitable to refigure a conveying system for several pipe sizes and velocities in order to establish the combination which is cheaper overall and which best fits the local conditions.

Air Volume per Pound of Conveyed Solids

Mechanical feeders which continuously and uniformly load the conveyor, permit lower air flow-rates per pound of material than does intermittent and irregular hand-feeding. Hand-feeding requires a flow-rate sufficient to take care of the maximum slug of solids. The average concentration is seldom more than one-third of the maximum.

Published data on the minimum air quantities for pneumatic conveying are limited. The designer is forced to depend upon experience and upon spot checks of existing systems. A typical test is one conducted to ascertain the rate of feed which would choke a system for conveying batched jute butts. Two experienced men fed a 30-in. pipe at the maximum rate they could sustain for 5 minutes. Although they fed 2,000 lbs of damp fiber in this short period, they were unable to block the system. The average air velocity was 4,300 fpm, corresponding to a flow-rate of 53 cu ft of air per lb of jute. It is believed that the system capacity is from 30% to 50% in excess of the feeding rate attained during the test.

Table 8-1. Velocities for Low-Pressure Pneumatic Conveying

Material	Velocity, fpm	
	From	To
Wood flour	4,000	6,000
Sawdust	4,000	6,000
Hog waste	4,500	6,500
Pulp chips	4,500	7,000
Tanbark, dry	4,500	7,000
Tanbark, leached, damp	5,500	7,500
Cork, ground	3,500	5,500
Metal turnings	5,000	7,000
Cotton	4,000	6,000
Wool	4,500	6,000
Jute	4,500	6,000
Hemp	4,500	6,000
Rags	4,500	6,500
Cotton seed	4,000	6,000
Flour	3,500	6,000
Oats	4,500	6,000
Barley	5,000	6,500
Corn	5,000	7,000
Wheat	5,000	7,000
Rye	5,000	7,000
Coffee beans, stoned	3,000	3,500
Coffee beans, unstoned	3,500	4,000
Sugar	5,000	6,000
Salt	5,500	7,500
Coal, powdered	4,500	6,000
Ashes, clinkers, ground	6,000	8,500
Lime	5,000	7,000
Cement, Portland	6,000	9,000
Sand	6,000	9,000

A comprehensive study of the flow of air-coal mixtures through several configurations of 8-in. and 12-in. pipes developed useful relationships between mixture density, velocity, and friction loss.[1] The coal had been reduced to 99% through 200 mesh, and 90% through 325 mesh. The tests

[1] "Pulverized-Coal Transport Through Pipes," by R. C. Patterson, *ASME Paper* No. 58-SA-24.

demonstrated that the critical zones were the horizontal runs rather than the vertical. At velocities between 2,400 and 3,600 fpm, heavy drifting took place downstream from long-radius bends, substantially reducing the effective cross section of the pipe. With velocities in the range of 4,200 to 5,400 fpm, the drifting was inconsequential or nonexistent. Plainly, at low velocities the material was sliding along the bottom of the pipe until the velocity was high enough to place it in suspension. The friction losses were high at the lower velocities, diminishing to about 125 to 150% of that of air alone, in the normal range of 4,000 to 6,000 fpm. The study concluded that air/coal ratios ranging from 1.3 to 2.0, and velocities from 4,200 to 5,400 fpm permit considerable latitude in piping layouts.

Dense materials require less air per pound than do lighter and bulkier substances. From 35 to 50 cu ft per lb should handle any material in Table 8-1, at the lower velocity quoted. It is probable that 15 to 20 cu ft is sufficient for the upper velocities listed. Mechanical feeds may cut these values in half if conditions are favorable.

Suction versus Pressure Systems

Once the material is in the air stream, it makes no difference, pneumatically, whether the conveying pipe is under suction or pressure. Practically, there may be definite advantage in one over the other under certain circumstances. The designer can choose among three types of system. He may introduce the material through the suction pipe, trapping it before reaching the fan; introduce it into the discharge pipe against the fan pressure; or he may feed it on the suction side, pass it through the fan and separate it from the conveying air on the discharge side. Figure 8-1 indicates the alternatives, schematically.

As a rule, the selection of the preferred type of system is not difficult. To illustrate, it may be advantageous to use the suction as a means for getting the material into the system but the nature of the material may be such as to preclude passing it through the fan. Figure 8-1a is then the correct type. Local conditions may dictate a fan location near the feeding point. Fragile materials then are best fed by mechanical charger into the pressure pipe beyond the fan. This is the arrangement shown in Fig. 8-1b. In other cases, such as the handling of coarse wood wastes, non-inflammable or non-abrasive materials, the conveyed matter may be passed through the fan without danger. In the last instance, any one of the three types will be satisfactory.

Leakage of pressure systems is always outward. Hence, poisonous and other hazardous substances should be conveyed entirely by suction wherever possible. Spark-proof bronze wheels and adequate tramp-iron traps minimize fire hazards. The long shavings wheel or the one-piece, smooth, wool wheel will pass large quantities of stringy materials without

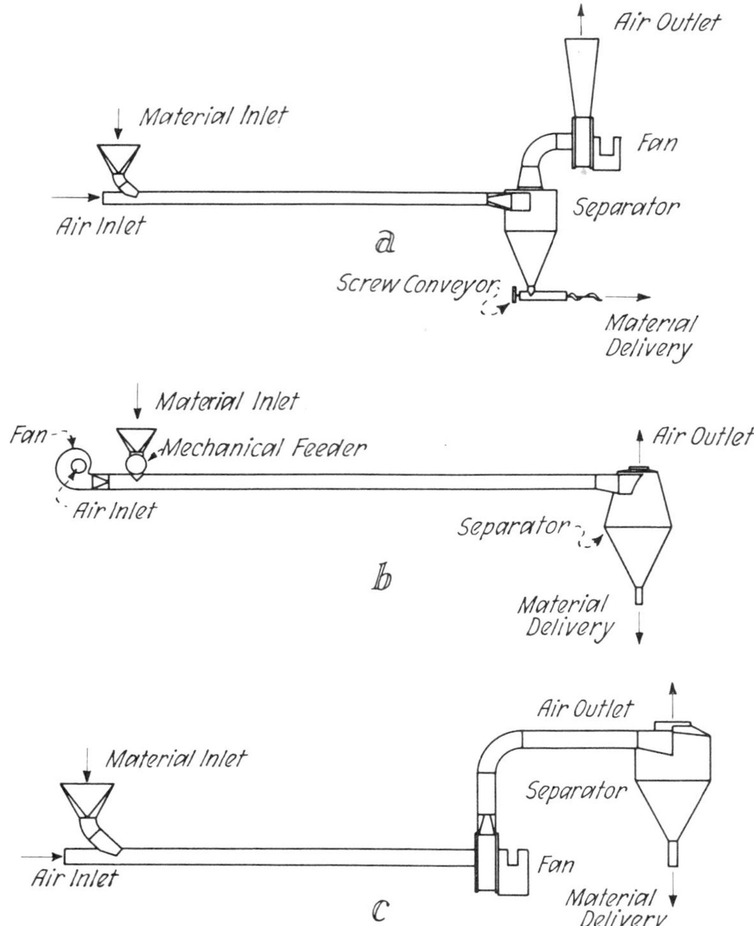

Fig. 8-1. Basic types of low-pressure pneumatic conveyors.

clogging or losing balance. The life of the fan may be improved by the use of chilled or white-iron casing liners, by the use of hard alloys or by using extra thick casing sheets. Neoprene or rubber linings and fan wheels coated with these materials also are helpful. By these and other expedients, the suction-pressure system, Fig. 8-1c, is enabled to invade the fields of the all-suction and all-pressure types.

Unloading and Feeding Devices

The dust discharge pipe of any separator operating under negative

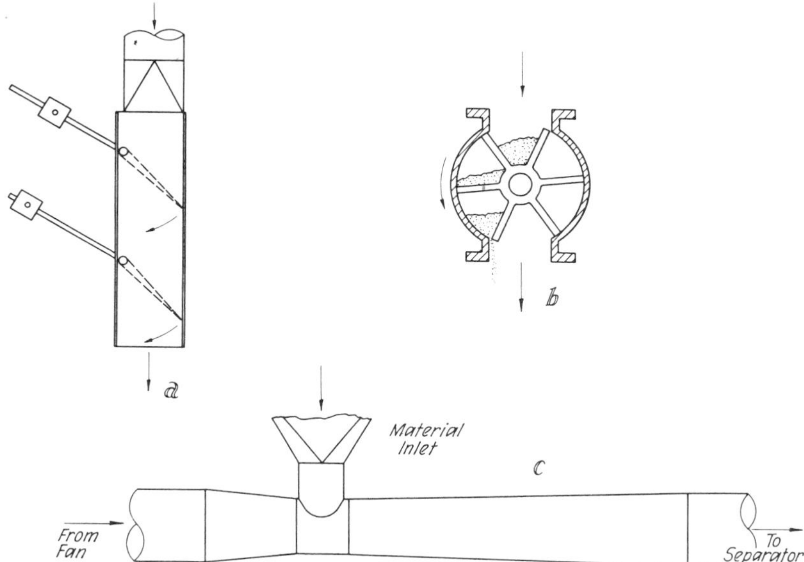

Fig. 8-2. Unloading and feeding devices.

pressure must be sealed against the atmosphere. The entrance of air through the dust discharge would destroy the suction at the feeding point and would cause settlement in the pipes. If the separator is of the cyclone type, the admission of air through the dust outlet will interfere seriously with vortical separation. In Fig. 8-2a and b, appear two forms of sealing device which permit the delivery of material without the entrance of air. Figure 8-2a is a simple gravity dump of the airlock type. By adjustment of the counterweights, the valves may be made to dump under different loads so that only one valve is open at a time. Counterweight adjustment is somewhat critical and most modern dumps of this type are motorized with the blades operated in sequence through suitable linkage. Gravity unloaders deliver intermittently. A power-driven unloader such as Fig. 8-2b delivers continuously and is more positive in action than the gravity valve just described. The wear is moderate if the rotational speed is not excessive. The ordinary screw conveyor, also, is a satisfactory seal if the discharge end is kept submerged in material.

Pressure systems may be fed through seals similar to Fig. 8-2a and b or by screw conveyor. Another type is the venturi feeder, Fig. 8-2c. When constructed as part of the fan discharge pipe this device reduces the static pressure at the material inlet to atmospheric or below, so that no inlet seal is needed. The venturi tube may be used alone or in combination with mechanical feeders such as Fig. 8-2b. In the latter case, the power-driven feed wheel functions solely as a metering device to regulate the flow of material into the system. Since it is no longer needed as a seal, clearances may be liberal and the wear reduced correspondingly.

Venturi Tube Theory

A simple venturi tube is shown in Fig. 8-3. It consists of convergent and divergent cones joined by a short, parallel throat section. The pressure relationships in the various sections, for the condition of perfect pressure conversion, are shown in the illustration. These follow Bernoulli's theorem. When the static and velocity pressures at the discharge end of the unit are known, and the desired static pressure in the throat has been established the throat velocity pressure may be obtained from the expression:

$$h_{v2} = h_{v3} + \frac{h_{s3} - h_{s2}}{1 - k_1}$$

where k_1 is the loss factor in tapered enlargements as taken from Fig. 5-15. The static pressure at the inlet includes the outlet static and all intermediate conversion losses. It is derived from the throat static and velocity pressures as follows:

$$h_{s1} = h_{s2} + (1 + k_2)\,(h_{v2} - h_{v1})$$

The constant, k_2, is the loss factor for tapered contractions and may be taken from Fig. 5-16.

Good proportions for venturi feeders are:

Entrance cone included angle, 20°
Discharge cone included angle, 10°
Throat length $\gtreqless$ throat diameter.

The process of computing throat diameter must start at the delivery end of the venturi since the only known factors are the discharge resistance, including collector back-pressure, and the flow conditions downstream

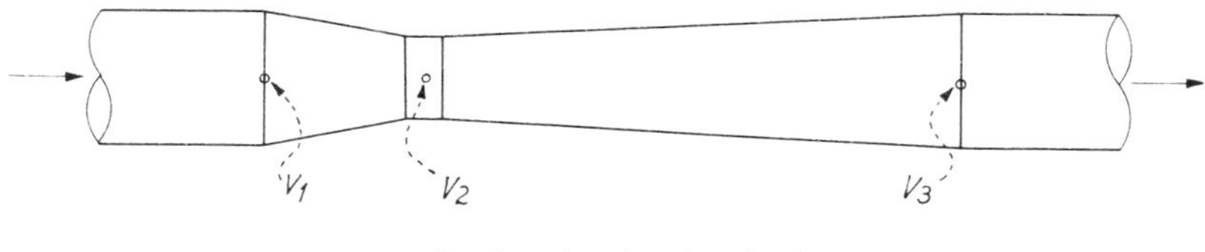

Fig. 8-3. Pressure relationships in simple venturi tube without losses.

from the venturi. When the throat pressures have been established, the pressure against which the fan must work can be computed.

The venturi feeder differs from the simple venturi tube by the addition of a feeding hole in the wall of the throat. The presence of this opening introduces an additional loss because of the discontinuity of the throat surface and because of the admission of air and material at this point. For convenience, this loss may be included in the factor k_1 used in the computation of the throat velocity pressure.

The loss factors for the entering cone and the expansion piece may be taken from Figs. 5-15 and 5-16, with the expansion factor increased about 10%. The static-pressure drop from inlet to outlet of a well-designed venturi feeder is usually from 15 to 20% of the static pressure at the delivery end of the tube.

Another form of venturi has a throat of rectangular cross section into which an adjustable tongue projects. The tongue is pivoted so that the throat velocity can be regulated to suit. The hopper connection points downstream at an acute angle to ease the passage of material into the air stream. A somewhat similar effect is produced by the introduction of a vacuum booster, Fig. 5-21, at the throat.

Typical All-Pressure Conveying System

There appears in Fig. 8-4, a typical system for conveying bulk granular material under pressure. The feeding device consists of a power wheel and venturi tube. The proportions of the latter are shown in enlarged detail in Fig. 8-5. The velocities in the entrance and exit cones and in the throat are shown in the lower diagram. The upper curves show the corresponding pressure changes.

Tandem Fans

The distance through which a conveying system can operate with a single fan is limited by the maximum static pressure difference which the fan can produce. This, in turn, is limited by the safe tip-speed at which

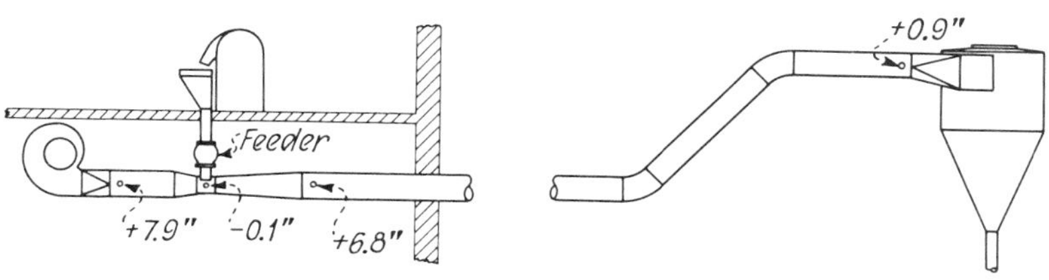

Fig. 8-4. Pressure conveying system.

the wheel can be operated. If long, stringy materials such as rags, jute or hemp fiber, or long damp shavings must be passed through the fan, it is best to limit the tip speed to about 10,000 fpm. This speed will produce a total static pressure (sum of inlet and discharge static pressures) approaching 8 in. of water. All-suction or all-pressure systems such as Fig. 8-1a and b permit maximum fan speeds. Well-built and well-balanced wheels may be run as fast as 15,000 fpm, producing static pressures of from 17 to 20 in. of water depending upon the blade design. If higher pressures are needed, two or more fans may be connected in series. When so connected, the pressures are additive. Thus, if two identical fans, run at equal speeds, are connected in tandem, the pressure difference between the inlet of the first and the outlet of the second is exactly twice that produced by either fan operated alone.

The general arrangement of a long-distance conveying system using tandem fans is shown in Fig. 8-6. The drawing also shows a diagram of the static pressures present in the different parts of the system. So far as the building arrangement will permit, the fans are spaced to produce the smallest departure from atmospheric pressure. The greatest compression is 10.8 in. of water, or about 2-1/2% of atmospheric. The maximum rarefaction is nearer 1-1/2%. Had the fans been concentrated near the inlet or near the collector, the compression or rarefaction might have

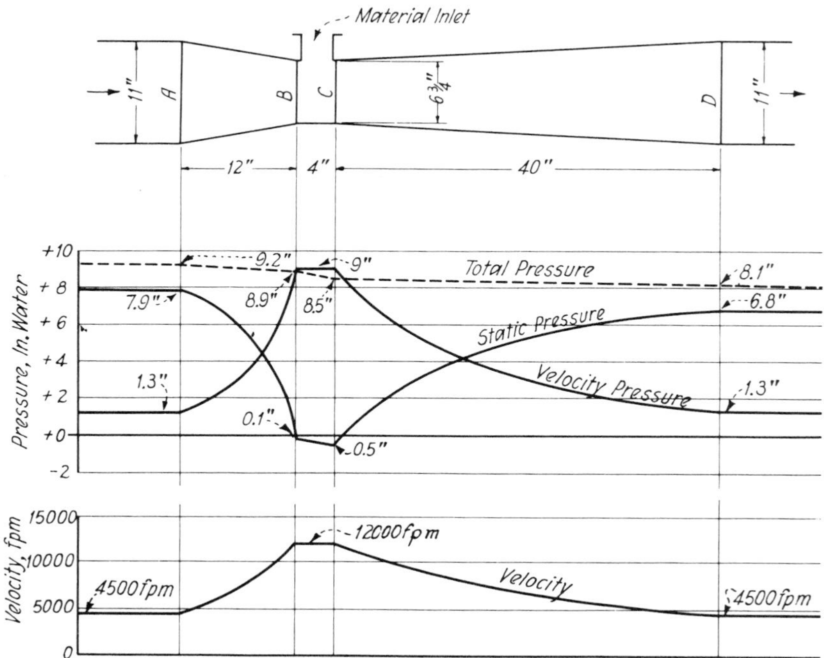

Fig. 8-5. Velocities and pressures in venturi charger.

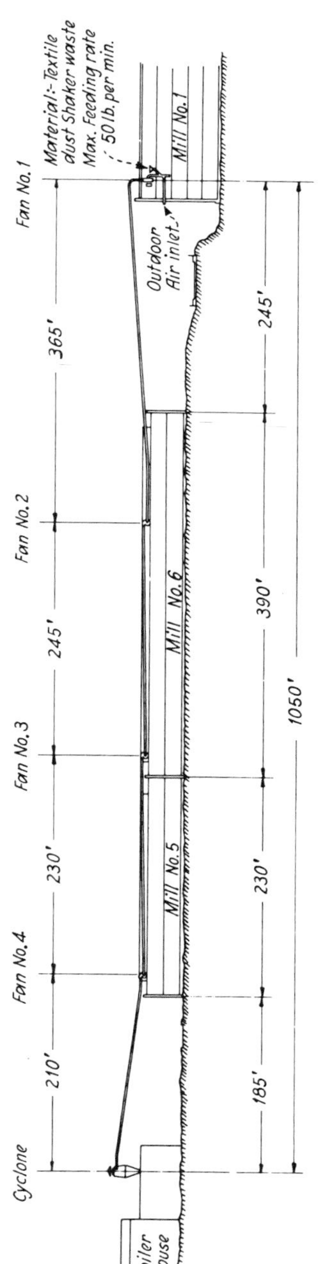

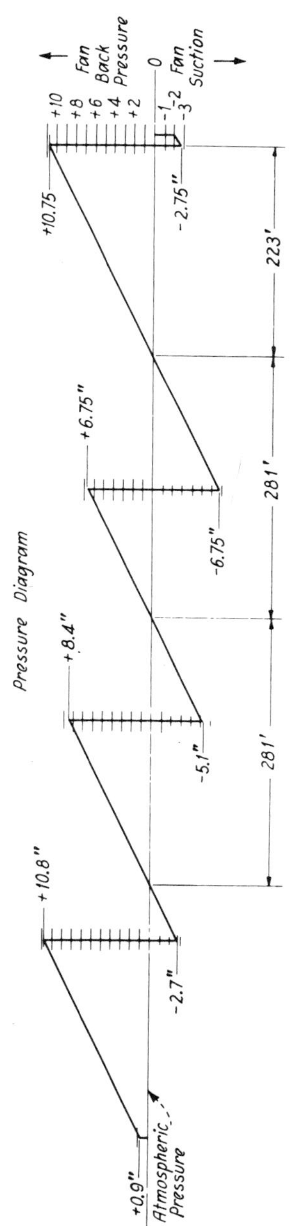

Fig. 8-6. Conveying system with tandem fans.

reached 12% or more. The corresponding change in volume would have produced a progressive increase or diminution of velocity along the system.

Inspection of the pressure diagram shows that the static pressure passes through zero between the outlet of one fan and the inlet of the next. If material is to be introduced into the system at more than one point, these points of zero static-pressure are the most favorable for preventing inward or outward leakage through mechanical chargers.

Double Fans

Figure 8-7 shows a double fan connected as a two-stage, or compound fan. This system conveys textile fiber through a 30-in. pipe at the moderate velocity of 3,500 fpm. It will be observed that the pressure drop through the cross-over connection is about 0.8 velocity head. The pressures shown were measured when the system was handling air only. Slugs of fiber passing through the system cause the pressures to fluctuate wildly. The pressure at the inlet of the second fan surges from about 2 in. of water below atmospheric to about 1.5 in. above. The changes are so rapid and violent that no accurate readings are possible with a water-filled manometer. Double fans are not common today but the results would be similar if two separate single fans were used.

Belt-Driven Fans

Design uncertainties are considerable in most conveying systems. The

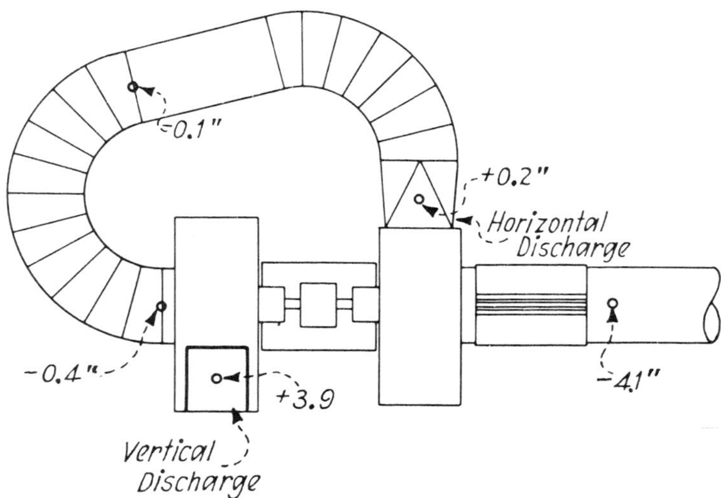

Fig. 8-7. Double fan connected as two-stage compound fan.

friction loss when moving air only may vary 5 percent or more from the calculated amount. A further uncertainty is introduced by the factor applied from Fig. 5-2, to compensate for the effect of the conveyed solids on the friction loss. The combined error in calculated pressure may easily be as much as 10 percent of the total. In the long system shown in Fig. 8-6, the error may be more than 5 in. of water. The simplest means for bringing the pressures in line with the calculated values is to belt drive the fans, so that simple and cheap pulley changes will adjust the speeds as needed.

Economical Pipe Sizes

The smallest practicable pipe size should be specified for a pneumatic conveying system. The combination of small pipes and high velocities results in high friction losses but the carrying capacity of the system increases more rapidly than does the power consumption. Fans, separators, and piping become smaller, cheaper, and easier to install. The first estimate for the system in Fig. 8-6 proposed a 24-in.-diameter pipe. As finally installed, an 8-in pipe was used. Table 8-2 gives comparative data for this system as calculated for three pipe sizes.

Table 8.2. Influence of Pipe Size on Cost of Pneumatic Conveying System

Pipe Dia., In.	Air Vol., cfm	Static Pressure, In. Water	No. Fans	Motor Size, hp	Total Power Consumption, hp	Increased Cost, Percent	
						First Cost	Power Cost
8	1,600	54	4	7-1/2	25	0	0
16	5,300	18	2	15	27	48	8
24	11,300	11	1	40	35	85	40

Relay Systems

When a number of dust collecting systems or a single large system is located at considerable distance from the ultimate destination of the refuse, there may be economy in the use of a relay fan. Large airflow is necessary for dust control purposes but results in a low dust loading per cubic foot of air. If the material can be separated from the air used for its collection at a point close to its origin, a smaller system of the high velocity conveyor type can be used to deliver it to its remote destination. Figure 8-8a shows a conventional dust gathering system delivering the collected refuse to a cyclone on a remote building. In Fig. 8-8b the main cyclone has been placed near the primary fan. The concentrated refuse then feeds from the main cyclone to the inlet of a small fan which blows the material across the yard into a correspondingly small cyclone.

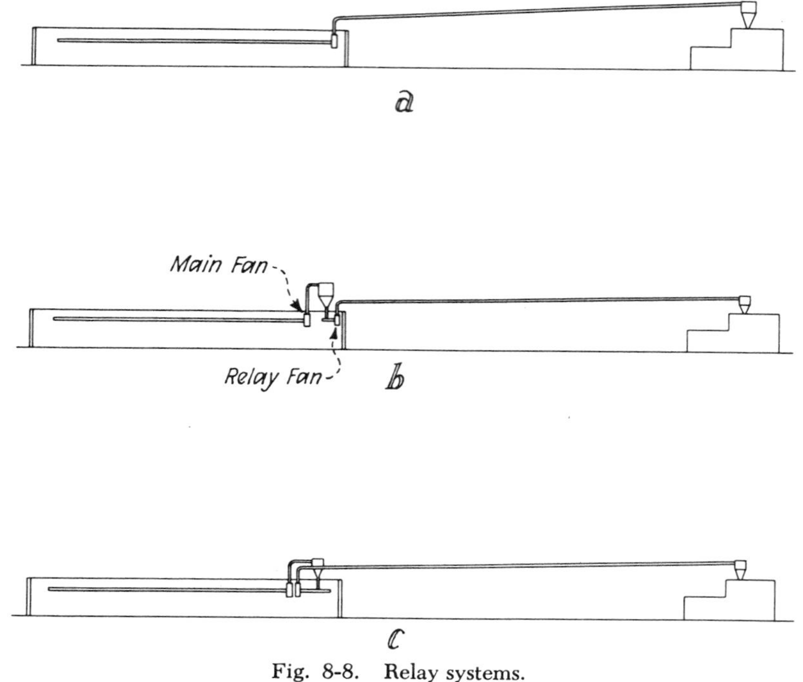

Fig. 8-8. Relay systems.

The relay system is the recognition of the dual function of a dust collecting system, namely, dust control and dust conveying. While each situation must be analyzed individually, it may be said that a system handling 15,000 cfm for a discharge distance of 200 ft or more, usually can be broken into a gathering unit and a conveying unit.

Figure 8-8c represents a double fan, one side of which is used as a relay fan. As a rule, this is not as cheap an installation as that employing a separate small fan since it does not take full advantage of the possible reduction in pipe diameter and cyclone size. If several gathering systems are located in the same building, one of the smaller units may be used as a relay system for the remainder. Also, when rearranging or enlarging existing systems, the possibility of using part of the present installation as a relay system should not be overlooked. The alternative arrangements should be sketched roughly and the more promising ones estimated in detail for first cost and power consumption.

Special Considerations for Conveying and Relay Systems

Systems employing two or more fans must be operated by definite schedule. The most remote fan must start first or some positive means must be adopted to prevent feeding material into the system before adequate conveying velocities are built up in all pipes. Ample handholes and cleanouts must be provided. They are not needed often if the system is designed properly but they save expense and damage to the system in cases of accidental clogging. When handling fibrous or hygroscopic materials, the conveying air should not be taken from warm and humid rooms. Exposed runs of piping will sweat internally in cold weather and will be difficult to keep clear. If possible, the conveying air should be drawn from outside.

CHAPTER 9

Centrifugal Exhaust Fans

In order to select the fan for an exhaust system it is necessary to know exactly what work the fan is expected to do. Its purpose, of course, is to establish and maintain a prescribed rate of airflow through the various elements of the system. The requirements of the system are expressed in terms of the desired flow-rate and the static pressures at the fan inlet and outlet. Until these factors have been established the fan cannot be chosen. Not all manufacturers express fan performance in the same terms. Therefore, in order to fit the fan to the work it is necessary to understand the basic significance of the static pressures at the fan and to interpret the capacity tables in terms of these pressures.

Analysis of System Pressures

Shown in Fig. 9-1 is an exhaust fan connected to an elementary exhaust system. Projected below it are the velocity, static, and impact pressures occurring in the various parts of the piping. The velocity pressures are positive in both suction and pressure pipes and are so indicated in Fig. 9-1a. The static pressure, on the other hand, is negative in the inlet pipe and positive in the discharge pipe.

The static pressure at the pipe mouth is the negative pressure required to establish inward flow. It provides the energy to overcome the inlet loss and to provide the inlet velocity pressure. The pressure drop between the inlet and the fan represents the friction loss in the pipe and any other resistances present between these points. Similarly, the fan-outlet static pressure is made up of the separator back pressure and the discharge-pipe friction. Static pressures are plotted in Fig. 9-1b.

The total, or impact pressure, it will be recalled, is defined as the algebraic sum of the static and velocity pressures occurring simultaneously in a given cross-sectional plane of a pipe. In Fig. 9-1c, these pressures have been combined to form the impact pressures throughout the system.

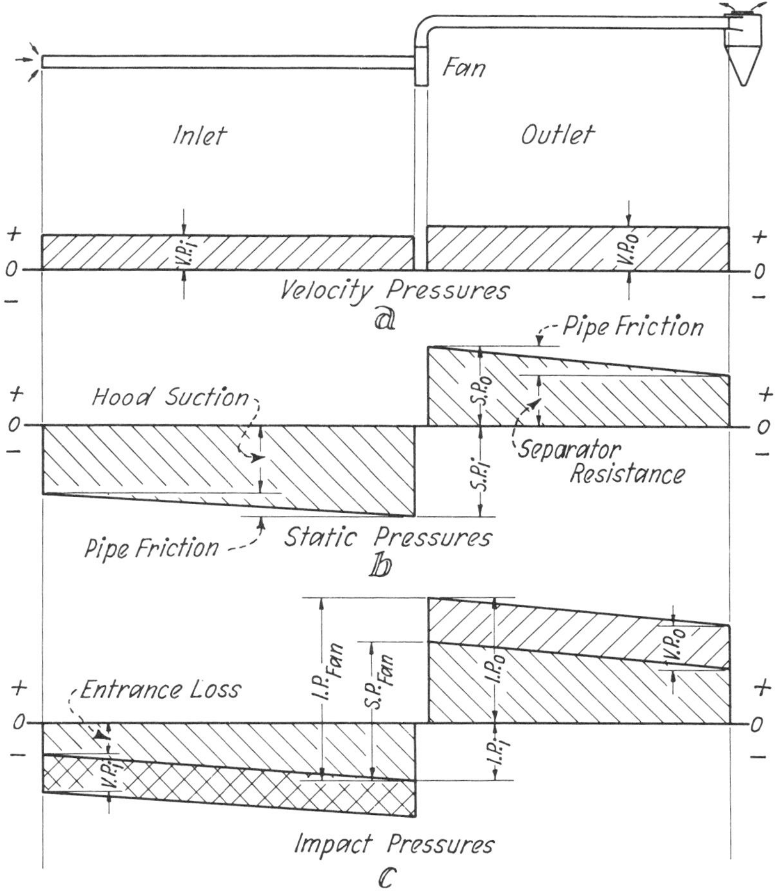

Fig. 9-1 Pressures in exhaust systems.

Thus, at the pipe entrance, the positive velocity pressure combines with the negative static pressure to produce a negative impact pressure. The total impact pressure which the fan must produce is shown to be the algebraic difference, or, disregarding signs, the sum of the inlet and outlet impact pressures. This is the entire energy output of the fan per cubic foot of air and is the pressure used in determining the power output of the fan and the mechanical efficiency.

Fan Rating Pressures

For purposes of fan rating, the fan static pressure has been defined as the total impact pressure at the fan minus the velocity pressure in the discharge duct. This is indicated in Fig. 9-1c. Most performance tables use the fan static pressure instead of the impact pressure against which to list volumetric capacity. It is evident that to select a fan from a table prepared in this manner the system pressure requirements must be expressed in the same terms. It must be emphasized that the fan static pressure is not the algebraic difference between the static pressures at the fan inlet and outlet as plotted in Fig. 9-1b, but is this value minus the inlet velocity head. Inspection of Fig. 9-1c shows that the fan static pressure includes resistance losses only.

Referring again to Fig. 9-1b and c, it is evident that the algebraic difference of the static pressures at the fan becomes numerically equal to the fan impact pressure when the inlet and outlet velocities are equal. Since this is the common condition existing in most exhaust and conveying systems, the impact pressure at the fan can be determined by the simple measurement of two static pressures. Moreover, these static pressures are the ones which the designer calculates while designing the piping. It should be noted that the fan static pressure of an operating system cannot be checked by static measurements alone but must include the much more involved measurement of mean velocity. Be certain that the velocity at the fan inlet is compared with the design velocity of the main. A higher fan-inlet velocity will mean an added acceleration loss and an increase in the inlet velocity pressure that must be added to the system pressure requirements. On the fan discharge side a higher outlet velocity than at the stack discharge can produce a measurable regain; sometimes more than enough to overcome the discharge duct resistance and actually produce a negative SP at the fan outlet.

Inlet and Outlet Connections

To produce rated airflow, the inlet duct must permit uniform flow into the fan inlet. Abrupt turns as the air approaches the inlet will crowd the air unevenly into the fan with poor distribution or "loading" of the fan wheel.

Power Consumption

A pressure of 1.0 in. of water is equal to 5.19 lb per sq ft. Hence, the work done in moving a cubic foot of air per minute against an impact pressure of 1.0 in. of water is 5.19 ft lb per min. Therefore, the power necessary to maintain flow may be expressed in horsepower as:

$$Ahp = \frac{5.19\,Qh_1}{33{,}000} = 0.000157\,Qh_1 \quad \text{or} = \frac{Qh_1}{6{,}356}$$

where:

Q = volume per min., cfm,
h_1 = impact pressure, in. of water.

This is the power output of the fan and would be the power input if the efficiency were 100 percent. The actual input is the air horsepower divided by the mechanical efficiency. When selecting a fan for a given system, the power consumption is taken from the performance table without going through the calculation of the air horsepower.

In dust-collecting systems the effect of the dust loading on the power required to drive the fan is negligible. The power demand is that for handling air only. In a conveying system, however, the power needed to move the material is an important fraction of the total. The best current information states that the power output of the fan is best expressed as:

$$Mhp = \frac{WH}{33{,}000}$$

where:

$W =$ the weight of the mixture in pounds per minute,
$H =$ the developed head in feet-of-air of the carrier air only.

Again, the input horsepower is Mhp divided by the fan efficiency.

Effect of Air Density on Power Consumption

A fan operating at constant speed and connected to a given piping system will deliver a constant volume of air regardless of density. Pressure and power vary directly as the density. In Fig. 9-2 is plotted the influence of temperature, altitude, and barometric pressure on the density of air. Roughly, the pressure and power decrease about 4 percent for each 1,000 ft of altitude above sea level and about 1 percent for each 5F increase in temperature above that of standard air.

Heat of Compression. The energy expended in developing the static pressure is released in the form of heat. Air temperature rise will be approximately 1 degree F for each 2 in. static pressure developed. While temperature rise will not make significant density changes, the added heat can be helpful in preventing condensation in the discharge stack where wet scrubbers are exhausted. Also the heat pickup can offset heat losses through exposed duct and collector surfaces where cleaned air is returned to plant areas.

High Temperature Operation. Exhausters of standard construction will withstand gas temperatures up to 750F but will require bearing protection for temperatures in excess of 300F. A heat slinger which is a small heat-conducting fan wheel attached to the shaft between the fan housing and the inboard bearing, will protect bearings up to 600F temperature. For higher temperatures, the separation of bearing bracket from fan housing to form a "heat gap," or the use of water or oil-cooled bearings is the usual practice. Protection of drive motor becomes important also. Insula-

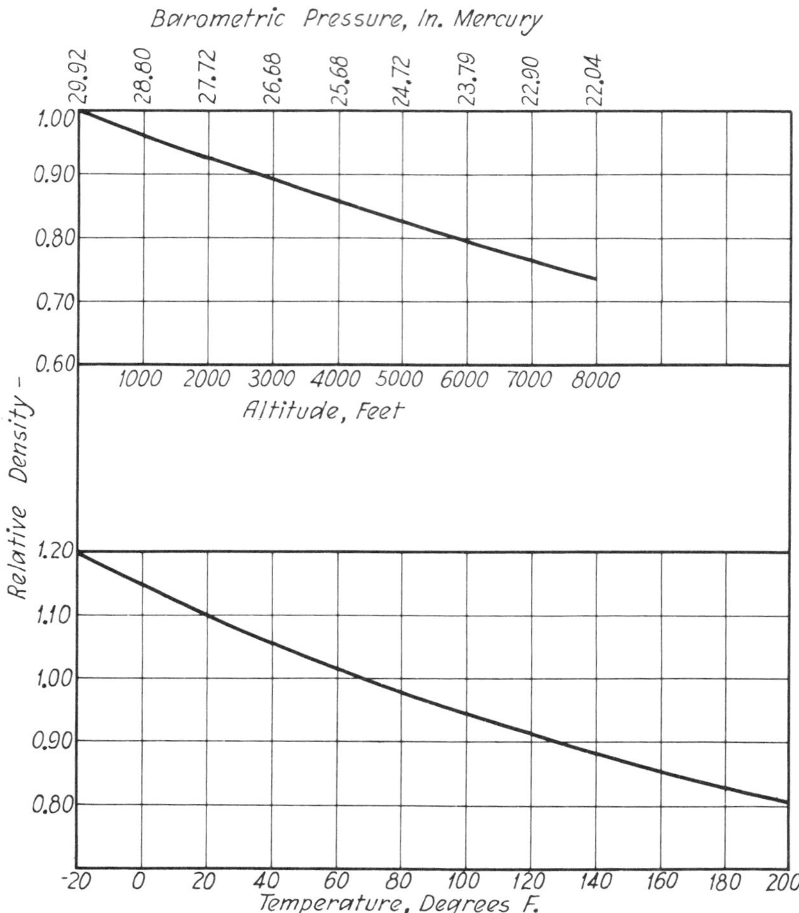

Fig. 9-2. Effect of temperature, altitude and barometric pressure on air density.

tion from heat conducted through the supporting steel can be obtained by air gaps between motor base and supporting steel. A radiant heat shield between fan housing and motor is also suggested. Even with this protection, the motor may operate in ambient temperature high enough to cause excessive temperature rise at full motor loads.

Performance Curves of Centrifugal Exhausters

When tested for rating purposes, exhaust fans are connected to inlet and discharge pipes in which impact and static pressures are measured and the flow rate determined. A symmetrical throttling device in the dis-

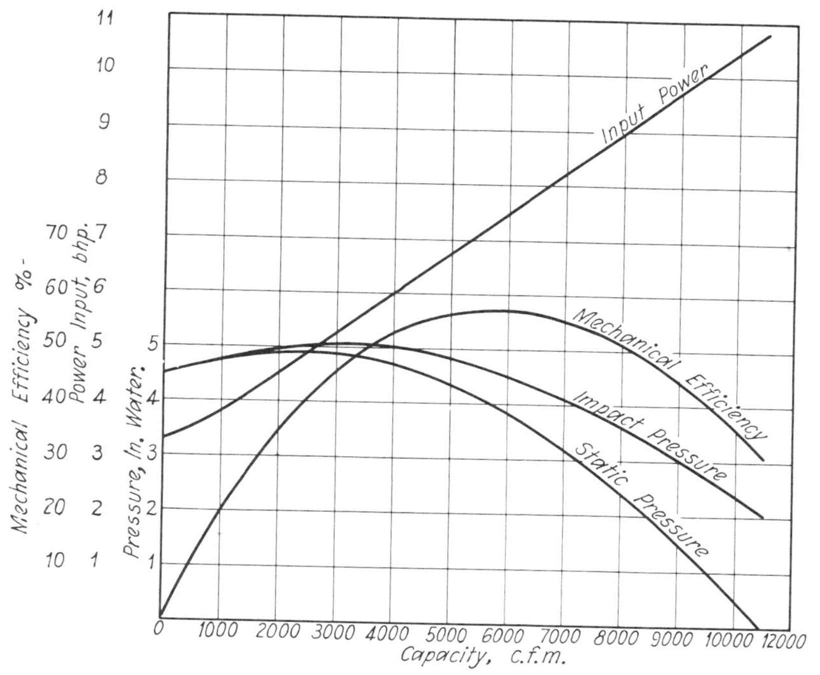

Fig. 9-3. Performance curves of centrifugal exhauster operating at constant speed.

charge pipe permits the load to be varied so that several points on the performance curve may be established. A group of curves such as in Fig. 9-3 may be drawn from the test data for a single speed. A family of similar curves covering the entire range of useful speeds may be derived from the original set by the application of certain well-established laws of fan performance. These form the basis for the published performance tables of the manufacturer.

Effect of Speed on Fan Characteristics

At any other speed than the one for which the original curves were plotted, the following relations are true when the air density remains constant and the flow is throttled through the identical orifices used in the original test:

1. The capacity is proportional to the speed.
2. The pressure is proportional to the square of the speed.
3. The power is proportional to the cube of the speed.
4. The efficiency is independent of the speed.

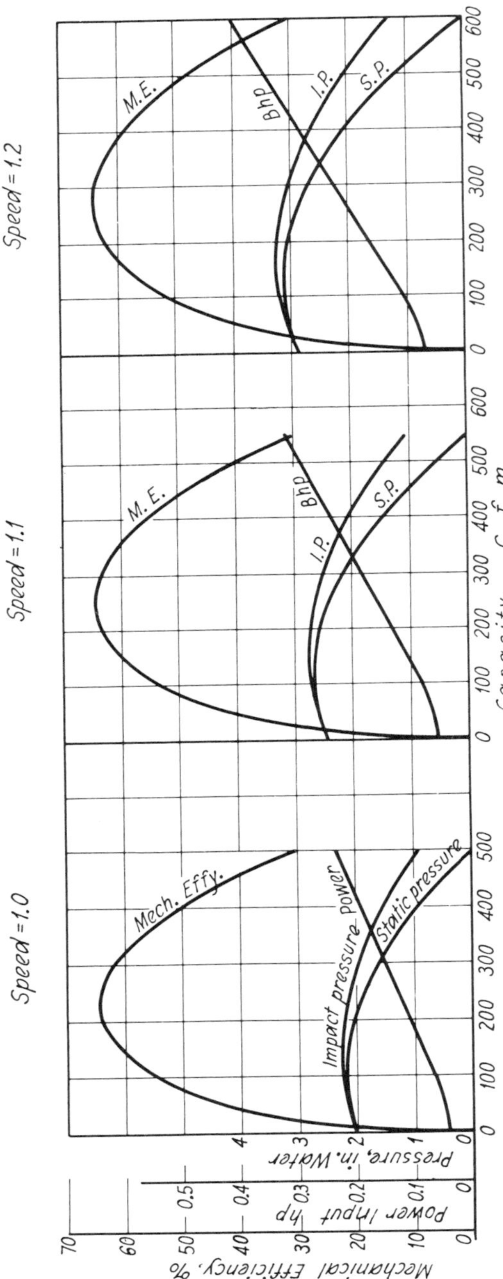

Fig. 9-4. Effect of speed on performance of centrifugal exhauster.

These laws are illustrated by the performance curves of Fig. 9-4 which represent the characteristics of a fan operated at three speeds whose ratios are 1.0, 1.1, and 1.2. The capacities at a given discharge opening are also in these ratios. The pressure ratios are 1.0, 1.21, and 1.44 and the power ratios 1.0, 1.33, and 1.73. The efficiency at any opening is constant at all speeds.

Effect of Size on Fan Performance

If a series of fans of uniform proportions and differing only in size is investigated for performance, a single efficiency curve plotted against relative capacity will be found to represent the entire series. Furthermore, the basic shapes of the pressure and power curves will be identical for all sizes although differing in numerical values. The influence of the wheel diameter on the performance, at constant peripheral speed, is as follows:

1. The capacity is proportional to the square of the diameter.
2. The power is proportional to the square of the diameter.
3. The pressure is independent of the diameter.
4. The efficiency is independent of the diameter.

These relationships derive from the fact that pressure is a function of peripheral speed; that capacity is a function of wheel volume; and that the power is proportional to the product of capacity and pressure.

Effect of Direction of Rotation

When a centrifugal fan is operated in the wrong direction, it will still exhaust 40 to 50% of rated air-volumes. Consequently, exhaust systems often operate at less than design exhaust volume because of incorrect rotation.

Fan Types

For most industrial exhaust systems for solid particulates, the centrifugal fan will be either a radial blade or backward-curved blade design. The slower speed, forward curved, "squirrel cage" design used for some air supply applications has little application in exhaust system work because of its sensitiveness to material build-up and/or wheel wear, plus a very unstable area at lower performance ratings.

Material Handling Fans

The radial blade, or "paddle wheel" design is often called the workhorse of industrial exhaust systems. It is of rugged construction, has relatively few flat-surfaced blades. It resists abrasion well, and can handle suspended material with a minimum of accumulation, or bridging. It is large in size, lower in mechanical efficiency than the backward-curved design. It is recommended for woodworking, buffing, and similar applications where the collector is on the downstream side of the exhauster. Also, it is suitable for systems handling condensable mists or vapors, and for the exhaust of wet collecting devices where water carryover during malfunctions can wet the exhauster wheel surfaces and encourage accumulations and unbalance.

Where excessive wear is encountered on the fan wheel due to abrasive dusts sliding outwardly on the blade surfaces, protective coatings of rubber or other abrasive resistant materials should be considered. Often, increased life can be achieved at the expense of some loss of efficiency by fabricating blades of floor plate or by welding beads about an inch apart, parallel to the shaft on the leading blade surface. The theory is that the raised surfaces will cause material in contact with the blade surfaces to be deflected away from the blade and be conveyed through the fan wheel with reduced blade-contact.

Wheel Types

The planing mill exhauster is a paddle-wheel type fan. Although a few fans employ warped blades, by far the larger number are radial or forward curved. The number of blades ranges from 4 to 18 in the principal makes of fan. The simplest form is the cast wool wheel, Fig. 9-5a. The number of blades is either 4 or 6 and the material is usually cast iron, bronze, or aluminum alloy. The maximum safe speed for gray-iron wheels is not much over 5,000 fpm tip speed. Nickel-iron or cast steel wheels may be run much faster. Heat-treated, cast aluminum-alloy wheels are in daily operation at 12,000 fpm and have the further advantage of being nonsparking.

Wool wheels of the same general form may be built of steel sheets, and when so constructed, are capable of higher speeds. In either form, the wheel is made as smooth as possible in order that fibrous materials may pass freely.

The long-shavings wheel, Fig. 9-5b, consists of a hub into which is cast a number of structural spokes and six or eight steel blades riveted to the spokes. These blades are usually radial. The addition of annular sheets or side plates converts this wheel into the shrouded, or rim-type wheel. Wheels with side plates are somewhat more efficient than open wheels but should not be used on stringy materials such as long fiber, rags, or curly shavings.

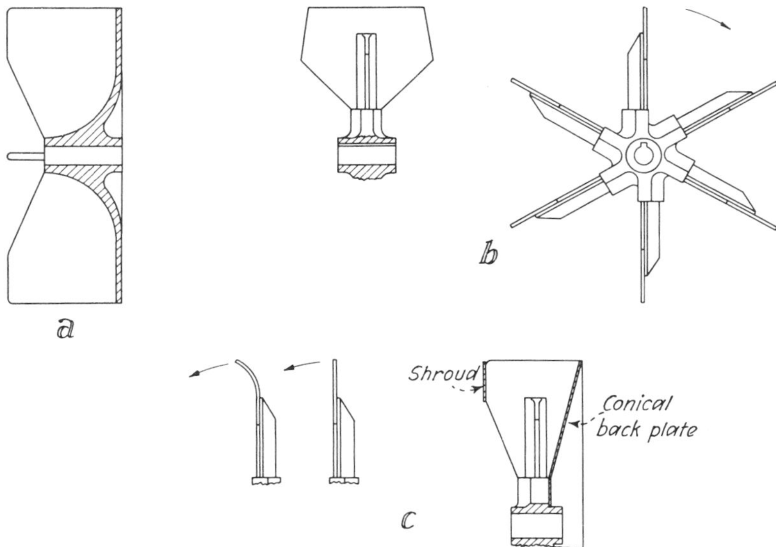

Fig. 9-5. Exhaust fan wheels.

Slow-speed wheels often are equipped with cone back plates as in Fig. 9-5c. When handling other than stringy materials, a shroud may be added to the inlet side of the wheel. Both radial and forward-curved blades are shown in the small detail. Although the efficiency may be no greater, the forward curve at the tip of the blade will produce a higher pressure at a given peripheral speed than will the radial blade.

Fans for Gaseous Materials

Fans operating on the clean air side of high efficiency dust collectors, or those handling vaporous contaminants are not limited as to blade form. The blade may be forward-curved, radial, or backwardly inclined. Vector diagrams of the velocity at the blade tip show that the air leaves the backwardly inclined blade at lower velocity than the tangential velocity of the wheel. As a result, the conversion to static pressure in the fan casing takes place with lower loss than is present in fans of the other types. The air from both radial and forward curved blades is moving faster, relative to the casing, than the tip-speed of the wheel.

The blades of the wheel shown in Fig. 9-6a are flat plates welded to a back plate and shroud. A more refined form is the airfoil blade of Fig. 9-6b. The efficiency of each type is good; both forms have good stability

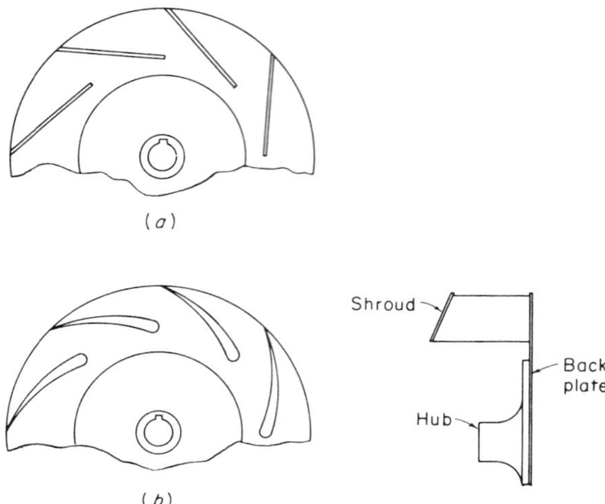

Fig. 9-6. Fan wheels with backwardly inclined blades.

at light loads, a region wherein many fans pulsate badly. The airfoil fan, when well designed, is usually less noisy than other types.

An important feature of the backward-blade fan is its load-limiting characteristic. The pressure-volume curve, Fig. 9-7, falls steeply and, because the volume increases more slowly than the pressure falls, the

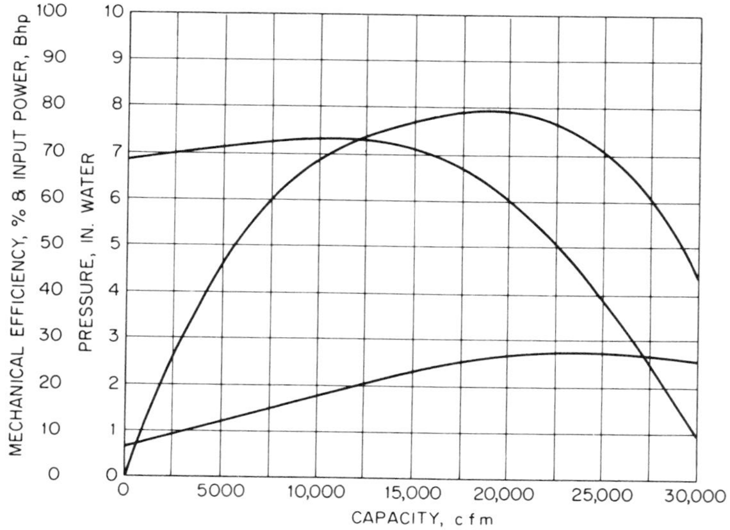

Fig. 9-7. Typical performance curves of backwardly inclined blade fans.

power curve flattens and droops. This attribute is especially useful when the system resistance fluctuates as, for example, during the build-up of the dust mat on filter fabric. In this instance the flow through the system remains approximately constant while the fabric passes from a clean to a loaded condition. Likewise, the power input has changed very little, which permits the selection of a motor to closely fit the system requirements with little danger of overloading.

Fans manufactured to the standards of the Air Moving and Conditioning Association, Inc., are fabricated in four series, based on tip-speed and maximum pressure; Class I, up to 3-3/4 in. TP; Class II, up to 6-3/4 in. TP; Class III, up to 12-1/4 in.; and Class IV for higher pressures. For industrial operations, Class II could be considered the minimum design as the heavier shaft and bearings will prove helpful even for lower pressure applications.

Special Fans

Fans can be built to order to meet most industrial needs. A wide range of materials is available to withstand corrosion, abrasion, or heat. Stainless steels, nonferrous metals such as nickel and Monel, cast acid-resistant alloys and fiberglass can be used for casings and wheels. In addition, fans of standard construction and materials can be coated with protective paints, rubber or various plastics and resins. Other modifications can adapt fans to high temperature use.

Fan Drives

It is seldom possible to design an exhaust system so that a fan with a direct connected alternating current motor can operate at the optimum pressure and capacity. Small differences in speed produce relatively large changes in pressure and power since these quantities vary with the square and cube of the speed respectively. The small number of common synchronous speeds, 600, 720, 900, 1,200, 1,800 and 3,600 rpm, makes it difficult to fit the fan and motor to the needs of the system. Moreover, the spread between speeds is so great that none but the most major changes can be made. Thus, to drop back from an 1,800 rpm motor to one at 1,200 rpm will reduce the volume by 1/3 and the pressure by more than 1/2.

While the trend in power drives has been away from belts, the belt drive offers to the exhaust fan a degree of flexibility at low cost which is not duplicated by any other type of power transmission. The modern "V" belt permits large speed ratios, short center distances and good efficiency. Small speed changes of the sort necessary for the correction of pressure deficiency or to allow for moderate increases or decreases in the size of the system may be made by a simple and inexpensive pulley change.

Noise and Vibration

Many exhaust systems are objectionably noisy. The characteristic sound is a high-pitched, penetrating hum or whine which may be audible throughout an entire building or for considerable distances outside. No practicable way to reduce this noise substantially is known to us at this time. The offhand solution of the layman is to insulate the fan from the building by means of rubber, cork or composition pads and to connect it to the piping through nonrigid sleeves. While these expedients will render mechanical vibration less objectionable, they are valueless as a means of suppressing noise. Even as an attack on vibration, they treat the symptom rather than the disease. Putting the fan wheel in dynamic balance, or even good static balance, will usually accomplish greater reduction of vibration than will expensive insulating materials.

The primary source of noise in an exhaust system is the fan. To a much lesser extent the vibration of unstayed sheet metal surfaces in the piping system contributes to the general noise level. The rush of air into hoods also is a factor. Nevertheless, the fan is the source of most of the noise and is the point from which it is transmitted, through the air column in the piping, to each hood and to the outside air at the discharge outlet. Fortunately, the point of minimum noise-level is close to the point of maximum efficiency.

While the exact mechanism surrounding the generation of noise in a fan is not entirely clear, a major factor is related in some way to the passage of the blades past the cut-off of the casing. Considerable disturbance occurs at this point; pressures change sharply from one side of the cut-off to the other; and the passage of each blade sends forth a compression wave into the air column in both the suction and discharge pipes. Figure 9-8 records a series of static pressure measurements taken at various points in a fan case. Pressure tap No. 1 is located at the cut-off and is taken as the reference point for the angular location of the other taps. Pressures at stations 1 to 4, inclusive, were unstable and difficult to measure with accuracy. The difference between these pressures and the markedly higher ones at stations 15 to 20, inclusive, indicates that the zone of the cut-off is a region of special significance.

Further information is derived from a brief study of sound frequency or pitch as related to the number of blades and the wheel speed. The characteristic sound output of the fan consists of a fundamental tone and its harmonics, the latter seldom distinguishable by ear. It is found that the frequency of the fundamental coincides with the number of blades passing the cut-off per second. This has been verified with wheels of various numbers of blades and with radial and both forward-and backward-curved blades.

The pitch is related to apparent loudness through the characteristic of the human ear which causes a greater sensation of loudness for certain frequencies than for others even though the sound energy remains constant. Thus, for a given energy-level, sounds in the neighborhood of

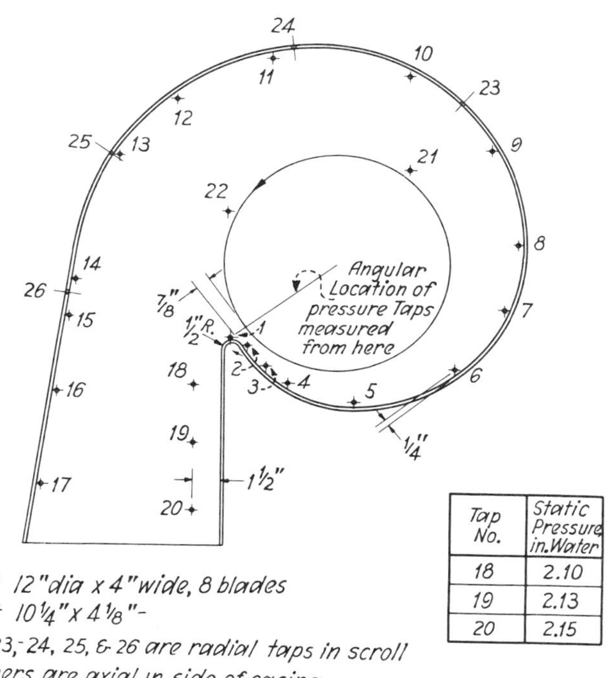

Tap No.	Static Pressure in. Water
18	2.10
19	2.13
20	2.15

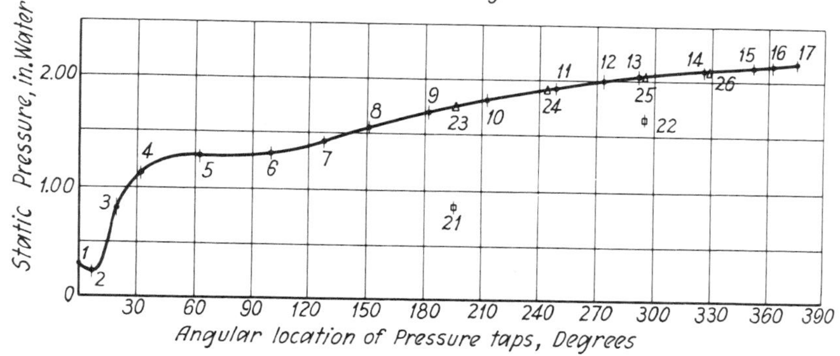

Fig. 9-8. Static pressures in fan casing.

2,000 cycles per second[1] appear to be louder than those at either lower or higher frequencies. Field observation will confirm the conclusion that lower-pitched fan noise is less irritating than that produced at higher pitches. Consequently, the combination of rotational speed and number of blades which gives the lowest number of blades per second passing the cut-off is likely to be the least objectionable.

A sturdy support is essential to minimize vibration. It must oppose the dynamic as well as the static loadings and as the size and tip speed increase, the dynamic load becomes increasingly significant. When total pressures exceed approximately 6 in., the mass of the supporting base should equal twice the fan weight. On larger fan sizes this can most easily be obtained by mounting on a concrete pad. Concrete is an excellent supplement to the structural steel supports for elevated fan locations.

Ejector Systems

When the conventional system is unsuitable because of high gas temperatures, explosive mixtures or corrosive vapors, the ejector system finds application. As shown in Fig. 9-9, flow in the exhaust piping is induced by the aspirating effect of a high-velocity air jet. Ejector systems require from 5 to 10 times the power of ordinary systems because of the inefficiency of energy transfer between the high-speed jet and the induced air.

The nozzle velocity usually lies between 8,000 and 15,000 fpm and the ratio of inspirated air to high pressure air is from 3:1 to 6:1. Air ejectors have not been investigated fully. In consequence, our design rules are empirical. The steps are as follows:

1. Calculate the air horsepower of the exhausted air using the volume of induced air and the total or impact pressure in the zone of the high velocity nozzle.
2. Multiply this by 6 to allow for the inefficiency of energy transfer. The resulting figure is the air horsepower of the high speed jet calculated from its volume and velocity pressure.
3. Compute the jet velocity from the expression:

$$V = 4674 \sqrt[3]{\frac{\text{Jet air hp}}{\text{Jet area (sq ft)}}}$$

The performance of a straight stack similar to Fig. 9-9b is not greatly inferior to that of the more elaborate venturi ejector, Fig. 9-9a. Its cost, of course, is considerably less. The ejector is incapable of working against substantial pressure. The highest vacuum induced in the suction system

[1]This is the third octave above middle-C on the musical scale.

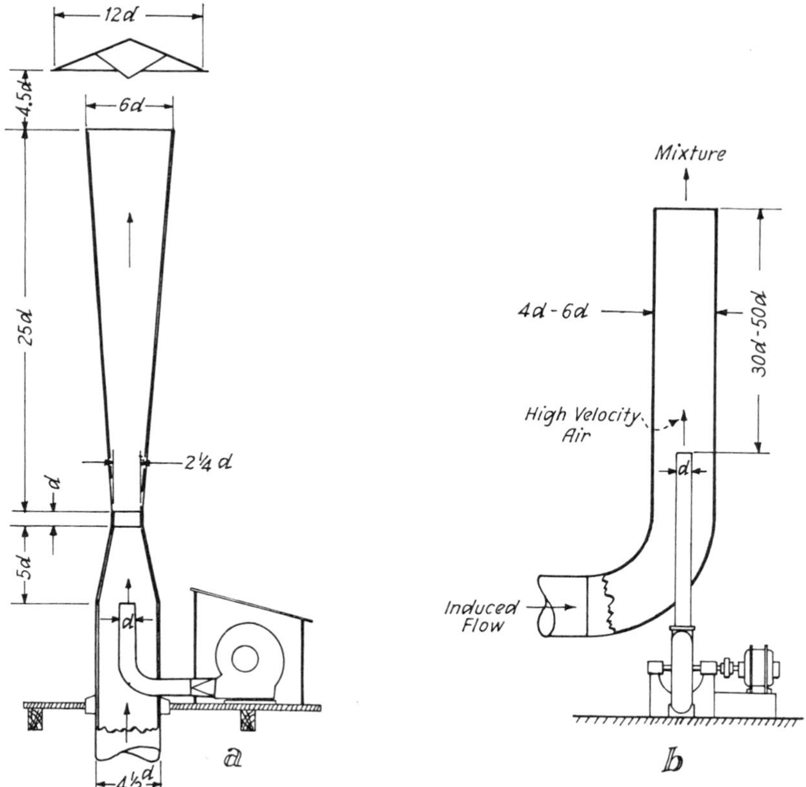

Fig. 9-9. Ejectors.

is not likely to exceed 1-1/2 in. wg and 1.0 in. or less is more common. It must discharge directly to the atmosphere because even a small back-pressure will kill the aspiration and may actually cause back-flow.

Dust-Separating Fans

A fan may be so constructed as to combine the functions of an exhauster and a centrifugal separator. All fans of this nature concentrate the solids on a portion of the blade surface by inertia or centrifugal force and discharge the solids and air into separate casings or into compartments of the same casing. Because of the high velocities present, careful design permits good separating efficiency without sacrificing air-handling economy. At least one type appears to be capable of separating particles of 20-micron size with regularity.

Fans also may be constructed with washing nozzles mounted in the inlet. The effectiveness of air washing fans depends to a considerable extent upon the fineness of the spray droplets, upon the completeness of coverage of the air stream and upon the length of time during which both dust and water are jointly in suspension. Accumulation of sludge in the casing and on the fan blades may present a problem.

CHAPTER 10

Axial-flow Fans

While the centrifugal fan predominates in industrial exhaust work, the axial-flow fan has become more prominent in recent years. For the most part, the two forms are not competitive. The centrifugal fan is unchallenged as an air mover in systems carrying solids in large quantities. The axial-flow fan, on the other hand, is often the first choice when large volumes of smoke, steam, and the like are to be exhausted. At low dust loadings and moderate volumes and pressures, the choice is often determined by local considerations of system arrangement, personal preference, delivery, price, or some other, non-technical reason.

The axial-flow fan, as its name implies, is one in which the direction of airflow parallels the rotational axis of the wheel. This is in contrast with the radial flow which takes place in a centrifugal fan. Familiar examples are the common desk-fan or the domestic kitchen-ventilator. In accordance with the standard nomenclature of the Air Moving and Conditioning Association, Inc., axial-flow fans are classified as propeller, tubeaxial, and vaneaxial fans. While the three types differ substantially in construction their operating principles are identical in that each is an airscrew.

Propeller Fans

The propeller fan consists of two or more blades mounted on a central shaft and revolving within a narrow mounting-ring. Figure 10-1 is a schematic illustration of a typical propeller fan. These fans are usually designed to operate in the range from free delivery to about 1/2 inch of water. When driven at blade-tip speeds of from 12,000 to 16,000 fpm they are capable of operating against pressures up to 1-1/2 inches but at sacrifice of capacity and efficiency. Moreover, the noise level may become objectionable at these speeds.

Because of its pressure limitations, the propeller fan finds its principal

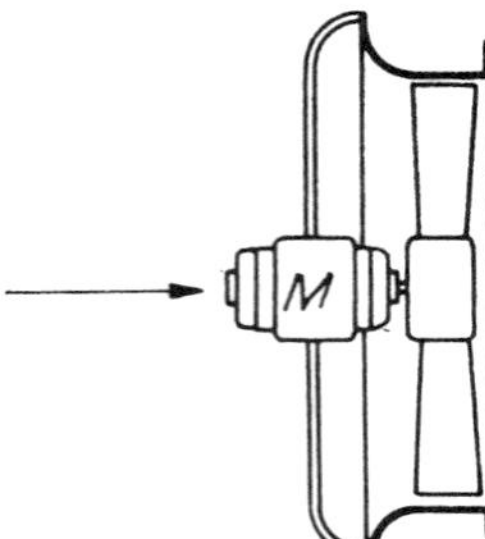

Fig. 10-1. Propeller fan with motor on inlet side.

application in general room ventilation when mounted in a side wall or roof monitor and discharging directly to the atmosphere. Frequently, the location of hot processes or welding booths is such that they can be exhausted to the open air through short and direct piping. When this is possible the propeller fan may be the logical choice. Although there are few suitable applications for this type of fan where more than the simplest duct work is involved, it is, without doubt, the cheapest fan both in first cost and in power consumption when the static pressure can be kept below 1/2 inch of water.

Tubeaxial Fans

An axial-flow fan consisting of a single propeller wheel mounted in a cylindrical casing is called a tubeaxial fan. In the cheaper forms it is no more than the open type of propeller fan with its wheel and motor encased in a tube for ease of installation in a duct. The more refined tubeaxial fans are designed with shorter blades of airfoil section mounted on hubs of such diameter as to blank off the less-effective portion of the

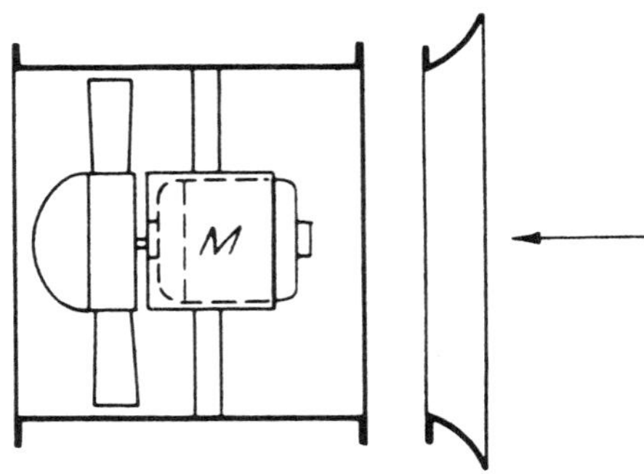

Fig. 10-2. Tubeaxial fan.

wheel through which reentrant air may flow when working at higher pressures. A fan of this type will give satisfactory service at pressures as high as 2-1/2 inches of water. This ability broadens the scope of application so that they are capable of operating against the resistance of considerable duct work. Figure 10-2 represents a tubeaxial fan.

Vaneaxial Fans

The air stream leaving an axial-flow wheel has an appreciable rotational component. If rotation can be suppressed, a considerable gain in static pressure and efficiency can be attained, increasing as the pressure increases. In the vaneaxial fan, this is accomplished by the addition of straightening vanes so shaped as to pick up, without shock, the air leaving the blades.

The vaneaxial fan is characterized by short, stubby, airfoil blades mounted on a hub which may be as large as 75 percent of the wheel diameter. The motor housing is the same diameter as the hub so as to create minimum interference to the air stream. The downstream end of the motor housing is enclosed by a rounded cap similar to that covering the wheel hub or by a bullet-shaped tail, to reduce eddy losses. The radial straightening vanes provide a convenient means of centering the motor housing in the casing. Since there appears to be but little advantage in shaping the vanes to an airfoil section, they are press-formed of heavy sheet metal. The number of guide vanes is so selected that there is no divisor common to both the vanes and the fan blades. By this means pulsating flow is minimized and the noise level is reduced. Figure 10-3 shows the general arrangement of a typical vaneaxial fan. Figure 10-4 is representative of the proportions and appearance of the fan wheel. The five blades of this wheel deliver the air stream to six straightening vanes.

Single-stage, vaneaxial fans may be operated at pressures as high as 6 or 8 inches of water. Double-stage fans are capable of much higher pressures, but since the system requirements for most applications sel-

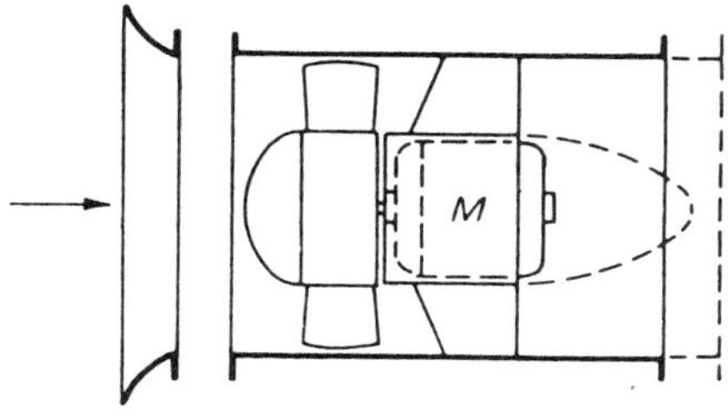

Fig. 10-3. Vaneaxial fan.

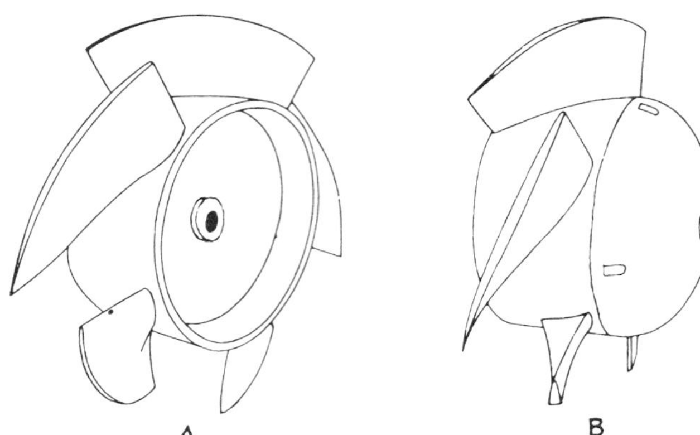

Fig. 10-4. Fan wheel of a typical vaneaxial fan; (A) without hood, and (B) with hood.

dom exceed the range of the single-stage fan, the double-stage design has little or no usefulness in the industrial exhaust field. Commercial single-stage vaneaxial fans will meet the most exacting pressure and volume requirements ordinarily encountered.

Direction of Flow

Unlike the centrifugal fan, reversal of rotation of an axial-flow fan will reverse the direction of flow. A similar effect will result if a tubeaxial or vaneaxial fan is inadvertently turned end for end in a duct during installation. The result is a fan which blows instead of exhausting. The manufacturer's directional arrows should be followed during installation but if these are obliterated the correct mounting is indicated by the location of the motor or belt drive. In the tubeaxial fan the drive is at the inlet end whereas the drive and straightening vanes of the vaneaxial fan are at the delivery end of the casing.

Propeller fans and tubeaxial fans deliver about one-half of the design volume when the rotational direction is reversed. For the vaneaxial fan the flow at reversed rotation is only a small fraction of the designed flow.

Representative Installations

Figure 10-5 shows a propeller fan mounted in a wall opening and exhausting from the hood which encloses it. A fan so mounted can exhaust large volumes of contaminated air at low power-consumption. The pressure drop at the hood mouth is negligible so that the only static resistance is that of the automatic louvers. The motor is mounted on a bracket attached to the hood face, free from exposure to corrosive vapors.

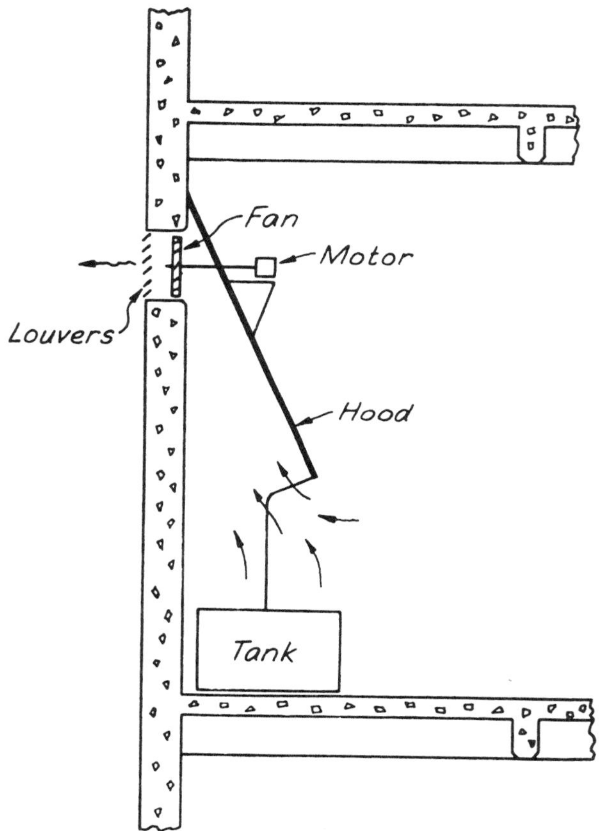

Fig. 10-5. Propeller fan exhausting from tank hood.

Figure 10-6 illustrates a similar fan installed in a vertical duct serving two branch pipes. This is a common arrangement when a short, vertical pipe discharges through the roof. The vaneaxial fan in Fig. 10-7 is exhausting a series of hoods over the doors of oil fired furnaces. The discharge pipe runs vertically from the first floor to the roof of a 6-story building. The velocity in the system is abnormally high in order to keep the discharge pipe as small as possible for certain structural reasons. As a consequence the system resistance is high enough to require a vaneaxial fan whereas a tubeaxial fan would ordinarily be called for.

Fan Characteristics

The characteristic curves of Fig. 10-8 are typical of axial-flow fans. The pressure-volume curve shows how these relationships change as the

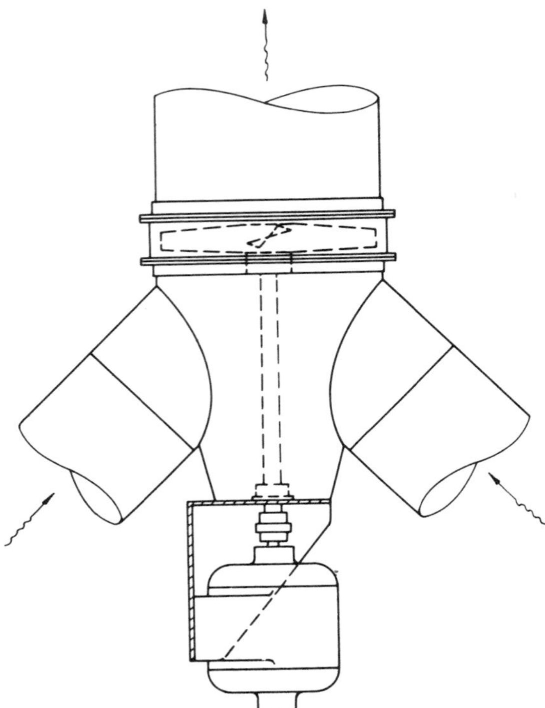

Fig. 10-6. Vertically mounted propeller fan in duct.

flow decreases from the condition of free delivery to that of no delivery. Starting at the free-delivery point (the base line), the pressure rises as the volume decreases until what is known as the stalling point is reached. This is the point at which the flow lines begin to depart from the inlet side of the blade surface and is the region in which eddies and vortices begin to form. It corresponds to the stalling or "burbling" point of an airplane wing whose angle of attack has been increased until a loss of lift occurs.

As might be expected, the region between the stalling point and the no-delivery point constitutes an undesirable operating zone. The stalling dip is a symptom of instability and the sudden rise of the noise level which accompanies it is an infallible sign of serious flow disturbance. It is evident that the system characteristics must be matched with the fan characteristics lying to the right of the stalling point. It is this feature of axial-flow fans which makes their application to systems of fluctuating characteristics somewhat more critical than the application of centrifugal fans.

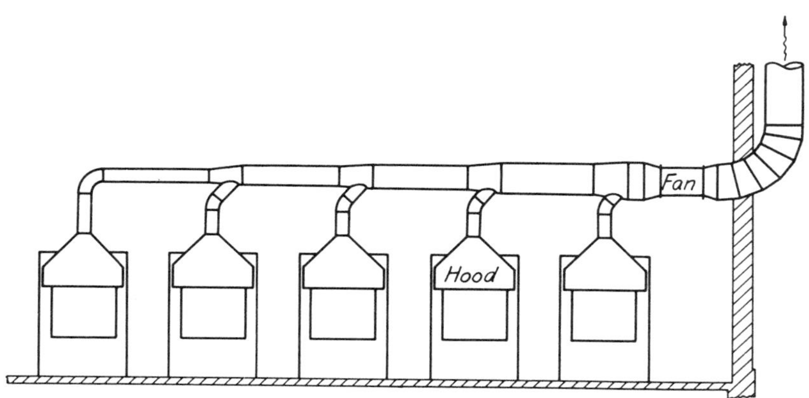

Fig. 10-7. Vaneaxial fan exhausting furnace hoods.

In Fig. 10-9 are plotted the pressure-volume curves of four axial-flow fans of different types but of the same diameter and speed. The four performance curves are of the same basic shape although the stalling dip becomes more pronounced in the higher pressure fans. The parabolic lines representing system characteristics intersect the pressure-volume lines of each fan at the design point or point of highest efficiency.

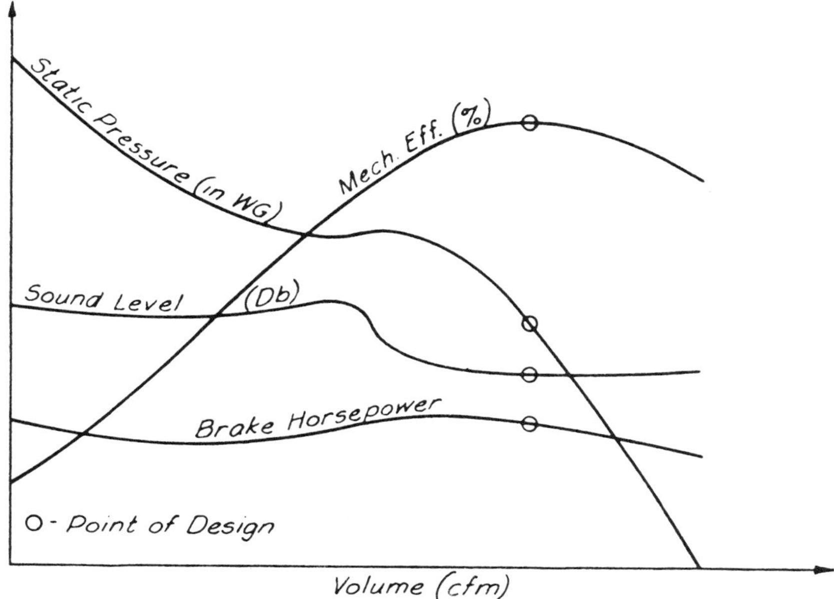

Fig. 10-8. Characteristic curves of an axial flow fan.

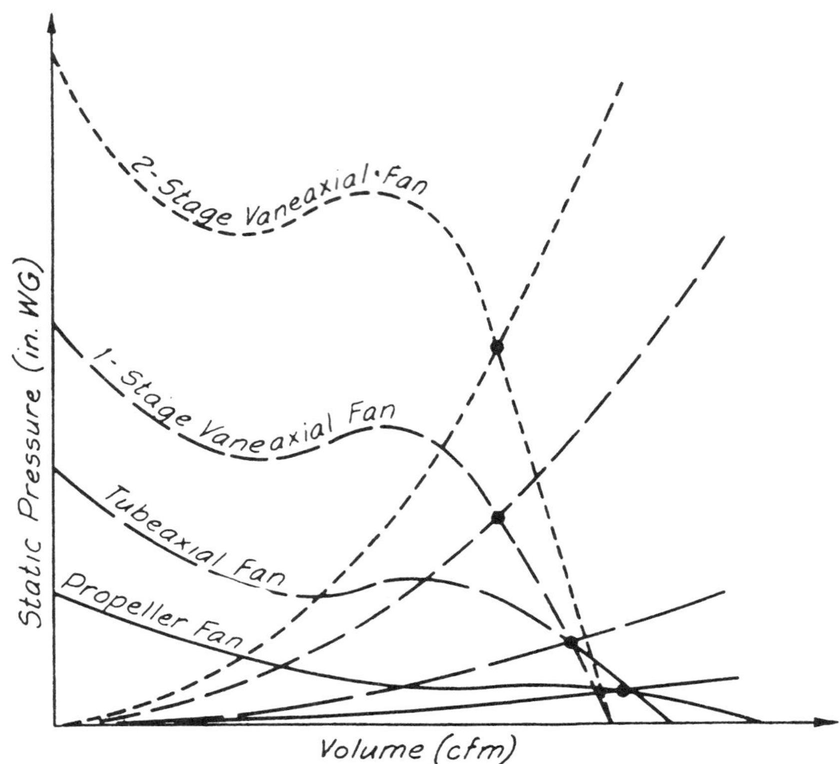

Fig. 10-9. Performance of different types of fans.

Sound Level

The predominant source of noise in a fan system is the air stream itself. Vortices and eddies are set up at fan blade-tips, at the trailing edges of blades, at the entering edges of stationary vanes, and, in fact, at any point where the flow is not smooth and continuous. For minimum noise all structures entering the air stream should be faired and should be stiff enough to avoid flutter. It is imperative that the blades and vanes be unequal in number to avoid the drumming sound of pulsating flow.

Noise becomes more serious as speeds and pressures increase. Designs must necessarily become more refined as they pass from the simple propeller-fan operating at low pressures, through the tubeaxial, to the vaneaxial type. More machined surfaces are required in the higher-pressure fans both for smoothness of surfaces and to control the aerodynamic shape. In addition, tip clearance of blades must be kept small since the efficiency drops and the noise level increases as the clearance increases.

Axial Flow versus Centrifugal Fans

The choice between the axial-flow fan and the centrifugal fan frequently is determined by factors other than pressure and volume characteristics. Some of these in favor of the axial type are:

1. Greater compactness
2. Straight line installation
3. Higher efficiency.

The centrifugal fan, on the other hand, may be chosen because of:

1. Better ability to cope with uncertain or fluctuating operating conditions
2. Better accessibility of the motor and greater ease of providing sturdy support
3. Lower noise levels for comparable system characteristics
4. Natural adaptability to duct systems requiring 90° turns.

Note: In preparing this chapter, the authors have drawn on and acknowledge their indebtedness to consulting fan engineer, Frank P. Bleier, "Design, Performance and Selection of Axial-Flow Fans," Reference Section, *Heating and Ventilating*, Vol. 43, No. 10 (October, 1946), 83-94.

CHAPTER 11

Structural Details and System Planning

Ductwork used for industrial exhaust systems is usually rolled but may be spirally wound. Material can be either galvanized or black iron for normal ambient air service. Galvanized is the more frequent for duct sizes usually encountered in inplant ventilation systems. Longitudinal joints for black iron are normally butt welded; for galvanized the joints are butt joint seam welded or lap joint riveted or spot welded, and the exposed crack soldered air tight. Girth joints can be welded; lapped in direction of air flow and connected with rivets or tee lugs and then soldered; or flanged. Flanged joints are attractive at selected locations as they permit easy dismantling for cleaning or for the replacement of worn sections.

The length of each section or "joint" usually is made equal to the width of the sheet adopted as the shop standard. For example, a common sheet-size is 36 in. by 96 in. which will make pipe in 36-in. lengths and up to 30-in. diameter with a single longitudinal seam. In order that piping may be lapped in the direction of air flow, each section is tapered slightly. The small end is made equal to the nominal pipe-size and the large end is made ¼ in. greater in circumference. The corner of the longitudinal lap is clipped at the small end of the section as in Fig. 11-1, so that only one thickness of metal need be forced into the next section. The preferred lengths of laps are given in Fig. 11-1 and the circumferential rivet spacing in Table 11-2.

In Table 11-1 the recommended thickness of metal for various classes of service is also listed. While reasonable life may be expected of piping made to these specifications, no accurate prediction is possible. Nevertheless, barring accidents, a well-built woodworking system should last from 10 to 15 years and one handling a heavy abrasive load, from 2 to 5 years. The elbows of a conveying system handling abrasive materials will cut through in 12 months or so, while the piping will last about twice as long.

Nickel-chromium, white iron castings have given good service when handling silica, feldspar, cullet (broken glass), fluorspar, borax and other constituents of glass through 5- and 6-in. pipes at speeds of 5,000 to 9,000 fpm. Steel piping 5/8 in.-thick cut through rapidly in this service. Elbows of

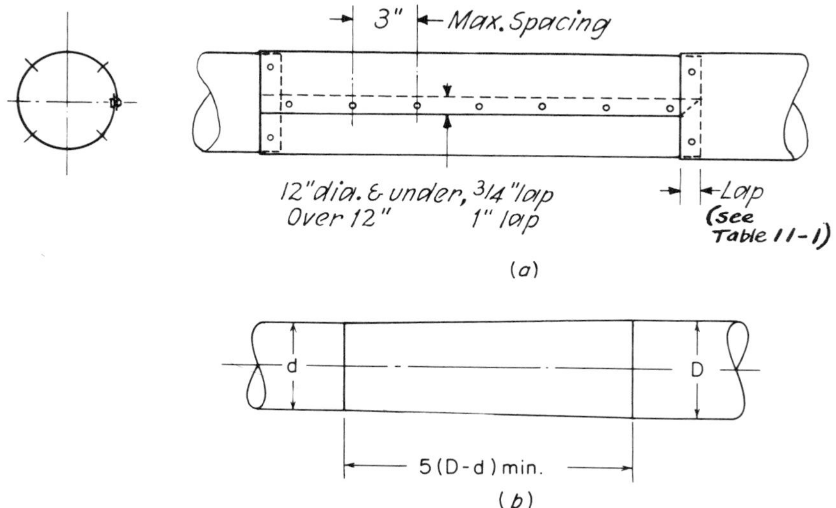

Fig. 11-1. Straight pipe and tapers.

rectangular cross-section with renewable, bolted back-plates often are used to combat extreme wear.

Many special alloys, all somewhat costly, have been developed to resist chemical attack. Also, there are a number of coatings, sprayed or dipped, that will provide protection under specific conditions. Rigid polyvinyl chloride, fiberglass-reinforced polyesters, and other nonmetallic materials for fabrication of hoods, ducts, exhausters, and collectors find substantial use for such service.

Galvanized piping of 22 gage may have a useful life of no more than 6 months when conveying fumes from pickling tanks. Asphalt-coated black steel pipe when heavily treated should last for 10 years in this service as should steel pipe with 3-ply rubber lining.

Tapers

Figure 11-1b shows the minimum, permissible length of tapers. It is preferable to make tapers equal in length to the sheet width as has been recommended for pipe. The eccentric taper whose bottom lies in the same plane as the bottom of the pipe is thought to be a little less susceptible to clogging than a plain conical concentric taper. When the expansion angle is small, there is no noticeable difference in performance.

Branches should enter tapers from the top or sides rather than the bottom. Tees entering the main from opposite sides should be staggered to minimize interference of opposing streams.

Gages of metal, length of laps and rivet spacing should be the same as for straight pipe of the same diameter as the large end of the taper.

Table 11-1. Recommended Thickness of Sheet Metal[1]

Pipe Diameter, In.	Thickness, U.S.S. Gage			
	Class I	Class II	Class III	Class IV
8 and under	24	22	20	16
Over 8 to 18	22	20	18	16
Over 18 to 30	20	18	16	14
Over 30	18	16	14	12

Class I Includes nonabrasive applications such as paint spraying, woodworking, textile, pharmaceutical, and food products.

Class II Includes moderately abrasive materials and light concentrations of highly abrasive applications such as metallic grinding, buffing and polishing, grain dusts.

Class III Includes highly abrasive materials in moderate to high concentrations such as abrasive cleaning, rock crushing and screening, dryers and kilns, fly ash from boiler stacks, foundry shakeout, and sand handling. Also low pressure conveying of moderately abrasive materials such as tobacco, chemicals, wood dust.

Class IV Includes heavy duty applications with high production rates and/or two and three shift operations such as steel and cement mills, foundries. Also for low pressure conveying of abrasive materials such as sand, ashes.

[1] The Sheet Metal and Air Conditioning Contractors' National Association introduced a more complex table of recommended duct sizes in 1975. As of this printing the schedule shown in Table 11-1 is still in extensive use.

Table 11-2. Rivet or Spot Weld Spacing for Circumferential Seams

Pipe Diameter, In.	No. Rivets
8 and under	4
9 to 12	5
13 to 18	6
19 to 24	7
25 and over	9-in. centers

Elbows

Two-piece or mitre elbows should not be used in exhaust work. Five-piece construction is satisfactory for elbows 6 in. in diameter or smaller, and seven-piece construction for larger sizes. A single pattern for a 90° elbow of a given diameter and throat radius will make elbows of other angles. Thus, a 5-piece pattern will make 22½°, 45° and 67½° elbows and a 7-piece will make 15°, 30°, 45°, 60°, and 75° elbows. Elbows should be made from metal at least two gages heavier than the pipes to which they connect. Do not use lock seam elbows for substantial work where rigidity and wear resistance are important.

Tees

Figure 11-2a shows the usual 45° round tee. While smaller angles of junction are preferable, the tees become structurally weak. It will be seen from the cut that the notched flange at the heel of the tee is already inaccessible for riveting and is difficult to reach with a soldering copper. The "shoe" tee, Fig. 11-2b, escapes this weakness. No data are available as to the relative pressure-losses of the two types, but there is no evidence that the pressure drop through the shoe tee is excessive.

Equalizers

Equalizers are fixed dampers for regulating the distribution of air between branches. The style x, Fig. 11-2c, consists of a sheet of heavy steel inserted in

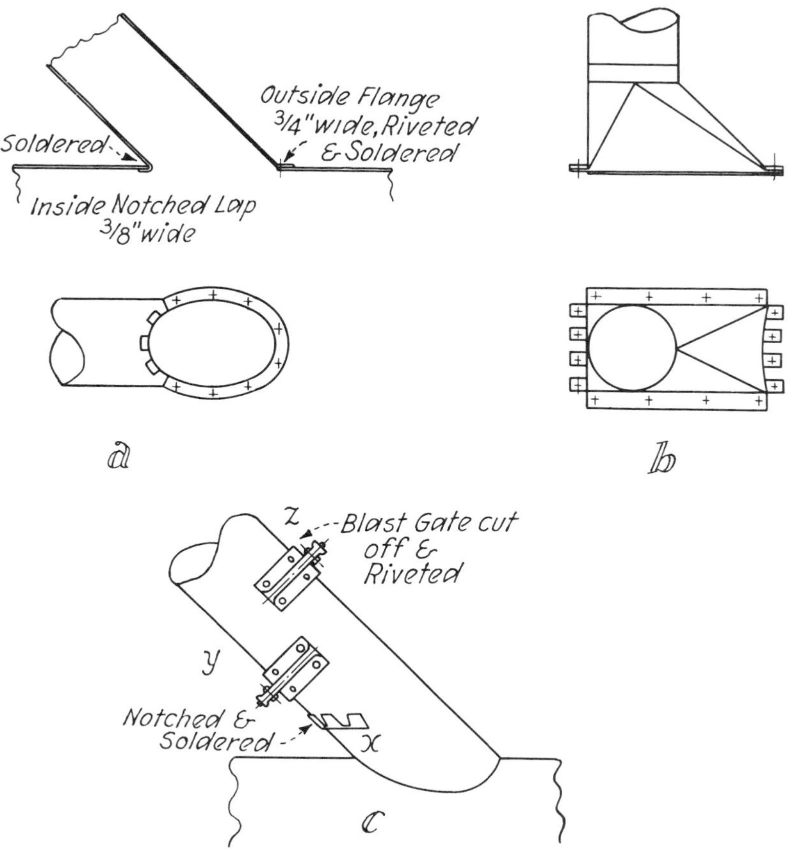

Fig. 11-2. Tees and equalizers.

a saw slot near the heel of the tee. After adjustment, it is cut off, notched, and soldered in place. At y and z are blast gates whose slides have been cut off and riveted. Equalizers must be as near tamper proof as possible. If closely preceded by an elbow, the equalizer should be inserted in the pipe on the same side as the elbow throat. This location will lessen wear and will prevent clogging.

Blast Gates

The use of blast gates to provide exhaust only when needed from an intermittent operation is seldom an economy for the reason that the designer must calculate mains for velocities about 50 percent higher than the minimum allowable values so that closed gates will not cause settlement of material in the pipes. During the times when all gates are open, the friction loss is excessive.

The common blast gate is shown in Fig. 11-3a. This style is suitable only for small pipes and light duty. A more rigid gate, supported on all sides, is the skeleton blast gate, Fig. 11-3b. It is especially suited to systems handling fibrous or stringy substances. The lever gate, Fig. 11-3c, is used in overhead pipes and may be controlled by chain and pulleys.

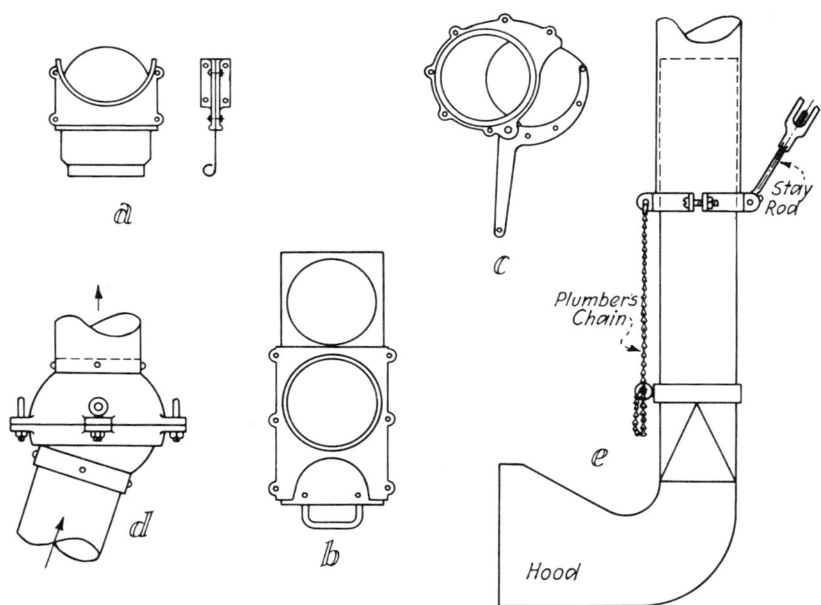

Fig. 11-3. Blast gates, ball joints, and telescope joints.

Ball and Telescope or Slip Joints

The cast-iron ball joint, Fig. 11-3d, permits lateral movement of the hood in all directions. Cast lugs and eye bolts permit attachment of stay rods. Slip joints, Fig. 11-3e, allow axial pipe-movement and when connected to ball joints make possible great freedom of hood adjustment. There are situations for which they are more suitable than the cheaper hose.

Cleanouts

The suction main and fan are connected by a sleeve, Fig. 11-4a. The distance L from the end of the main to the fan casing should be great enough to permit removal of the fan wheel without disturbing the main pipe. Sleeves may be hinged along the side opposite the bolted angles or may be a single rolled sheet, sprung into place. The latter is the tighter connection.

Cleanouts should be provided in all mains and in the discharge pipe at intervals of about 10 ft. The blind end of the main should be capped. A handhole should be cut at the lower end of each riser for the removal of heavy objects. Cleanouts are needed near equalizers and in switches and dampers. The slide cover, Fig. 11-4b, sufficiently dust-tight and waterproof for outdoor use, is placed on the side of the pipe. Figure 11-4c is a friction cap often used on automatic fire dampers for inspection and replacement of fusible links.

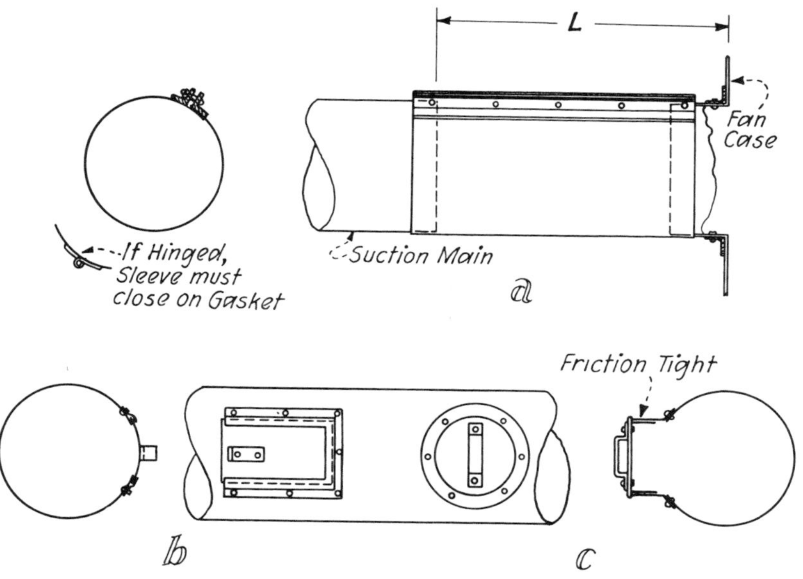

Fig. 11-4. Pipe sleeve and hand hole covers.

Large doors in dust arresters, cyclones, and pressure pipes should be gasketed. They should be of the lift-off type or loosely hinged so that the cam clamps can pull them tightly against the gasket.

Back Pressure Dampers

When two or more pipes under pressure enter a dust separator, a back-pressure damper in each pipe is essential to prevent reverse flow of dust in any pipe whose fan is idle. The damper should be close to the separator and must be horizontal so that an accumulation of dust on the blade cannot

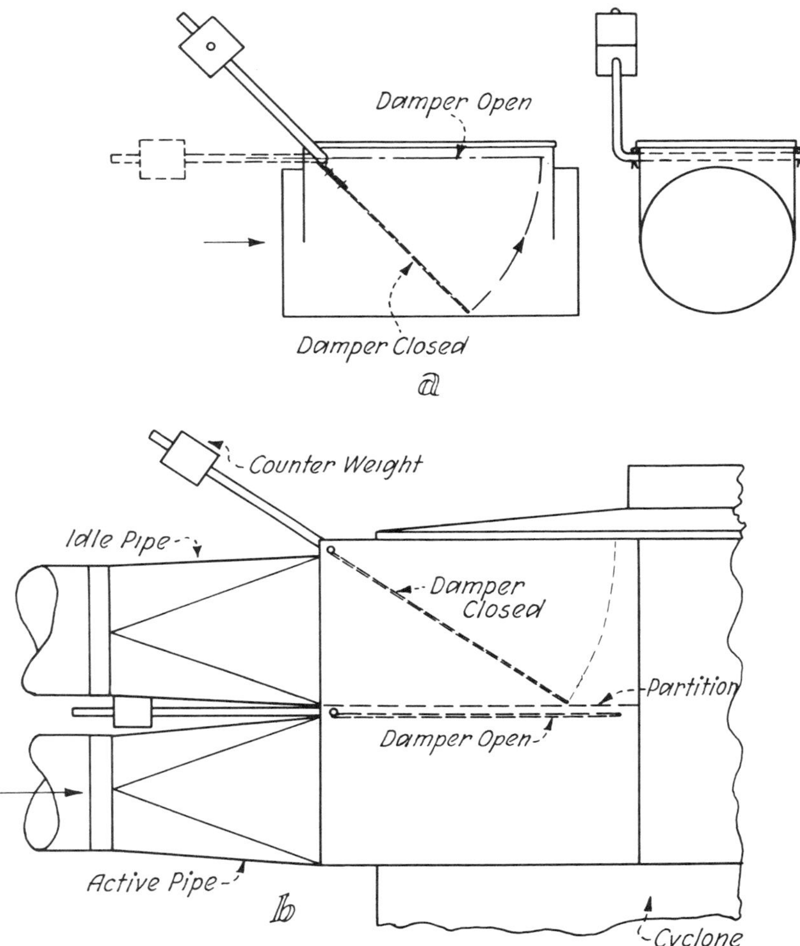

Fig. 11-5. Back pressure dampers.

prevent the damper from opening when the fan starts. A damper for installation in round pipe is illustrated in Fig. 11-5a. Figure 11-5b is a multiple damper mounted in a cyclone inlet. Dampers must be ruggedly built, using nothing lighter than 16-gage sheets for the blades and sides.

Switches

A single-blade switch is shown in Fig. 11-6a and a double-blade, long shavings switch in Fig. 11-6b. With the flow as shown by the arrows, the latter seldom clogs when passing fibrous materials. The flat sides and blades should be made of 16-gage leveled sheets to insure free action. Handholes are necessary for the removal of refuse caught on the blades or between blade and housing. Sometimes, a vacuum door is added to prevent collapse of piping due to the momentary suction formed when the stream is diverted. This is a simple door, opening inwardly, and closed against a felt gasket by a spring hinge. Similar diverters constructed of machined castings are found in many conveying systems where material must be directed to several bins.

Pipe Supports

Interior piping should be supported by metallic straps and hangers similar to those in Fig. 11-7a. Bands usually are rolled from black iron or angles. Hangers are straight, bent, or twisted, as required, and usually are formed on the job.

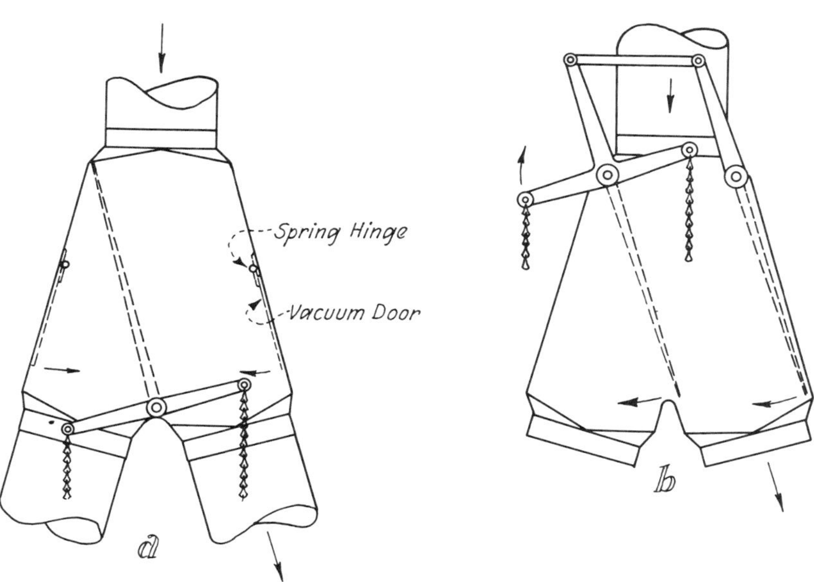

Fig. 11-6. Switches.

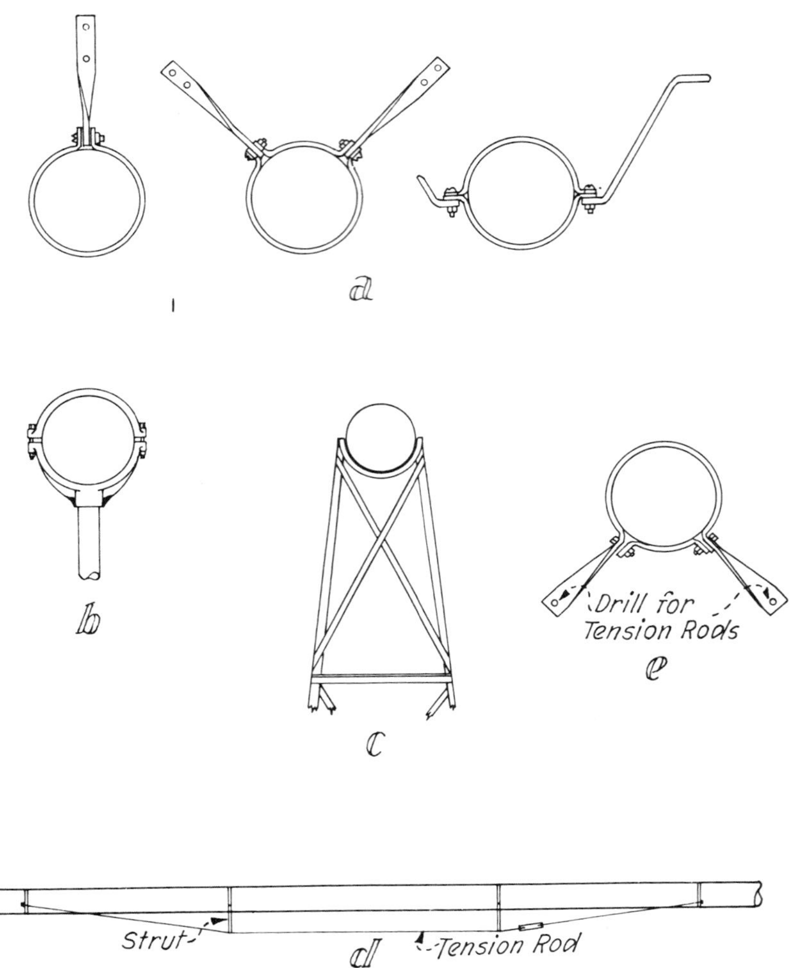

Fig. 11-7. Pipe supports.

Long runs of outdoor piping of small sizes such as are common in pneumatic conveying may be supported on iron-pipe standards set in concrete. The pipe saddle and strap shown in Fig. 11-7b are cast iron. Steel "A" frames, as in Fig. 11-7c, are common. When the span between supports is so long that sagging occurs, the pipe may be stiffened by tension rods and struts as shown in Fig. 11-7d. A detail of the strut construction in Fig. 11-7e shows how double tension rods may be used to reduce the tendency to sway in the wind.

System Size

No arbitrary limits can be placed on the maximum size of an exhaust system. Nevertheless, there are drawbacks to a single system serving a large number of contamination sources. An installation broken into two or more smaller systems offers less interruption to production in the event of accidental shutdowns or stoppage for repairs, alterations, or machinery rearrangement. Reexamination is warranted if the size of such a system much exceeds 20,000 to 30,000 cfm.

Overhead, Floor-level, and Under-floor Piping

Although overhead piping is conspicuous and shuts off light, it saves floor space and can cross aisles without interfering with traffic. Floor-level piping, on the other hand, takes up usable space unless it can be placed under

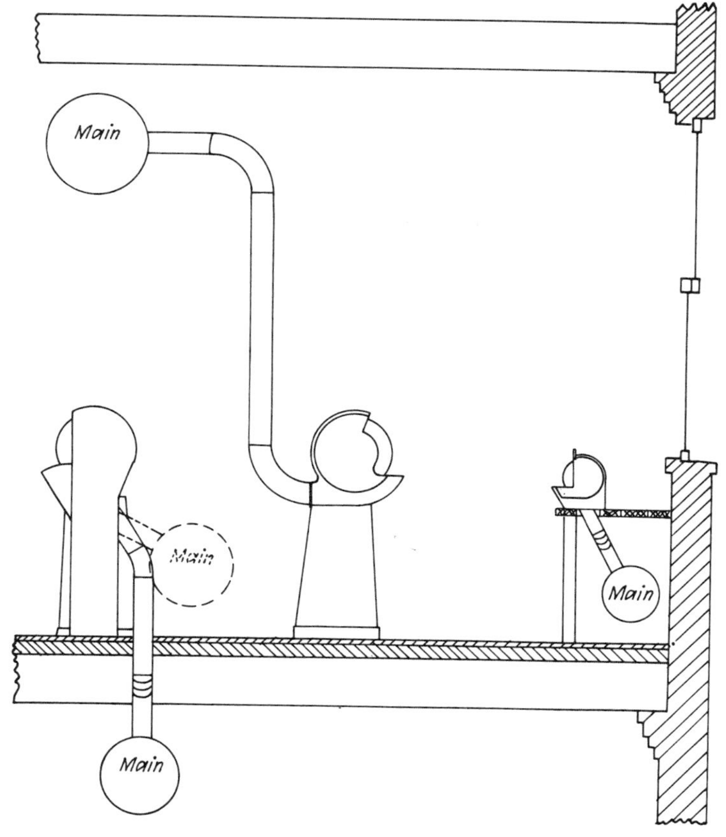

Fig. 11-8. Exhaust main locations.

benches. Housekeeping always suffers, however, when piping is so located. Exposed pipes at working level are subject to damage by trucks and usually block passages between machines. The sole advantage is that branches are short and direct. Under-floor piping combines the advantages of the other schemes but has the drawback of high cost, particularly when holes must be cut through concrete or composition floors. Figure 11-8 shows the several arrangements.

The practice of some architects of specifying exhaust piping to be embedded in poured concrete has little to recommend it. It produces a workroom pleasing to the eye and has some sound-deadening effect but its drawbacks are many and serious. Not the least is the loss of flexibility: machines once positioned are fixed forever; no expansion is possible.

System Arrangement

When the designer lays out a system on the drawing board he tries to place the fan and dust collector so that all piping runs will be as short and direct as the building structure and the various obstacles will permit. The points of contaminant generation are fixed by the machinery or process arrangement. Often, the spot to which the collected material is to be delivered is prescribed. Usually the fan location is somewhat more flexible.

Figure 11-9 shows representative system arrangements. That shown in

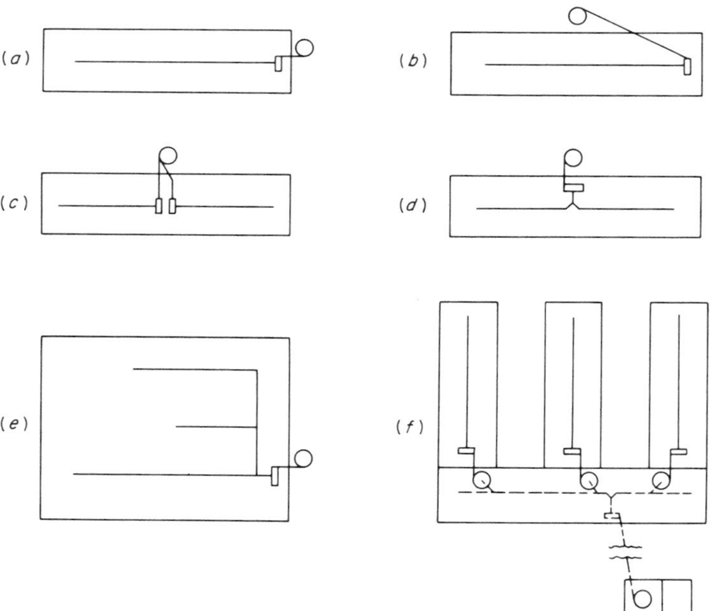

Fig. 11-9. Representative system arrangements.

Fig. 11-9a is suitable for a long narrow building when the length of the suction main can be kept within reasonable bounds; perhaps 200 feet. The collector is shown at the end of the building. When it must be located midway of the building length it is evident that either Fig. 11-9c or d is superior to Fig. 11-9b. The former shows the system broken into two approximately equal sections, each served by its own fan, and both fans discharging into a single collector. A layout such as in Fig. 11-9e is common; a suction main and one or more submains serve scattered dust sources. Figure 11-9f represents an "E"-shaped ground plan consisting of finger-like buildings joined by a cross building and having a remote location for the point of dust disposal. The three gathering systems feed rooftop collectors, the dust outlets of which are connected to the combined gathering and relay system in the cross building. The relay arrangement eliminates long runs of large-diameter discharge pipe.

TYPICAL CONSTRUCTION SPECIFICATIONS FOR LOCAL EXHAUST SYSTEM

General

All exhaust systems shall be constructed with the materials recommended herewith and shall be installed in a permanent and workmanlike manner. Interior of all ducts shall be smooth and free from obstructions with joints either welded or soldered air-tight.

Materials

1. Ducts shall be constructed of black iron welded or of galvanized sheet steel riveted and soldered unless the presence of corrosive gases, vapors and mists, or other conditions makes such material impractical. Galvanized construction is not recommended for temperatures exceeding 400 F. Welding of black iron lighter than 18 gauge is not recommended.
2. For average exhaust systems on non-corrosive applications, the following metal thicknesses shall be those of Class __ construction. (See Table 11-1 for Class Specification.)

	MINIMUM U.S. Standard Gauge for Steel Duct			
Diameter of Straight Ducts	Class I	Class II	Class III	Class IV
To 8″	24	22	20	16
Over 8″ to 18″	22	20	18	16
Over 18″ to 30″	20	18	16	14
Over 30″	16	16	14	12

Brown and Sharpe gauge numbers have been used to indicate thickness of aluminum sheet as compared with U.S. Standard gauges for steel sheet.

Where aluminum duct is indicated, the following equivalent B & S gauges should be used:

Steel—U.S. Standard Gauge	26	24	22	20	18	16	14
Aluminum—B & S Gauge	24	22	20	18	16	14	12

3. For exhaust systems on corrosive applications, consideration should be given to non-corrosive materials or coatings.
4. Elbows and angles shall be a minimum of two gauges heavier than straight lengths of equal diameter.
5. Hoods shall be a minimum of two gauges heavier than straight section of connecting branches.
6. Where flexible piping is necessary, a non-collapsible type of flexible piping shall be used and it shall be kept at a minimum.

Construction

1. Longitudinal joints of ducts shall be lapped and riveted or spot welded on 3″ centers maximum, or butt welded.
2. Girth joints of duct shall be made with inner lap in direction of air flow, with 1″ lap, diameters to 19″, and 1¼″ laps for diameters over 19″; or flanged or butt welded.
3. Elbows and angles shall have a centerline radius of two pipe diameters whenever possible. Large radii are recommended for heavy concentrations of highly abrasive dusts. Construct elbows 6″ or less in diameter of at least five sections, over 6″ diameter of seven sections. Prefabricated elbows of smooth construction may be used. Angles pieced proportionately.
4. Hoods must be free of sharp edges or burrs and reinforced to provide necessary stiffness.
5. Use straight-through weather caps unless otherwise specified.

System Details

1. Connect duct to fan inlet with split sleeve drawband at least one pipe diameter long, but not less than 12″.
2. Transitions in mains and sub-mains to be tapered; taper 5″ long for each 1″ change in diameter when possible.
3. All branches shall enter main at the large end of transition at an angle not to exceed 45°; 30° is preferred. Connect branches only to top or sides of main with no two branches entering diametrically opposite.
4. Provide dead-end caps within 6″ from last branch of all mains and sub-mains.

5. Provide access openings or cleanouts every 10′ and near each elbow, angle or duct junction in horizontal sections, except for non-corrosive gases and vapors containing no particulate matter.
6. Support ducts sufficiently to place no load on connecting equipment and to carry weight of system if plugged with material. Maximum supporting interval 12′ for 8″ or smaller ducts, 20′ interval for larger ducts.
7. Provide 6″ minimum clearance between ducts and ceiling, wall or floors.
8. Where blast gates are used for adjustment of system, place near connection of branch to main. Provide means of locking after adjustments have been made. Butterfly-type dampers shall not be permitted.
9. Fire dampers, explosion vents, etc., should be installed in accordance with National Fire Protection Association Codes or local fire ordinances.
10. Rectangular ducts can be used only when clearance prevents the use of round ducts. Rectangular ducts must be made as nearly square as possible. Weight of metal, lap and other construction details are to be equal to round duct construction whose diameter equals the longest side.
11. Support fans and motors on common vibration absorbing mounting.
12. Exhaust fans installed in a hazardous area shall be spark-resistant and shall have non-ferrous blade or wheel and a non-ferrous ring about the opening through which shaft passes. Provide electrical grounding for all fan parts.

CHAPTER 12

General Exhaust Ventilation and Air Supply

General ventilation is a usual supplement to local exhaust ventilation and at times a substitute for local exhaust. Effectiveness is so interlocked with air supply systems that both subjects are included in this chapter.

General Ventilation

Applications generally fall into two groups: The ventilation of areas with little or no local exhaust ventilation and with minimum contaminant generation; and as a major contaminant control system either supplemental to local exhaust or as a substitute.

Area Ventilation

Where ventilation is needed for comfort considerations or to eliminate stagnant air in the work areas, volumes of 1 to 2 cfm per sq ft of floor space will suffice; often, the lower value is suitable for winter, and the higher value is suitable for summer. Where heat release operations are concentrated, these values can be checked against heat release calculations to verify that the resultant temperature rise at the work stations will be in the acceptable range. Table 12-1 indicates heat release ranges for personnel; Table 12-2 indicates heat release from typical process heat sources.

Volumes can increase to 5 cfm per sq ft where modest quantities of contaminant must be purged from the area. For industrial application, the use of ventilation guides in cfm per sq ft of floor area is more realistic than the usual air changes per hour used in commercial building ventilation texts. Industrial buildings vary greatly in height, yet where workers are located at floor level, it is the floor area that controls the ventilation flow rates. If a ventilated zone involved the first 10 ft of elevation from the floor, note that 1 cfm per sq ft of floor area would equal six air changes per hour.

Where area ventilation is used to remove smokes, fumes, and vapors released over areas too large to make local exhaust practical, the exhaust volumes will be in the 10 to 25 cfm per sq ft of floor area range. Experience

Table 12-1. Estimates of Energy Metabolism (M) of Various Types of Activity[a]

		M, Btu/hr
	Sleeping	250
	Sitting quietly	400
Light work	Sitting, moderate arm and trunk movements (e.g., desk work, typing)	450–500
	Sitting, moderate arm and leg movements (e.g., playing organ, driving car in traffic)	550–600
	Standing, light work at machine or bench, mostly arms	550–650
Moderate work	Sitting, heavy arm and leg movements	650–800
	Standing, light work at machine or bench, some walking about	650–750
	Standing, moderate work at machine or bench, some walking about	750–1000
	Walking about, with moderate lifting or pushing	1000–1400
Heavy work	Intermittent heavy lifting, pushing or pulling (e.g., pick and shovel work)	1500–2000
	Hardest sustained work	2000–2400

[a] Values apply for a 154-lb man, and do not include rest pauses.

Table 12-2. Heat Gain from Lighting, Machinery, and Process

Electric lights	Btu/hr = watts × 3.413
Machinery—motor in room	$\text{Btu/hr} = \dfrac{\text{motor h.p.}}{\text{efficiency}} \times 2544$
motor outside room	Btu/hr = Motor h.p. × 2544
Metals—cooling from elevated temperatures	Solid-state only
Aluminum (1000#)	Btu/hr = 220 × temp. loss °F
Brass, bronze, copper (1000#)	Btu/hr = 90 × temp. loss °F
Iron, steel (1000#)	Btu/hr = 120 × temp. loss °F
Lead (1000#)	Btu/hr = 30 × temp. loss °F
Magnesium (1000#)	Btu/hr = 250 × temp. loss °F

from similar applications will be an excellent guide in volume selection. Where contaminants are released in a relatively uniform rate, dilution ventilation calculations will give an indication of probable exhaust requirement. For such a mathematical approach, factors of safety from 2 to 5 would be applied dependent on the effectiveness of air supply distribution to the ventilated area.

The most difficult operations for which to forecast general ventilation needs are those where contaminants are released from hot processes and the upward thermal thrust aspirates and sets in motion a large volume. Exhaust volumes will be a function of building height, temperatures transmitted to the surrounding air, and area of heat release surfaces.

Again experience with similar applications is the better guide to exhaust volumes, but, in general, if the vertical thrust cannot be intercepted by a horizontal barrier, the volumes of air set in motion and intermixed with the contaminant will be discouragingly high. For example, for a 10 ton ferrous induction melting furnace it is 40,000 cfm; for a 150 ton Basic Steel electric arc furnace it is 500,000 cfm.

Goodfellow and Bender[1] describe an interesting movie-scaling technique for establishing plume flow rates. Sixteen millimeter color movies using standard 18 frames per second (as low as 3 frames per second if available) can be analyzed to determine fume advances from frame to frame, using a known dimension such as the furnace diameter to establish the scale. The magnitude of the aspirated volume and the influence of distance from source to capture location is indicated in their exhibit, Fig 12-1.

Curtain Walls

Curtain walls provide an excellent method of forcing general ventilation air flow closer to the contamination generation zone. Without such a device, much of the air exhausted by roof or wall fans can short circuit the intended exhaust area.

Note that the use of such "draft curtain" walls, Fig. 12-2, forces the air supply to flow toward the floor of the contaminant free areas and keeps an inward flow of air toward the heat-treat furnaces. The addition of "smoke curtain" walls, Fig. 12-3, assures that air supply flows over the shell mold worker and does not short circuit to the roof or wall exhaust fan. The use of the curtain wall, Fig. 12-4, prevents the short circuiting of the air supply from the molding stations to the roof fan, bypassing the pouring area where general ventilation is needed to extract pouring smokes and fumes.

Opportunities to use this technique to improve general ventilation over a contaminated area are endless, and the improvement in air quality at floor areas rewarding.

Air Supply

Air supply systems perform such major functions as air supply to work stations for personnel comfort and as makeup air to satisfy general and local

[1] Goodfellow and Bender, "Design Considerations for Fume Hoods for Process Plant," *American Industrial Hygiene Association Journal*, July, 1980.

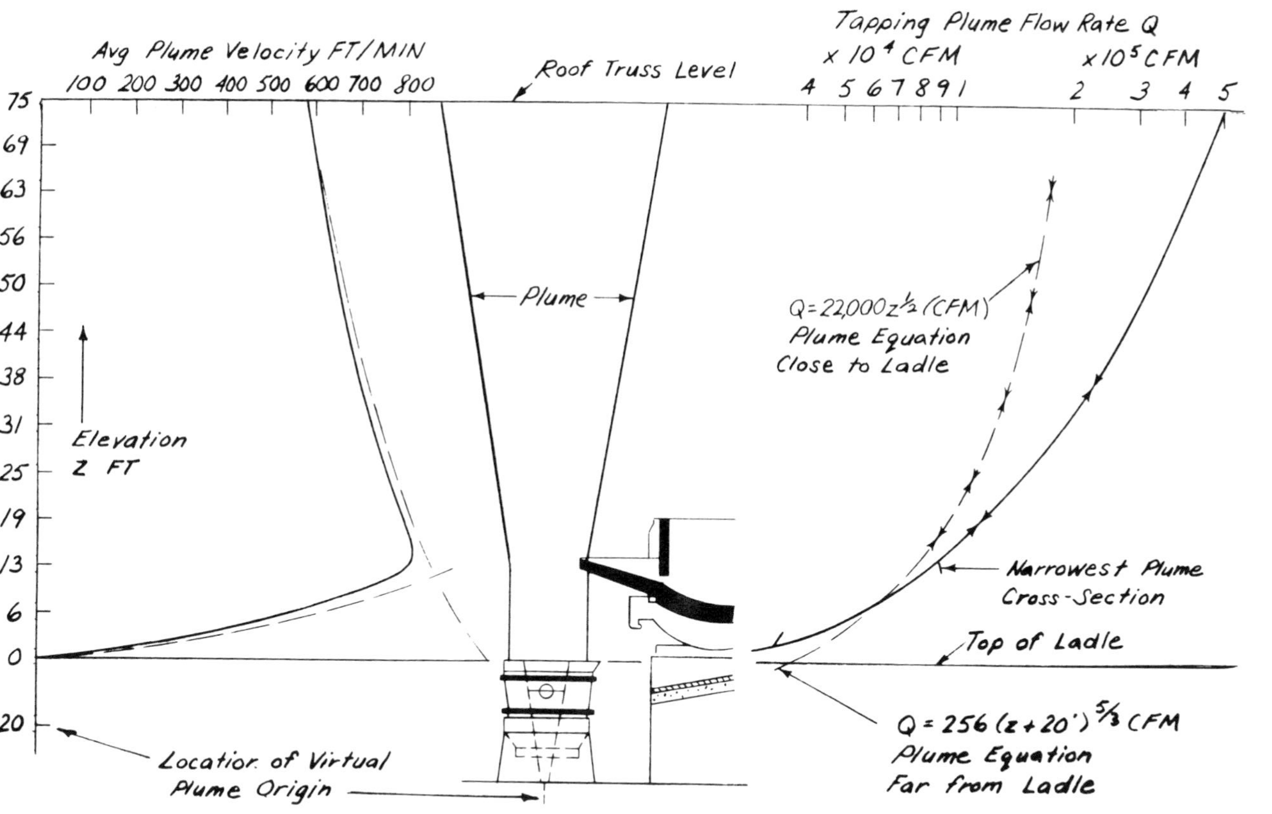

Fig. 12-1. Average plume velocity and flow rate during electric furnace tapping.

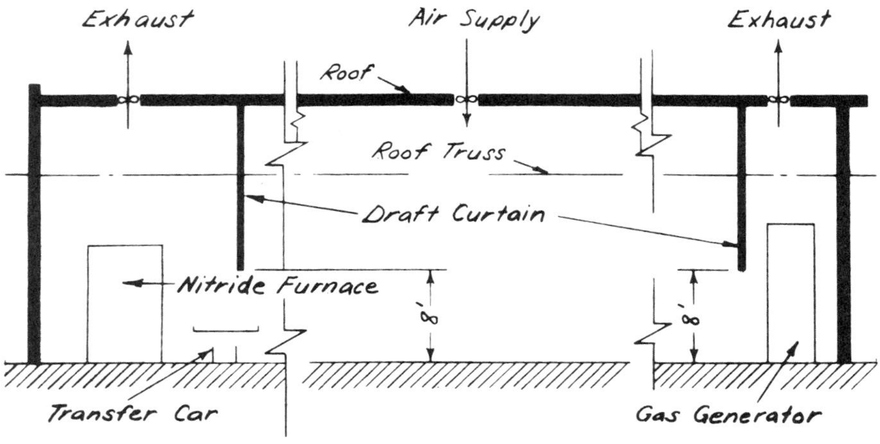

Fig. 12-2. Heat-treat section.

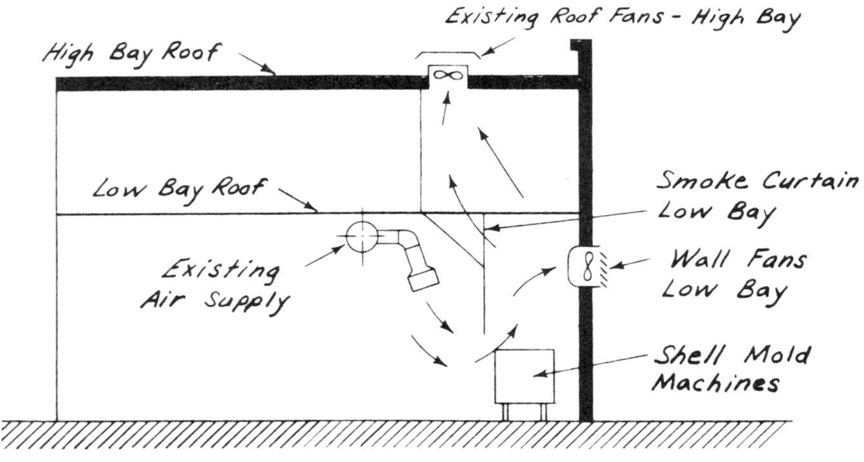

Fig. 12-3. Smoke curtain—shell core room.

exhaust systems. Often an installation will serve both purposes.

The effective method of supply air introduction will vary with local conditions but can include distribution to work stations to provide spot comfort ventilation; general distribution over a selected floor area; and the introduction of large volumes where exhaust system demand will provide the desired floor-level air flow patterns.

Spot Ventilation. Location of air supply outlets at each work station provides a maximum in comfort where spot cooling or heating is needed. The preferred location will be one where air impinges at the back of the

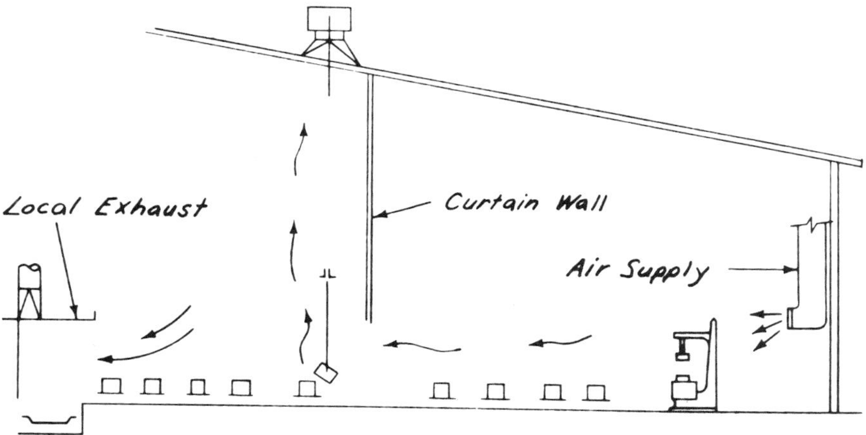

Fig. 12-4. Curtain wall.

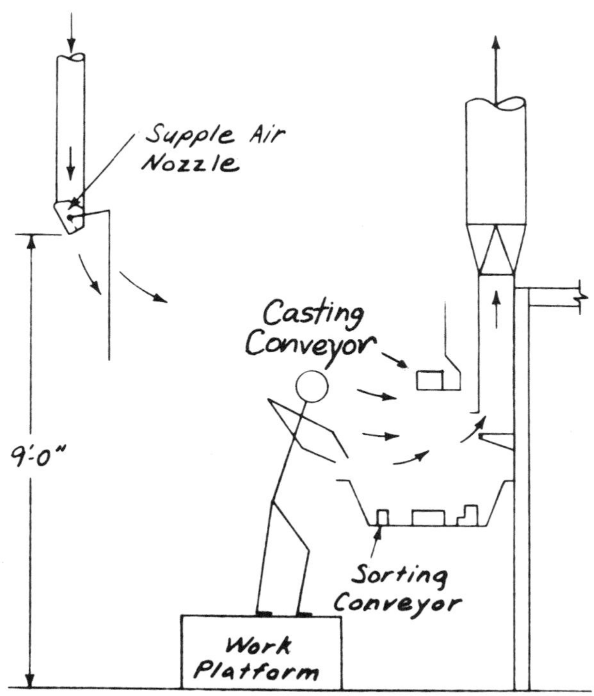

Fig. 12-5. Sorting conveyor ventilation.

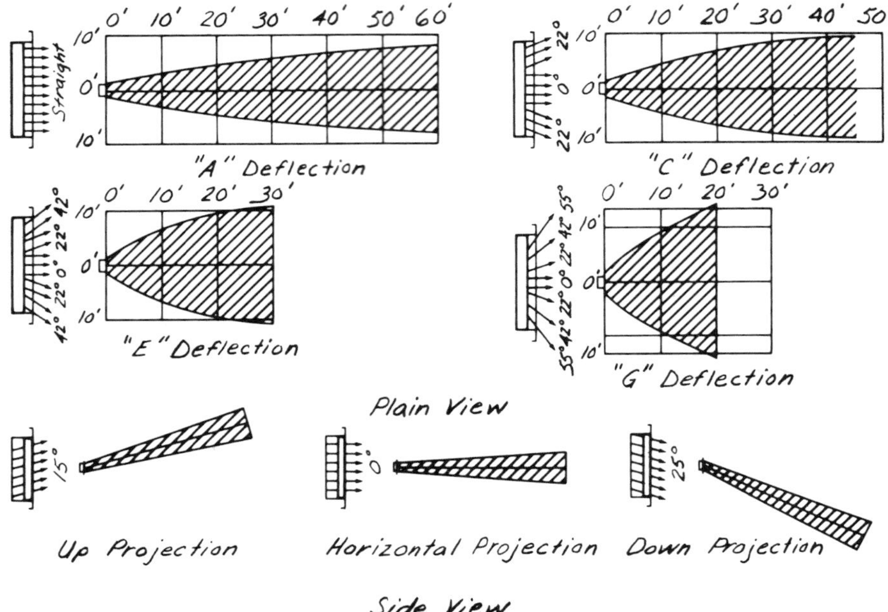

Fig. 12-6. Throw patterns and distance from different register adjustments. By permission—Hart & Cooley Manufacturing Co.

person, preferably between the shoulders and waist. See Fig. 12-5. Two-way deflection grilles may be adjusted to provide the desired flow patterns. See Fig. 12-6. Often horizontal deflectors are elevated during the heating season to reduce impact velocity.

Where a single discharge grille or nozzle serves only one person, means for adjustment of the flow pattern by the individual is desirable (see Fig. 12-5); where two or more people are involved or where work involves movement in and out of the air flow pattern, a fixed position of the louvres is almost mandatory.

One suggested range in air supply volumes and impact velocities is shown in Tables 12-3 and 12-4. Obviously the higher the impact velocity, the greater the heat transfer from the individual. Impact velocities many times those used for office and commercial air motion are common as Table 12-4 notes.

A secondary benefit of this spot air supply is the improved air quality at the work station because infiltration of contaminants from adjacent space is prevented. However, too large a supply volume or too high impact velocities can be as disruptive as man cooling fans on the effectiveness of adjacent local exhaust hoods, often requiring a compromise in the spot cooling design.

Area Ventilation. The cost of introduction of air to provide general

Table 12-3. Acceptable Air Motion at the Worker

Continuous exposure in air conditioned space:	50–75 fpm
Continuous exposure at fixed work station general ventilation or spot cooling:	
sitting	75–125 fpm
standing	100–200 fpm
Intermittent exposure—spot cooling or relief stations where worker is free to move about:	
Light heat loads and activity.	1,000–2,000 fpm
Moderate heat loads and activity.	2,000–3,000 fpm
High heat loads and activity.	3,000–4,000 fpm

Courtesy of John H. Clarke, retired, Films–Packaging Div., Union Carbide Co.

Table 12-4. Spot Cooling Air Volumes (Supply Air Temperature = 80 F)

Activity	Heat Load	Example	Air Volume/ Station, cfm
Light	Light	Bench work	1,000
Moderate	Moderate	Process equipment, Industrial boiler rooms	1,500–2,000
Heavy	High	Heavy machinery operation foundry pouring lines	3,000–10,000

Courtesy of John H. Clarke, retired, Films–Packaging Div., Union Carbide Co.

ventilation for that space is lower than the spot ventilation approach. Larger volumes can be discharged from a single outlet with discharge grilles adjusted for wide area flow patterns. The essential requirement of these systems is the production of ventilation flow patterns at work station elevations, preventing shortcircuiting to roof fans or adjacent high demand local exhaust points. A discharge point at the 8–10-ft level is usual. Two locations for supply main and branch ducts that are often found in industrial applications are:

(a) Downcomers supported from a building column.

(b) Horizontal mains, with discharge grilles, and extractors, if required, in side walls or on the bottom side of the duct.

Makeup Air. For exhaust systems to function, the need for a source of air supply is obvious. Without an adequate supply introduced through mechanical air supply systems, infiltration through door openings, cracks, etc., will be the air supply source which is seldom adequate, often produces cold drafty areas near outside walls, and provides no systematic air flow pattern to best accomplish exhaust system objectives.

Where exhaust systems create a negative pressure within the building, reduced flow can be anticipated through roof and wall exhaust fans which seldom are capable of operating against more than ¼ in. of differential pressure. Centrifugal fans connected to exhaust systems designed for 3–12 in. external static pressure will not be affected, although the exhaust air demand could cause reverse flow through gravity stacks, through roof monitors, and, on occasion, through roof or wall exhaust fans. While the major purpose is that of replacing exhaust air quantities, the supply should be introduced into relatively clean space some distance from the exhaust hoods to cause air flow patterns that will provide ventilation for those areas and prevent buildup of background levels from stray contaminants.

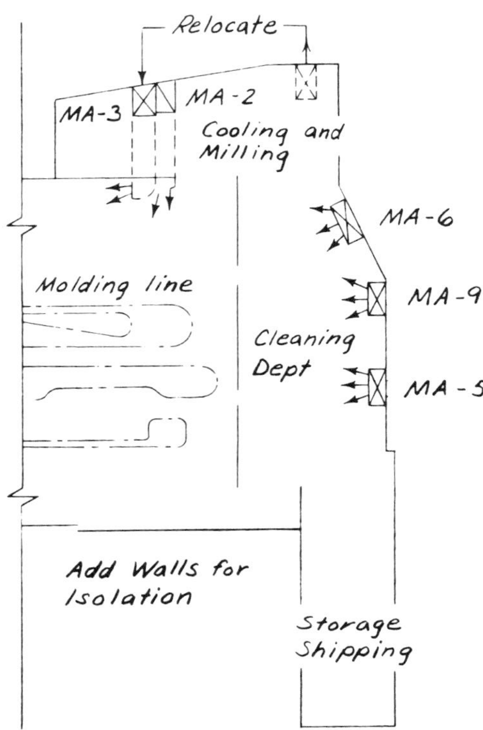

Fig. 12-7. Makeup air units.

Ideally, the total volume of air supply systems should equal the volume of local and general exhaust systems less the infiltration volumes forced into the plant by wind pressures on building walls. There is little justification for introducing any greater volumes and the recommendations of some designers to add an additional 10 to 15% beyond the exhaust system volume should be questioned. Actually, a supply air volume approximately 20% less than the total of the exhaust and infiltration volumes will cause no problem in the usual industrial building where the usual movement of materials occurs. The proper location of the supply can provide improved inplant ventilation as well as makeup. By introducing the makeup air for the foundry into the Cleaning Department, Fig. 12-7, the makeup air volume pressurizes the Cleaning Room and produces an outward air flow through the doorway in the dividing wall. Note also how the supply to the work stations did double duty by being forced to flow over the mold staging area toward the pouring and mold upsetting area, Fig. 12-4.

Makeup air can also be supplied through Central Stations, Fig. 12-8, where a supply of 20,000 to 30,000 cfm through a single distributor is usual and volumes up to 50,000 cfm are frequent. The supply plenum location should be some distance from the exhaust system hoods to serve a general ventilation function as well as that of makeup air.

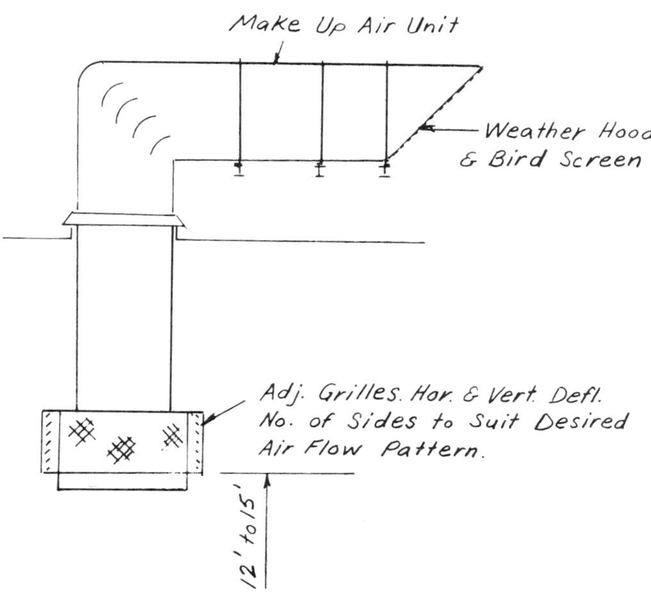

Fig. 12-8. Central air supply station.

CHAPTER 13

Monitoring Industrial Ventilation Systems

Because ventilation is a major means of controlling inplant air quality, a formal program of monitoring performance is highly desirable. The procedure need not be complicated, expensive, or time consuming, yet these major benefits can be realized:

1. Malfunctions can be quickly detected.
2. Effectiveness of corrective maintenance verified.
3. Evidence of maintained system performance provided.

Ventilation systems historically have had a low order of maintenance priority compared to production equipment. Where this has been the case, a new sense of urgency will have to be emphasized by Management and policed by Supervision. Monitoring can be a useless effort and a needless expense if corrective action is not promptly taken when deterioration or malfunction of the ventilation systems are detected and reported.

Monitoring approaches will differ among local exhaust, general exhaust, and air supply systems. Because local exhaust has a major impact on the air quality at the work stations, these systems deserve the more frequent quantitative measurements.

Monitoring Schedule

Local Exhaust. For the usual local exhaust system, assuming that air measurements are available when desired air flow was procured, these measurements could consist of pressure measurements and their comparison with previous data, on a basis such as:

Monthly

SP in main duct ahead of dust collector and/or exhaust fan (SP comparisons will give accurate indication of system performance except for systems where blast gates are used to adjust or alter air flow)

SP in critical branch ducts where air flow reduction would have a major impact on the work station air quality.

Installation of permanent gages mounted for easy access is recommended as they offer an opportunity for spot checking during usual trips through plant facilities. Magnehelic gages are especially suited for this service as the direct reading dial can be color coded for the acceptable range for each measuring station. A reduction from design values of less than 25% (a 13% reduction in air flow rates) should cause no problem as all design criteria include a substantial factor of safety.

Semiannually

VP at centerline of main duct.

General Exhaust Ventilation. Quantitative measurements are difficult to make for roof or wall fans that have no connected ductwork. In most cases, however, malfunctions can be traced and reported from visual observations, such as:

Monthly

Fan in actual operations. It is so easy to forget to start such remote equipment where manual starting is used.
V-belt drives have proper tension.
Barometric dampers are extended to their fully opened position.

Air Supply Systems. The monitoring procedure will vary with the equipment involved, but could include:

Monthly

Verify that system is in operation.
Check V-belt drives.
Check direction of fan rotation when fans are centrifugal.
SP across filters and/or coils to detect accumulations causing reduction in air flow.

Semiannually

Check air flow rates through typical discharge grilles, using Velometer or Anemometer.

Ribbons attached to outlet grilles provide an excellent means for spot checking performance, quickly indicating when a system is not in operation, and, often by visual comparisons, systems where supply air flow is marginal.

Field Measurements

Manometers The most useful single instrument in exhaust work is the common "U" tube. Static pressures are measured by this device without the aid of other instruments. One leg of the manometer may be inclined for the purpose of magnifying the differential movement by as much as 10 times. The inclined gage permits direct readings to the nearest hundredth of an inch, but because of its sensitivity it cannot be held in the hand and leveled by eye. It must be firmly attached to a rigid surface either magnetically or by permanent mounting. An inclined manometer or other suitable amplifying gage should always be used when pressures below 0.3 in. wg are to be measured with reasonable accuracy.

Gages are calibrated for either water or gage oil. If in doubt, measure the scale. For water the depression for 1 in. wg will scale 1 in.; for oil it will scale about 1-3/16 in. based on a specific gravity for oil of 0.85. For easier reading, water is often colored without changing its specific gravity. Commercial gage dyes are available, but colored ink, pastry coloring, etc. will do quite well.

Be certain that technicians reporting vertical U gage readings in a monitoring program are trained to read the total depression between the two liquid columns. There is a tendency to report only the difference between 'zero' and the liquid level on one of the legs, resulting in a 50% error. A fairly comprehensive study of a system may be made with no other apparatus than a waterfilled pocket "U" tube.

Magnehelic gages are direct reading and are a popular substitute for U gages. They are available in a wide range of increments and are relatively foolproof. An occasional check against a U gage is good practice, however.

The Impact Tube A simple instrument of great value is the impact tube, several varieties of which are shown in Fig. 13-1, a to e, inclusive. This instrument, connected to a manometer, will measure the impact, or total pressure, when pointed upstream in an air current. The velocity pressure is obtained by deducting the static pressure measured in the same cross-sectional plane of the pipe.

The impact tube is a primary measuring device of high, inherent accuracy. No calibration is necessary because its performance is in exact accord with theory. It is not recommended for velocities much less than 2000 fpm, unless connected to some form of multiplying pressure-gage such as the inclined manometer. Large percentage errors are possible under field conditions when reading pressures less than ¼ in. of water on the tube.

The dimensions of the impact tube are not critical. The minimum length from tip to bend should be about 8 diameters. There are no restrictions on diameter, 3⁄16, ¼, or 5⁄16 inch hard brass tubing are satisfactory. It is necesary only that the tube be stiff so that its unsupported length will not vibrate badly in the air stream. The small tubes shown in Fig. 13-1 have been used as searching tubes to explore the boundaries of jets and other small dimensional regions. A tiny tube drawn from glass tubing has been successfully employed in a study of the air currents following the rim of an abrasive wheel.

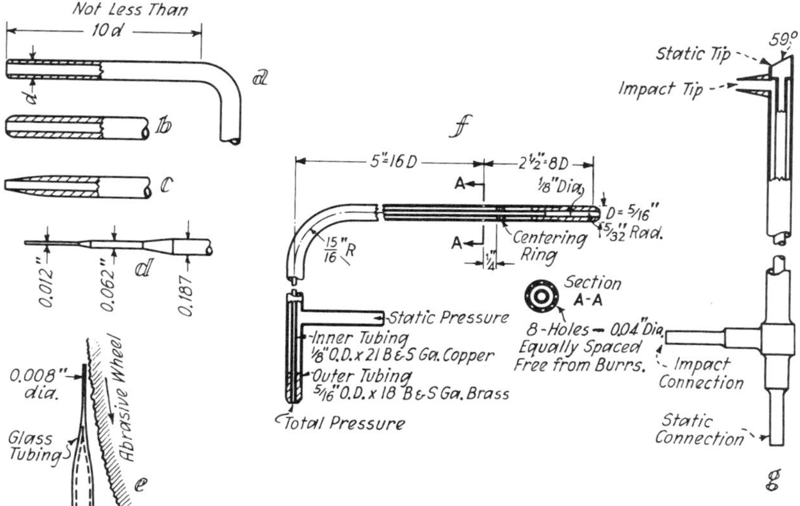

Fig. 13-1. Impact and pitot tubes.

The Pitot Tube The commercial pitot tube combines the impact tube with means for measuring static pressure. In its conventional form, Fig. 13-1f, it consists of two concentric tubes, the inner forming the impact tip and the outer constituting the chamber into which open the static pressure holes. When the inner and outer tubes are connected to opposite legs of a single manometer, the latter indicates the velocity pressure directly. Two manometers are required if the static pressure must be read separately.

Pulsating airflow causes the pitot or the impact tube to read high. These instruments measure the energy of flow, a variable which is proportional to the square of the velocity. Hence, in pulsating flow, the average of the surges of the water column is unduly influenced by the high values.

Measuring Tips The pitot tube is relatively foolproof. One should check the air passages of each tube by blowing into the ports; a fluctuation in the gage liquid level will assure clear passageways.

Be certain that the tip is parallel to the duct and pointed into the direction of air flow so that the air movement will impact on the open end. The right angle connection for the SP tap parallels the tube section inserted into the duct. It provides external evidence of direction and parallelism of the probe. Also watch for kinking of rubber hose connections. The likely places are close to the connection at either the pitot tube or the gage.

Anemometers The ordinary windmill anemometer is unsuitable for exhaust work, its range is too low and its bulk too great for use in ducts and it is much too delicate for shop use in measuring at hood faces and in booths.

A more rugged instrument is the Velometer, which is a swinging vane anemometer. One type is provided with a variety of impact nozzles which lend themselves very well to slotted exhaust hoods and air supply grilles or grids. The Velometer should be calibrated frequently, and, where major corrections are required, it may be desirable to retest those locations where the instrument had been used prior to the recalibration.

Location of Test Points

Test points for measurement of air flow and static pressures should be selected at sufficient points to provide background data against which performance can be measured during the routine monitoring of system performance.

Pitot tube traverses would be indicated to determine the volume in the main duct, Test Points T-5 or T-6, and preferably in each branch duct, Test Points T-1, T-2, T-3, T-4, Fig. 13-2. Include the centerline VP in the recorded data as it will make a useful reference point for future air flow monitoring.

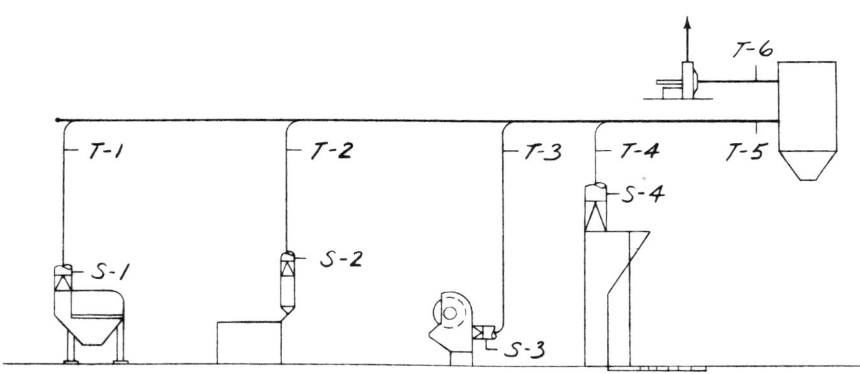

Fig. 13-2. Exhaust system test points.

Static pressure measurements should be included at each point where air volume is measured; these measurements will provide hood suction data, Test Points S-1, S-2, S-3, S-4, and pressure drop across the Collector, Test Points T-5 and T-6.

Where Collectors have inlet and outlet plenums typical of Fabric Collectors and some Wet Scrubbers, the Collector SP differential can be measured under two sets of conditions:

Flange to Flange measures the SP loss between inlet duct and outlet duct and as such includes the acceleration loss and turbulent loss involved in accelerating the air from the usual low velocity in the clean air plenum to the transport velocity in the duct connecting Collector to exhaust fan inlet or discharge stack.

Plenum to Plenum measures the differential between the air entering plenum and the clean air outlet manifold. It is the true measure of the resistance to air flow from the cleaning elements of the Collector for a specific air volume because the readings are not influenced by acceleration or deceleration loss.

In Fig. 13-3, the two approaches to Collector pressure drop reporting have been illustrated. The differential between T-6b and T-5b is representative of the energy required for the Collector element; between T-6a and T-5a it is the flange to flange energy demand.

The SP at T-5a will be practically the same as that of T-5b for Collectors with inlet plenums, because the velocity pressure of the air in the inlet duct cannot be easily converted to static pressure regain.

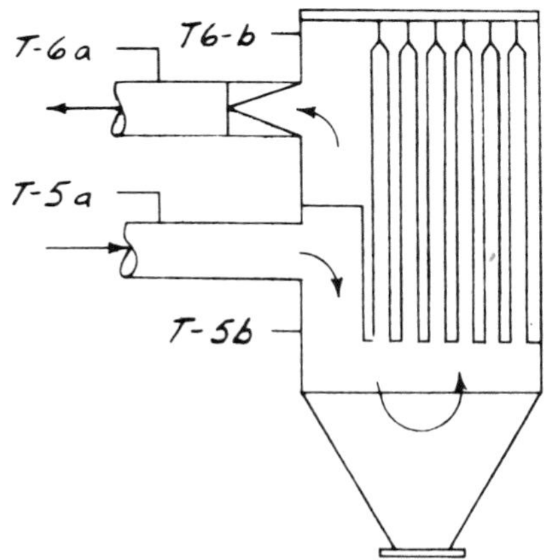

Fig. 13-3. Collector pressure relationships.

The SP at T-6b exceeds that of T-6a by the acceleration pressure needed to increase the air flow to discharge duct velocity plus the turbulence loss as the air is forced into the smaller cross section of the discharge opening.

Pitot and Impact Tube Traverses

The velocity across a given section of pipe is never uniform. Furthermore, flow conditions in exhaust piping are seldom such that the theoretical velocity distribution, Fig. 1-8, is attained. Consequently, a single pitot-tube measurement seldom can be translated into average velocity across the section. Velocities must be measured at several points and an average taken, weighting each velocity by that fraction of the total pipe-area which it represents. The usual practice is to divide the pipe area into imaginary rings of equal area and to measure the velocity pressure at four points in each ring along two diameters at right angles to each other. The four measuring stations in each ring are located on an imaginary circle which divides the ring into two equal, concentric areas.

Figure 13-4 shows a typical traverse. In the accompanying table the radii of the measuring stations are expressed in terms of the pipe radius. Ten readings are taken on each diameter, plus a centerline reading. These are translated into velocities and the 20 zone-velocities averaged, omitting the centerline velocity. Velocity pressures must not be averaged since they are proportional to the squares of their respective velocities.

Pitot-station radii are given in Fig. 13-4 for 3, 4, and 5 zones. Five zones, or 20 points, should be used for pipes 10 in. in diameter and larger, four zones from 5 in. to 10 in., and three zones for smaller pipes. When time is

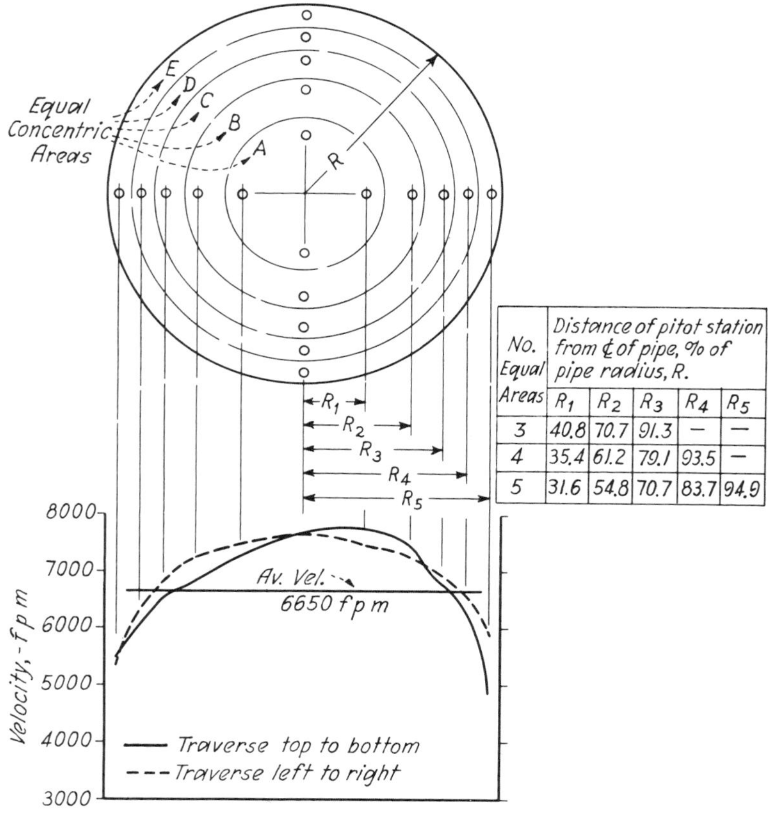

No. Equal Areas	Distance of pitot station from ℄ of pipe, % of pipe radius, R.				
	R_1	R_2	R_3	R_4	R_5
3	40.8	70.7	91.3	—	—
4	35.4	61.2	79.1	93.5	—
5	31.6	54.8	70.7	83.7	94.9

Fig. 13-4. Typical pitot- or impact-tube traverse.

limited, it is better to take 6 readings on each of two diameters or 12 readings, total, than to take 10 readings on a single diameter.

Preferred Location of Pitot Tube Traverse

The pitot station should be preceded by not less than 10 diameters of straight pipe where available. The longer the straight section, the more nearly normal the velocity distribution is likely to be. The velocity profiles shown in Fig. 13-4 were taken at the open end of a straight pipe, 27 diameters long. In spite of the long approach, the profiles show the effect of disturbed flow. The longest available straight section should precede the pitot station.

The necessity for a complete traverse instead of a single, centerline reading is well illustrated in Fig. 13-5. Distorted flow patterns are present in nearly all fan discharge pipes. The velocity profile in Fig. 13-5b shows that the velocity on the throat side of an elbow exceeds the mean and that the

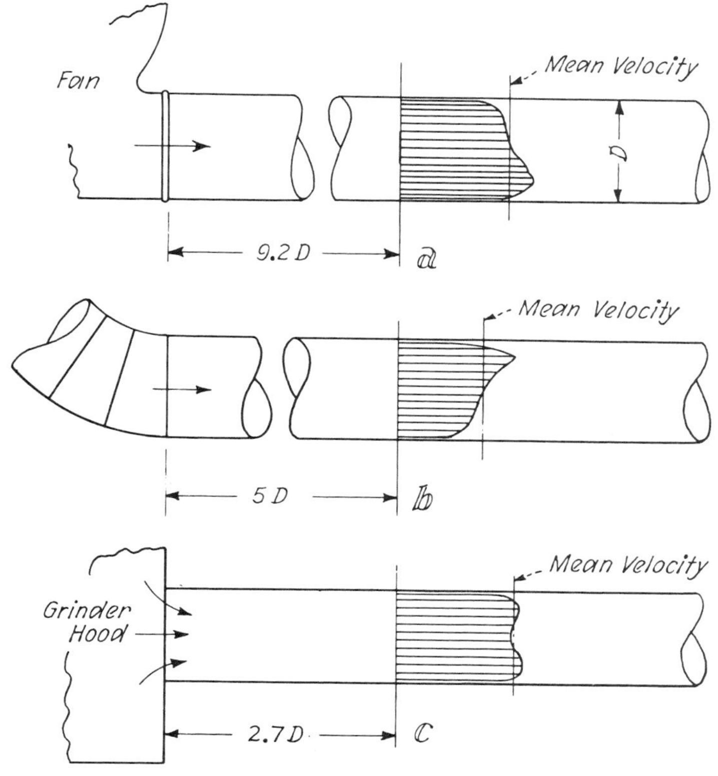

Fig. 13-5. Typical velocity profiles.

influence of the bend persists for several pipe diameters downstream. Figure 13-5c represents the velocity profile in a short branch-pipe leaving an exhaust hood. The depressed center is typical of profiles taken close to inlet openings. A single, centerline measurement can be converted to mean velocity only under more uniform conditions of flow than usually exist in practical systems.

However, with changes in flow rates, the profile will remain the same with all readings varying as the square of the change in velocity. When the volume was originally measured by a typical pitot tube traverse and the centerline VP recorded, a comparison of centerline readings can be used to quantitatively detect changes in flow rates during periodic performance checks. The time required for monitoring measurements is reduced, and the duct centerline provides an ideal point for repeated test positioning of the pitot tube.

Static-Pressure Holes in Pipe Walls

Static pressure measurements in industrial exhaust systems are generally made through the pipe wall. The size of the hole is not critical since reliable readings may be obtained from holes ranging in diameter from 0.02 in. to 1/4 in. and more. A convenient size which may be drilled with a light hand-drill, without excessive drill breakage, is 1/16 in. The inner end should be free from burrs. For field work, however, the removal of the inner burr may be difficult and, if so, is seldom worth the effort. Most field measurements are made and recorded in terms of tenths or twentieths-of-an-inch and hence are rough as compared with laboratory standards. In consequence, many of the customary precautions to insure accuracy are, in fact, unnecessary

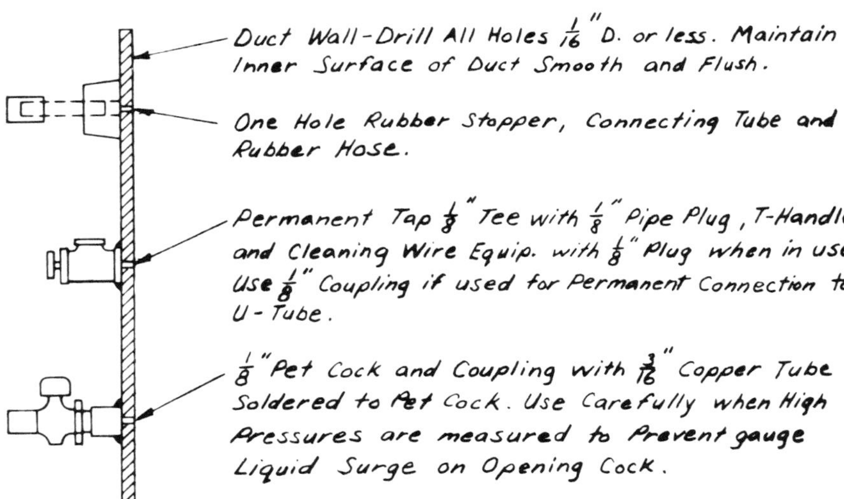

Fig. 13-6. SP tap details.

refinements. When periodic SP readings become part of a monitoring routine, permanent connections such as Fig. 13-6 are helpful.

Estimating the Volume Rate of Flow

The accurate way to determine the total air volume flowing through a system is to make a pitot traverse. When time or circumstances do not permit such a test, the volume may be estimated by one or more of the following methods.

1. Measure the pressure drop through a long run of pipe and find from Fig. 5-1 the volume which will produce this loss.
2. From hood suctions, branch pipe areas, and estimated entry coefficients calculate the combined flow.
3. Use the arithmetical sum of the inlet and discharge static-pressures as the impact pressure developed by the fan; measure the fan speed and HP then pick the volume from the manufacturer's performance table corresponding to these conditions.
4. Check by computing the volume from the probable minimum conveying velocity for the material being transported.

Admittedly, these methods are rough, with the hood suction estimates the most reliable, yet a fair degree of accuracy is possible as the example, Table 13-1, demonstrates.

Use of the air horsepower formulas

$$Ahp = 0.000157Qh \text{ or } Ahp = \frac{Qh}{6356}$$

where:

Q = the volume rate of flow, cfm and
h = the measured fan SP

Table 13-1. Flow Estimated by Several Methods

Method	Estimated Vol., cfm
By friction loss, 4 sets of readings at different locations	5,800 5,900 5,300 5,600
By hood suction	6,070
From fan tables	6,300
Check by estimated minimum conveying velocity	5,500
Average	5,800

offers another useful method for estimating air flow. The data required are motor horsepower, fan static pressure, and estimates of motor and fan efficiences. The formulas become

$$Q = \frac{(\text{HP} \times \text{Motor Eff.}) \times (6356 \times \text{Fan Eff.})}{\text{Fan SP}}$$

Flow Direction Finder

A tube developed for the purpose of finding the direction of flow or for measuring static pressures under difficult conditions is shown in Fig. 13-7.[1] The derivation of the 78-1/2° angle between static holes is illustrated in Fig. 13-7b. This curve shows the pressure variation indicated by a single hole in a smooth cylinder as the cylinder is revolved with respect to the direction of flow. The indicated pressure is nearly equal to the impact pressure when the hole faces the stream squarely. As the tube is rotated, a point is reached at which the measured pressure equals the true static pressure in the pipe. Fechheimer found this angle to be 39-1/4° for a tube of the dimensions shown. Further rotation is accompanied by a pressure drop which reaches minimum levels at about twice the critical angle previously mentioned. This value has been confirmed for velocities up to 16,000 fpm.

If two static holes are located as shown in Fig. 13-7a, connection of both legs of a manometer to the two pressure taps of the tube enables the latter to be used as a direction finder. Rotation of the tube until the manometer reads zero indicates the true direction of flow. If a second manometer is connected to one of the pressure taps, the static pressure may be read. Departure from the dimensions given may require special determination of the critical angle. If the holes are positioned 180° apart, the instrument may be used as a special pitot tube if individually calibrated.[2]

Test to Check Design Assumptions

Every design involves some degree of speculation. Some assumptions have been necessary and some design data have been incomplete or possibly inaccurate. Consequently, every new system should be checked against the original design figures. The first step is to check the fan speed. Next, static pressures are measured at all significant points. These include the suction at each hood, suction and back pressure at the fan, and the pressure drop through the separator. The original pressure and flow sketch similar to Fig. 6-1 should be used to select points for measurement in the suction main. If there is a long straight run of discharge pipe, the static pressure should be

[1] "Air Forces on Circular Cylinders," by Hugh L. Dryden, *Bureau of Standards Scientific Paper No. 394.*

[2] "Measurement of Static Pressure," by Carl J. Fechheimer, *ASME Transactions* (1926), pp. 965-977.

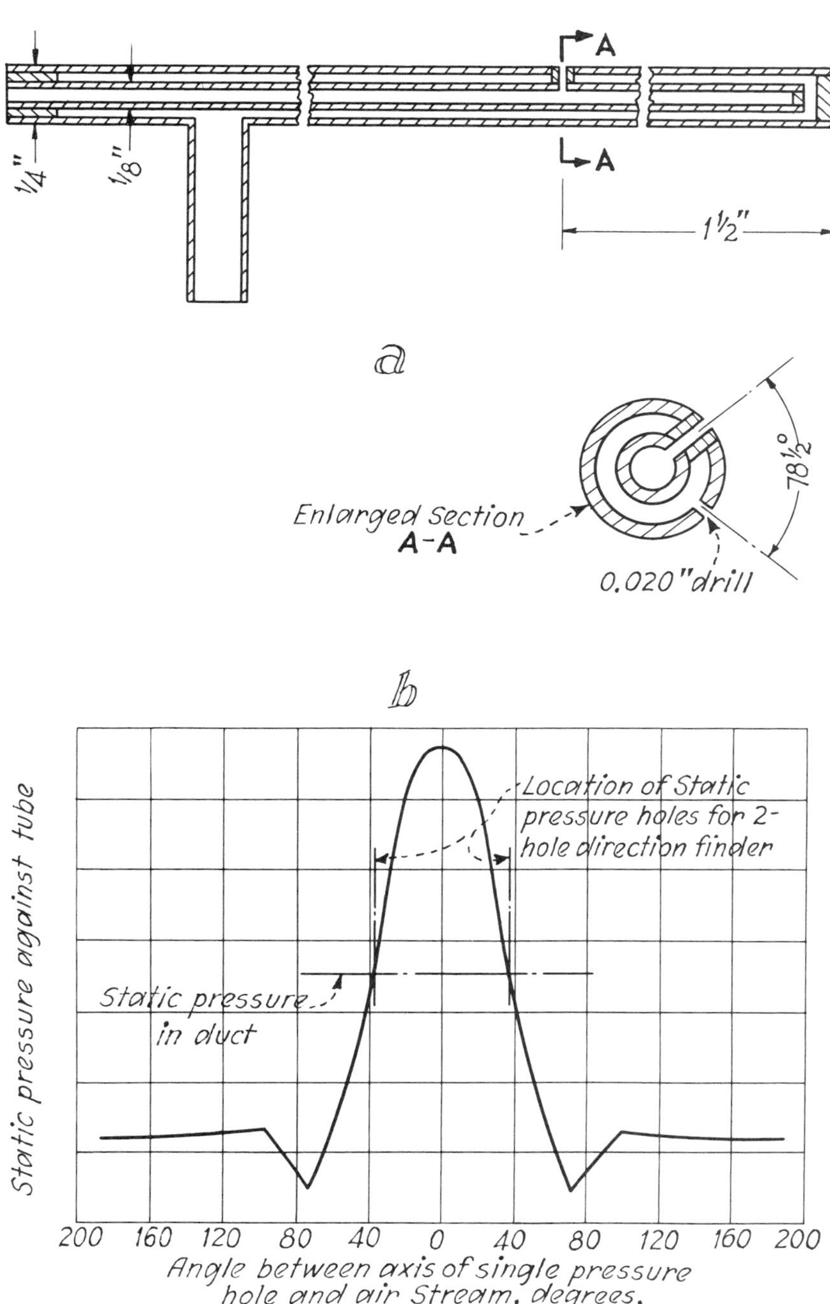

Fig. 13-7. Static pressure measuring tube or direction-finding tube.

taken at each end so that the friction loss may be checked against the friction chart, Fig. 5-1.

If the static pressures, as measured, check closely with the predicted pressures, it may be assumed that the air quantities are the same as those calculated. Exact agreement is rare, however, first, because design factors are not sufficiently well established and, second, because the erecting mechanics will have made departures from the original piping plan. Usually there will be a few places at which the test figures differ materially from those calculated. The engineer must then use his knowledge of airflow laws to deduce the reasons for the departure. Often it will be unnecessary to make changes in the physical system but the information obtained should be recorded and interpreted so that future designs may embody the lessons learned.

Locating and Diagnosing Trouble

In Fig. 13-8 are recorded certain pressure data obtained at the time of installation of a new system. The accompanying table indicates certain pressure changes as measured at various later dates. Each pressure change signifies a change in resistance of some part of the system. Correct interpretation of recorded variations enables the maintenance man to find and correct troubles promptly and economically. The analyses of the pressure readings of Fig. 13-8 are as follows:

Condition 1. The fan suction has dropped and the fan back pressure has increased by nearly the same amount. A small drop has taken place in the fan impact-pressure. The friction loss in the discharge pipe has increased as has the cyclone resistance. The latter changes indicate a definite increase in

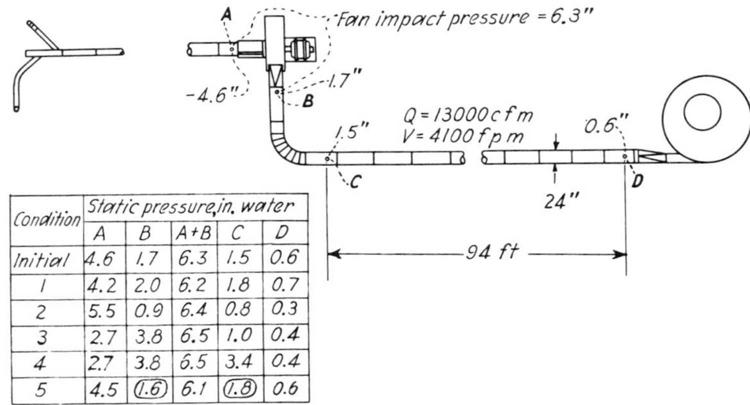

Condition	Static pressure, in. water				
	A	B	A+B	C	D
Initial	4.6	1.7	6.3	1.5	0.6
1	4.2	2.0	6.2	1.8	0.7
2	5.5	0.9	6.4	0.8	0.3
3	2.7	3.8	6.5	1.0	0.4
4	2.7	3.8	6.5	3.4	0.4
5	4.5	(1.6)	6.1	(1.8)	0.6

Fig. 13-8. Changed conditions within exhaust system as indicated by static-pressure measurements.

airflow rate. This can come only from decreased resistance on the suction side of the fan. The maintenance man should look for disconnected hoods, open floor sweeps, open handholes, and missing caps at the ends of mains and branches.

Condition 2. The fan suction has increased materially while the back pressures at *B*, *C*, and *D* have dropped. Reduced discharge resistances indicate a drop in air volume. The increased suction means increased inlet resistance. Closed blast gates or a clogged suction main will produce this pressure condition. If there is a previous history of clogging trouble, design changes may be indicated.

Condition 3. An abnormal pressure-drop has taken place between the fan outlet and the downstream side of the elbow. An obstruction will be found between *B* and *C*, probably at the elbow. The impact pressure at the fan has increased while the discharge-pipe friction and the collector loss have diminished. These factors indicate reduced volume.

Condition 4. This situation is similar to that of *Condition 3* except that the large pressure-drop occurs between *C* and *D*. Measurement at intermediate points will indicate whether the obstruction is localized or whether it has persisted long enough to cause general settlement throughout the pipe.

Condition 5. It will be observed that the pressure at *C* is recorded as being greater than that at *B*. There is nothing wrong with the system; the observer has misread his instruments or has transposed the figures. This is a common mistake which often passes unnoticed by inexperienced engineers. It represents an impossible condition since true static-pressures, both suction and positive pressure, are greatest in numerical value at the fan and diminish as the distance from the fan increases. The only exception is the rare instance in which velocity pressure is converted to static pressure by means of an efficient expansion piece.

Occasionally, two conditions of poor performance are observed which are not functions of the system resistances. Both are detectable through the sums of the pressures *A* and *B*. If the sum is slightly below the initial value, say 5 to 10 percent, the fan speed should be checked for belt slippage. If the difference is much greater, the direction of rotation should be examined. Reversal of rotation is not uncommon when 3-phase leads are reconnected after repair. The condition can go undetected for some time since a reversed fan will move air, although at much reduced volume.

CHAPTER 14

Isolation

As standards of acceptable workroom air quality become increasingly stringent, the need to supplement the usual local and general exhaust ventilation approaches becomes evident for many operations. Separation of the process from the worker can be accomplished by either isolation of the process or isolation of the work stations.

Isolation of the Process

This approach has long been a prime tool for effective local exhaust designs. Complete enclosures are common for bins, mixers, bucket elevators, abrasive cleaning, and a host of other processes. The concept has been expanded to include the housing of complete lines of process equipment whereby a negative pressure within the enclosures maintained by the exhaust ventilation prevents contaminant escapement to the adjacent work areas.

Isolation of the Worker

Separation of the work station from objectionable contaminant concentrations also has many applications, often used as a supplement where usual ventilation mechanisms fail to achieve the desired air quality.

Isolation can be in the form of an enclosure of the work space or the separation of the workspace from the process by distance or time.

Enclosing the Workspace

Enclosures fall into two general categories: complete, tightly constructed rooms with occasional door openings by workers; and enclosures with open observation, operating, or access openings.

Tight Enclosures. The exhaust volume needed for pressurization is quite small, probably not more than 2 cfm per sq ft of enclosure plan dimension. Where clean makeup air is readily available, an exhaust grille should be located in the lower part of the main access door and the makeup air introduced on the far side to purge the occupied space. See Fig. 14-1. Size the exhaust grille for 500 fpm. Because the supply volume is so small, comfort ventilation can best be provided by a recirculating room air conditioner.

Where a clean air supply cannot be readily introduced into the enclosure, such as a crane cab or a control pulpit remote from clean outdoor air, the air supply will have to be cleaned and recirculated. Recirculation maintains needed air movement for comfort and also quickly filters contaminant infiltration during access door openings. See Fig. 14-2. Such an arrangement will also reduce the filter maintenance as the only time a high concentration will be drawn from the outside atmosphere is when the access door is opened.

With the door closed, the circuit resembles that of a closed conveying system with the only air entering the outside air port being the volume needed to replace the exfiltration losses from the enclosure. Sizing the recirculation port for 750 fpm will maintain sufficient positive pressure within the enclosure and keep the size of the outdoor air port within usual space limitations. With the access door open, pressure within the enclosure reduces to atmospheric. At such times the negative pressure in the inlet plenum of the filter housing induces air flow of approximately equal velocities through the recirculating port and the outside air port. If that opening is three times the area of the recirculating air port, about 75% of the fan capacity will be available to produce an outward air flow through the open doorway.

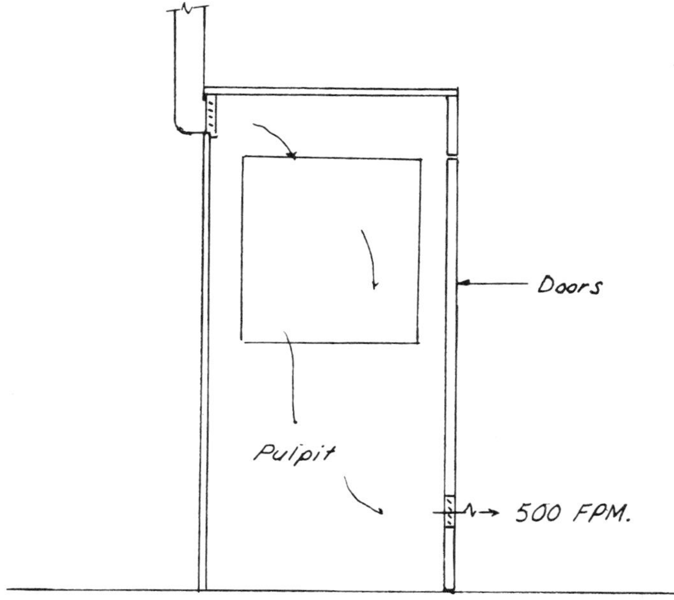

Fig. 14-1. Enclosed work station.

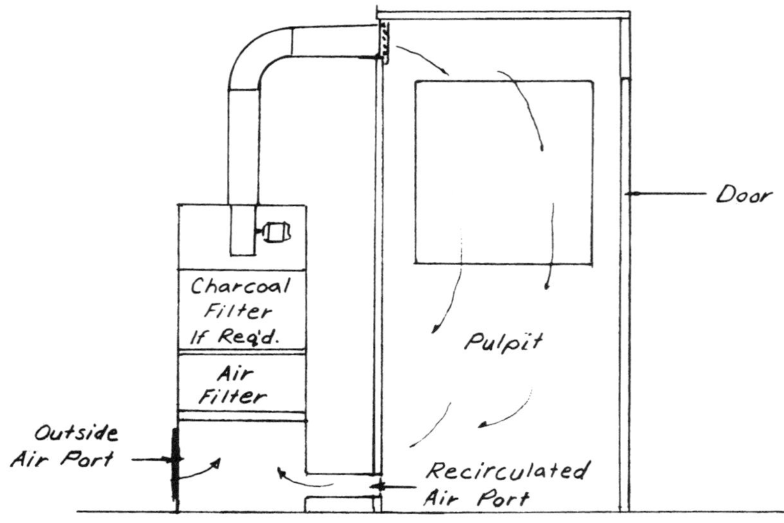

Fig. 14-2. Recirculated air.

Open Ports. For enclosures with open observation, inspection or access openings, the air supply volume will be increased to that necessary to maintain an outward flow through those openings of 125–150 fpm. The air supply is sufficient so that the introduction of tempered air is practical. The point of introduction should be remote from exhaust openings in order to provide an effective air flow pattern.

Cafeterias, locker rooms, and rest enclosures should be provided with sufficient supply air to maintain a 150 fpm outward flow through open doorways, with grilles in the doors to assure the venting of supply air when the doors are closed.

At times, tempering the supply air will provide sufficient air movement for comfort ventilation. Where large numbers of workers are involved, the use of a supplemental recirculated volume could be required.

Air Showers. The direction of a clean tempered air supply that will envelope the breathing zone of the worker provides a degree of isolation by reduction in contaminated air flow that can reach the worker from adjacent processes. Supply air must be introduced at relatively low velocities over a generous area. A typical air shower, Fig. 14-3, would approximate 5 sq ft in plan area with a supply volume of 150 cfm per sq ft of face area.

The direction of high velocity jets would usually defeat this objective. The high velocity aspirates contaminated air into the air supply and causes a turbulence in the work zone that reduces the effectiveness of local exhaust.

Air Supplied Respirator. While frowned on by OSHA regulations as not an engineered control approach, the "white cap" full head enclosure or the

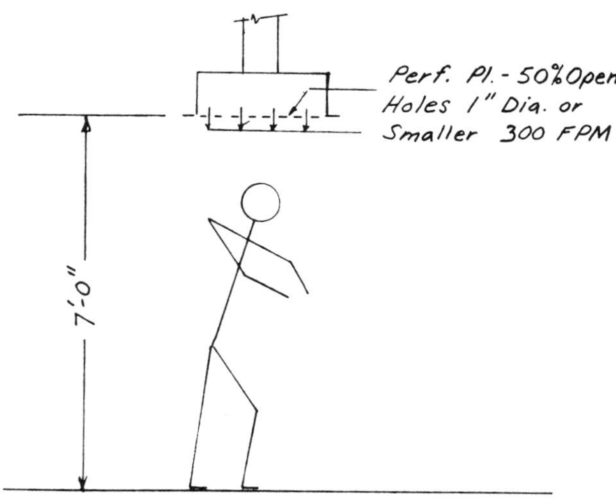

Fig. 14-3. Air shower.

air-supplied hard hat model provides an excellent mechanism for isolating the worker, providing a clean cool environment as well as superior eye injury protection.

Increasing the Distance between Worker and Process

Worker exposure can usually be decreased by removing him from the immediate contaminant generation source. At a more remote distance ambient air will have lower contaminant levels produced by the combined effects of local exhaust and general ventilation.

Remote Control Stations. For some processes the control panel can be located at a distance from the operation without seriously impairing the operator's view.

Mechanical Manipulators. The use of mechanical manipulators often places the operator at a control station some distance from the product requiring transfer, thereby reducing the need for close proximity to the zone of highest contaminant concentration. The introduction of robot mechanisms further reduces the work requirement to one of observation, which can be done at even greater distance and from within a ventilated control room, where indicated.

TV Cameras. Closed circuit cameras can replace workers where processes require constant observation to detect upset situations. The worker can then be stationed at a central location monitoring one or more TV screens. The control station can be enclosed and pressurized with a clean supply air when indicated.

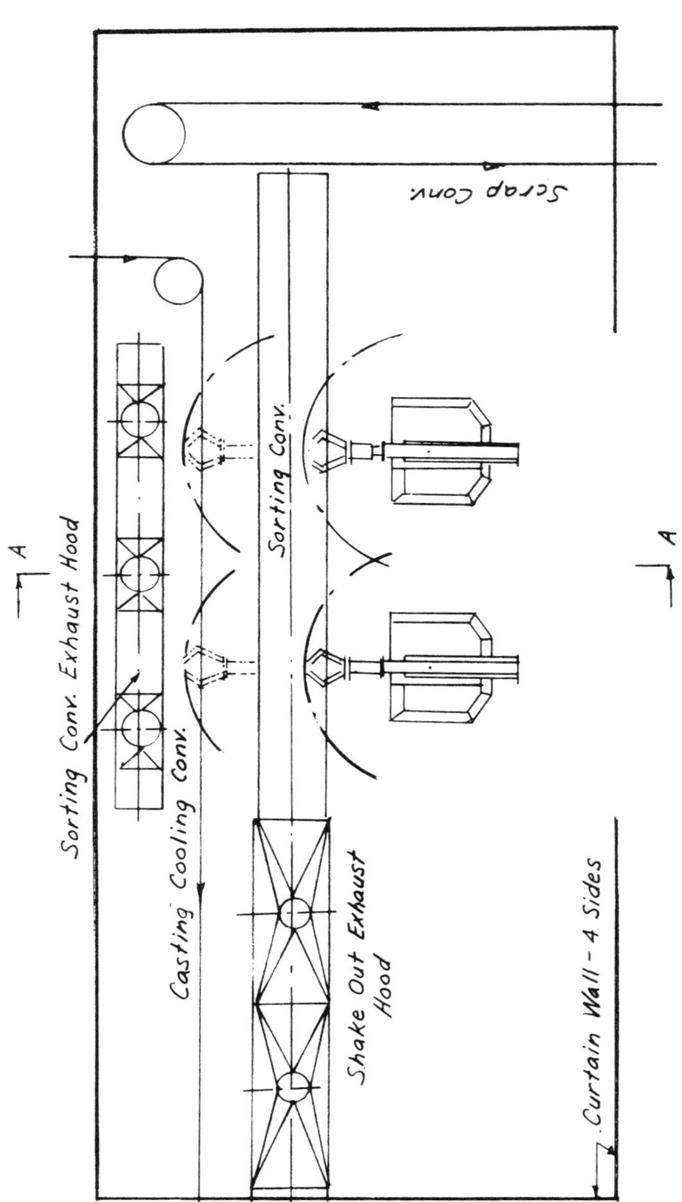

Fig. 14-4. Multiple control example. By permission—Smith, Hinchman & Grylls Associates, Inc., Detroit, MI and Cifunsia, Saitillo, Mexico.

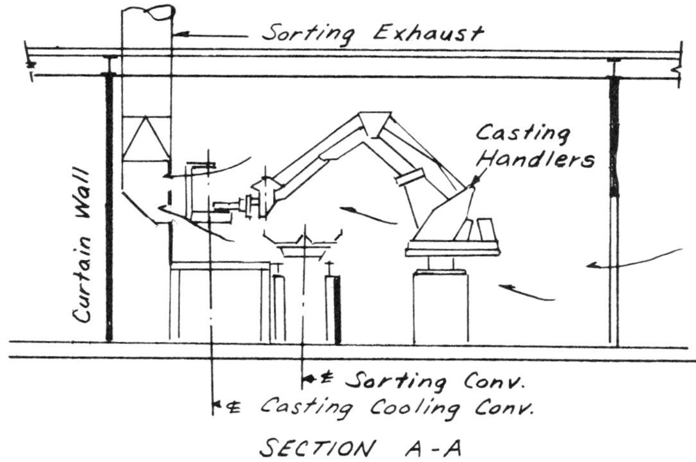

Fig. 14-4 (*continued*)

With the TV arrangement, the worker need be exposed to contaminants only during those times when his presence is required to correct malfunctions.

Combined Ventilation Techniques

The solution to many contaminant control problems will require more than a single control approach. In many cases, the solution will utilize all of the approaches discussed in this text; local exhaust with effective hood design, general exhaust ventilation, strategic air supply introduction, and isolation of the process or the worker.

The Gray Iron Foundry Shakeout and Sorting Area, Fig. 14-4, is an example:

(a) Shakeout is completely housed for maximum dust control.
(b) Side hood along the sorting conveyor is in an ideal location to exhaust the supplemental general ventilation.
(c) Walls enclosing the area isolate the area from adjacent foundry areas.
(d) Mechanical manipulators transfer casting from sorting conveyor to casting cooling conveyor, keeping operators removed from the contaminant release zones.
(e) Access opening in the wall opposite the conveyors causes lateral air flow to air-shower the work stations and provides general ventilation of the whole area while satisfying the demands of the exhaust system.

CHAPTER 15

Energy Conservation

The exhaust of tempered or cooled air from the work place to atmosphere represents a major part of the fuel consumption in climates where space heating or cooling is required for worker comfort.

Heat Loss

The fuel cost of replacing exhausted air will be a function of local outdoor temperatures, usual length of the work week, and the required temperature of the replacement air. For most operations supply air can be introduced to the work space at temperatures in the 55–65 F range because of supplemental heat generated by the industrial processes. The magnitude of the energy consumed can be recognized by the Fig. 15-1 calculations. Note that the exhaust volume of 10,000 cfm used in the sample calculations is only a fraction of the total air removed from the typical factory building by local exhaust systems, roof ventilators, wall fans, and other general ventilation units. Moreover, 1,000 degree days are encountered only in the southern states. (A degree day represents the Btu's required to raise one pound of air one degree F for a 24-hour period.)

See Table 15-1 for degree day values for representative U.S. and Canadian cities. Note that the degree days in Table 15-1 assume 24 hour days and 7 day weeks. For a 40 hr week, the number would be reduced by 40/168, reducing each 1,000 degree days to 238. Based on the Fig. 15-1 calculations and the degree days shown in Table 15-1, the magnitude of the heat loss for four typical cities has been illustrated.

Fuel Conservation

Opportunities for fuel conservation in ventilation systems may exist in some of the following areas:

(a) Reduction in tempered air discharged by roof or wall fans.
(b) Substitution of local exhaust for general ventilation.
(c) Recirculation of exhaust system air.

Btu loss = 10,000 cfm × 0.075 × 0.24 × 60 min.
(0.75 lbs/cu ft for air;
specific heat = 0.24)
= 10,800 Btu/hr/degree F

$$= \frac{10{,}800 \times 24 \text{ hours} \times 1000 \text{ degree days} \times 40 \text{ hours operation}}{168 \text{ hours week}}$$

= 61,714,000 Btu/heating season

$$\text{Fuel equivalent} = \frac{61{,}714{,}000}{140{,}000 \text{ Btu/gal} \times 0.90 \text{ efficiency}}$$

= 397 gal fuel oil

Degree Days per Heating Season
(based on 24 hour day, 7 day week)

Air Supply Temp.	55F	65F
Degree Days:		
Chicago	3743	6315
Indianapolis	2829	5297
Louisville	2294	4180
Memphis	1284	2950

Fuel Requirements
(gal oil/10,000 cfm supplied air/40 hour work week)

Replacement Air Supply Temp.	55F	65F
Gal of fuel oil to heat 10,000 cfm:		
Chicago	1486	2507
Indianapolis	1123	2103
Louisville	911	1660
Memphis	510	1171

Fig. 15-1. Heat loss calculations.

Table 15-1. Degree Days Per Year

State	City	55F	65F
AL	Birmingham	853	2408
AZ	Phoenix	229	1404
AR	Little Rock	1188	2811
CA	San Francisco	384	3264
CO	Denver	3440	5873
CT	New Haven	3237	5895
DC	Washington	2487	4626
GA	Atlanta	1165	2891
ID	Pocatello	4140	7985
IL	Chicago	3743	6315
	Springfield	3289	5370
IN	Indianapolis	2829	5297
IA	Sioux City	4732	7023
KS	Dodge City	2962	5034
KY	Louisville	2294	4180
LA	Shreveport	565	1938
ME	Portland	4572	7012
MD	Baltimore	2491	4533
MA	Boston	3602	6045
MI	Detroit	4089	6494
	Marquette	5842	8692
MN	Duluth	6774	9480
	Minneapolis	5417	7851
MS	Vicksburg	468	1822
MO	St. Louis	2745	4585
MT	Helena	5071	8054
NE	Lincoln	3850	6004
NV	Reno	1040	5891
NH	Concord	4640	6852
NJ	Atlantic City	2904	5175
NY	Albany	4302	6889
	Buffalo	4316	6821
	New York	3089	5348
NM	Santa Fe	3106	6063
NC	Raleigh	1080	3234
ND	Bismark	6468	9150
OH	Cleveland	3795	6154
	Columbus	3255	5323
OK	Oklahoma City	1835	3613
OR	Portland	1911	4468
PA	Philadelphia	2695	4855
	Pittsburgh	3028	5235
RI	Providence	3578	6014
SC	Charleston	336	1769
SD	Rapid City	4628	7163
TN	Memphis	1284	2950
TX	El Paso	919	2428
UT	Salt Lake City	3202	5553
VT	Burlington	4984	7620
VA	Richmond	1895	3725
WA	Seattle	2185	4968
	Spokane	3672	6353
WV	Parkersburg	2784	4829
WI	Milwaukee	4617	7372
WY	Sheridan	5236	7993

CANADA

Province	City	55F	65F
AB	Calgary	6788	10,046
BC	Vancouver	3057	6061
MB	Winnipeg	8440	11,360
NB	St. John	5651	8908
NS	Halifax	4964	7844
ON	Toronto	4901	7580
PQ	Montreal	6094	8806
	Quebec	6890	9749
SK	Saskatoon	8818	11,941

Buffalo Forge, *Fan Engineering*, Fifth Edition (Source Data—Heating and Ventillating; U. S. Weather Bureau Records.

(d) Reduction in infiltration of outdoor air.

(e) Conserving heat and power with interlocks to process operation.

(f) Heat recovery.

Roof and Wall Fans. The large air-handling capacity with low installation and operating costs of roof and wall fans tends to make their use more widespread than needed. Individual sizes and capacities are based often on abnormally high safety factors because of the low capital cost and power requirements. Consequently, this is an area where extensive loss of tempered air can occur during the heating season.

Roof fans, operating under suction, do not produce noticeable air flow at the floor level. They remove heat accumulations, smoke, etc., that reach the ceiling by convection. Their operation may unnecessarily remove thousands of cfm of warm air that must be replaced with outdoor air heated from outdoor temperatures to the comfort level within the production areas. The resultant fuel consumption occurs whether makeup air is strategically introduced through makeup air units or is allowed to infiltrate through cracks, roof monitors, or open doors and then heated by space heaters in the work areas.

For operations where roof or wall fans are used, the appraisal of potential savings is easy, rapid, and requires a minimum of instrumentation. Simply, each fan's function during the heating season is questioned. Its usefulness can normally be determined by stopping the fan and observing its impact on floor level air quality.

For belt driven fans the installation of a variable pitch sheave will also permit reduction in exhaust capacity to the minimum effective exhaust volume.

Local Exhaust Systems. Local exhaust of contaminants requires only a fraction of the exhaust volume used by general ventilation control methods. Replacing general ventilation by local exhaust systems to the greatest practicable extent will improve inplant air quality and greatly reduce the volume of room air discharged.

Excessive exhaust volumes from existing local exhaust systems are another potential. An appraisal would be indicated for operations where large air volumes are exhausted or where a number of identical operations are involved. Exhaust hooding should be improved wherever possible, and the exhaust volumes reduced to the point where satisfactory contaminant control is still achieved as indicated visually or by air sampling.

Recirculation from Exhaust Systems. The recirculation of air from exhaust systems during the heating season can provide substantial fuel conservation. Whether recirculation should take place is a matter of degree of risk. Air from systems handling radioactive materials or highly toxic substances should not be recirculated. The penalty for system failure is too great to make the risk worthwhile. On the other hand air from systems installed merely to abate a nuisance, for improved housekeeping, or for cosmetic reasons may be recirculated without question. Between these extremes, wood waste, grinding dust, textile fibers and most materials of vegetable of metallic origin may be recirculated safely after suitable cleaning. In most cases, failure of the separating element can be detected and repairs or bag replacement can be made before serious exposure to the contaminant takes place.

The risks involved are of no greater magnitude than those resulting from reduced exhaust volume from duct plugging or malfunction of fan or collector; from disruptive cross drafts from open doors, windows, man cooling fans; or from excessive contaminant generation from poor work habits.

While there is still no practical means of monitoring the air quality in the cleaned gas stream at the time this edition was printed (1982), conditions are more conducive to substantial recirculation because:

(a) Air quality sampling within the workspace is a relatively easy procedure with many qualified laboratories available for rapid analysis of sampling cassettes. A periodic area sampling program can detect increases in background levels caused by collector malfunction.

(b) Industrial Hygiene is a recognized profession with greatly expanded employment within industry as well as government.

(c) Greater awareness and acceptance by industry of air quality maintenance since the creation of the Occupational Safety and Health Administration.

(d) The need to conserve energy as an economic and patriotic way of life.

Recirculation will have the most appeal where:

(a) Particulate concentrations are relatively light to minimize collector maintenance.

(b) Recirculated air is a fraction of the total exhaust volume including local exhaust, general exhaust, and exfiltration. The lower the ratio, the greater the dilution factor and the lower the increase in background levels caused by inefficiencies of the collector. Ratios up to 50% would appear reasonable without extensive field studies to determine the contribution quantitatively.

(c) Recirculated air represents only a portion of the total exhaust volume. The supply of some makeup air will prevent significant build up of background levels and prevent air stagnation from continuous recirculation within a given zone. In many cases this objective can be achieved by discharging recirculated air to adjacent areas or buildings that have processes needing substantial exhaust to atmosphere.

While heat savings will be minor, recirculation from isolated unit collectors should cause no problem. Exhaust volumes are small and substantial diffusion occurs, especially when cleaned air is directed away from the area of contaminant generation.

Reduction in Infiltration of Outdoor Air. Where material handling requires frequent opening of doors in outside walls, the infiltration of cold outdoor air can be a substantial addition to the plant fuel consumption. Open doors introduce a "breezeway" effect and indraft velocities of 500–1,000 fpm are usual (75,000–150,000 cfm through a 10 × 15 ft door opening). The flow is produced from a wind pressure effect and will occur even when air supply and exhaust volumes are in balance. Mechanisms to reduce such an unwanted air supply include:

(a) Use of vestibules with two sets of doors to form an air lock.

(b) Reduction of door openings; using a door within a door when lift trucks and freight cars or trucks use the same passageway.

(c) Provide a wind screen in front of the opening necessitating a right angle turn by material handlers as they reach the outdoors.

(d) Provide a tempered air curtain from the two vertical sides of the door opening. See Fig. 15-2. High velocity jets impinge on the incoming air stream creating a turbulent zone to reduce the velocity pressure of the cold air blast. Volumes are in the 100 cfm per sq ft of opening range, with slot velocities of 1,000–1,500 fpm.

Interlock Exhaust System. Many contaminant producing processes operate on an intermittent basis or release contaminants only during specific portions of their cycle. Interlocking the exhaust system with the need for ventilation can produce significant energy savings in many ventilation systems. Such an interlock also prevents the routine startup of ventilation systems even though processes ventilated are on standby and not in operation.

Where large motors drive exhaust fans, frequent starting can be objectionable. The use of air- or hydraulic-cylinder-operated blast gates in the exhaust duct will practically accomplish the same function. The damper also permits partial air flow for area ventilation if needed. The intermittent operation of a large foundry shakeout and the savings potential illustrated in Fig. 15-3 are an example.

During the 105 min period observed, the shakeout was operated releasing dust and smoke only for the periods noted by the short solid vertical lines. By throttling back on the 40,000 cfm during the three cross-hatched time periods, Areas A and B, 2,000,000 cubic feet of air would be conserved. Should some exhaust be needed for ventilation of adjacent material handling, throttling the exhaust volume by 75% would still be practical, saving 1,500,000 cubic feet, represented by the three cross-hatched areas labeled "A." In either case the power savings would be substantial also.

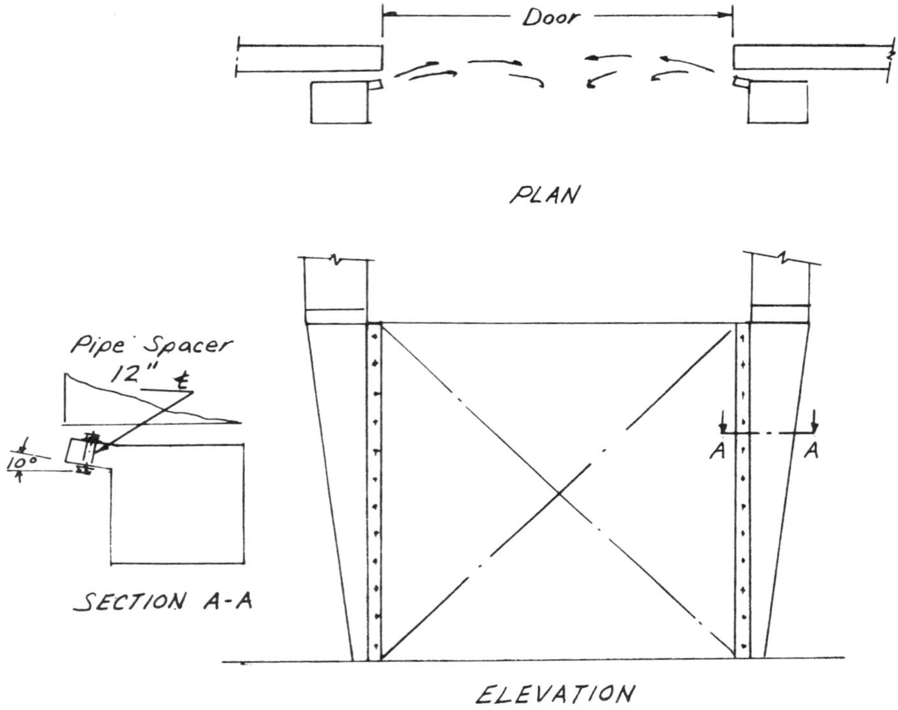

Door

PLAN

Pipe Spacer
12"
10°
SECTION A-A
A A
ELEVATION

Fig. 15-2. Air curtain door heater.

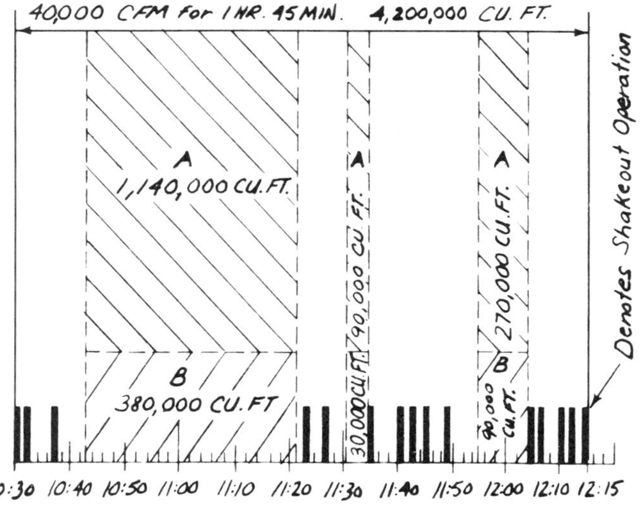

Fig. 15-3. Heat savings by interlocking exhaust with contaminant generation cycles.

Interlocking of roof or wall fans can provide similar savings in heat loss in some installations; in others, it takes the control of a trained Technician or Supervisor to manually start and stop such equipment. Key-operated start buttons prevent unnecessary fan operation at the whim of area production employees.

Heat Recovery

For many industrial buildings, heat recovery potential exists in two major areas: the recovery from hot air accumulations reaching the roof truss area and the use of heat exchangers to extract heat from exhaust stacks.

Heat Recovery from Roof Truss Accumulations. The potential for fuel savings from recovery of warm, relatively clean air accumulated in the roof truss area can be quickly checked by measuring temperatures at floor work stations and those in the roof truss area. The temperature differential cannot be translated into Btu values without knowing the exhaust or exfiltration volumes being vented to the atmosphere from this heat sink situation.

A check of roof fan capacity and an estimate of exfiltration will furnish that volume. Building construction and height will influence exfiltration rates. Values could be as low as three air changes per hour for tight, well-insulated buildings to 10 or more air changes per hour for high bay, monitor roof construction and generous window areas used for comfort ventilation during the warmer months. Recovery requires a mechanism that will reintroduce the heated room air back to the work station area. The methods include:

Vertical Space Heaters. The vertical space heater automatically takes advantage of the hotter intake air. The downward direction of the heated air assures that it reaches the floor area.

Reversed Roof Fans. Roof fans designed to remove heat accumulations during the warmer months can often be reversed, acting as makeup air supply systems during the heating season. The feasibility can be easily checked by reversing a fan and noting its impact on floor level temperatures. Like the vertical heater, the downward air flow will force the tempered air toward the floor area, but may produce noticeably cooler air motion at the impact areas. Delayed startup on a cold morning until temperature builds up within the building would be one solution; use of outdoor thermostats during extreme cold temperatures would be another. The use of deflectors or diffusers eliminates much of the cold air motion at floor level, but at the same time reduces the quantity of warm air reaching the work station.

Make Air Supply. The introduction of outdoor air through a distribution duct, Fig. 15-4, located in the roof truss area has attractions for some heat recovery applications. By introducing the cold outside air through a number of small-diameter discharge ports, good intermixing with the warm roof truss air occurs. A refinement of this approach modulates outdoor volume with plant air to maintain a minimum temperature within the air supply plenum.

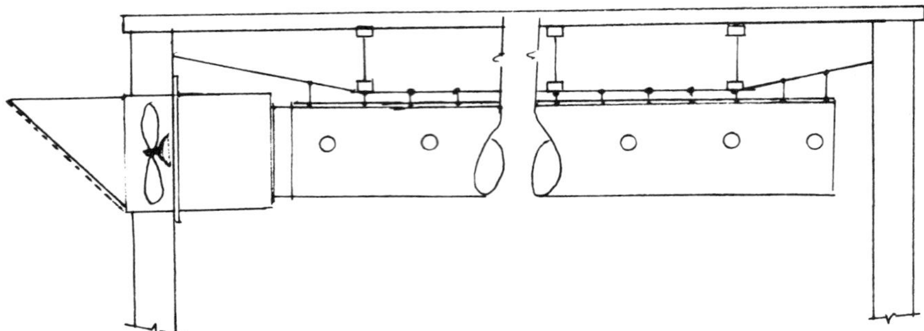

Fig. 15-4. Air supply at truss level.

The multiport air distribution reduces the delivery to the floor area but does eliminate the noticeable velocities introduced by reversed roof fans. These systems are especially attractive when the air supply is introduced to satisfy local exhaust system needs where exhaust hoods are in the floor level area and force air movement from the point of introduction to the exhaust hood opening.

Evaporative Cooling. Emphasis on energy conservation should reawaken interest in evaporative cooling as a substitute for refrigeration. Installed costs are low and power consumption is roughly one-fifth of that of equivalent mechanical refrigeration. They may replace or supplement the latter under suitable conditions with impressive power savings. Industrial applications need not be restricted to the dry climates of the southwest states, but can reduce peak temperatures even in locations of quite high relative humidity. The data, Fig. 15-5, show the potential for dry bulb reduction during a July day in Indianapolis. The spread between dry and wet bulb temperatures increases greatly as the dry bulb temperature increases in the afternoon and early evening hours, making substantial dry bulb reductions available during such periods with evaporative coolers. The example is typical for many U.S. locations, and with effectiveness can be calculated from hourly wet and dry bulb data recorded by U.S. Weather Bureau Stations and published by the Environmental Science Service Administration.

Evaporative coolers are not adapted to situations where temperature and humidity must be closely controlled.

Heat Exchangers. Heat exchangers have not found the broad market applications that were forecast for this energy conservation group. In many cases the capital costs, maintenance problems, or effective utilization of the recovered heat have been disappointments. Heat exchanger technology is beyond the scope of this book, but a study in depth by plant engineers is suggested during their evaluation for a specific application.

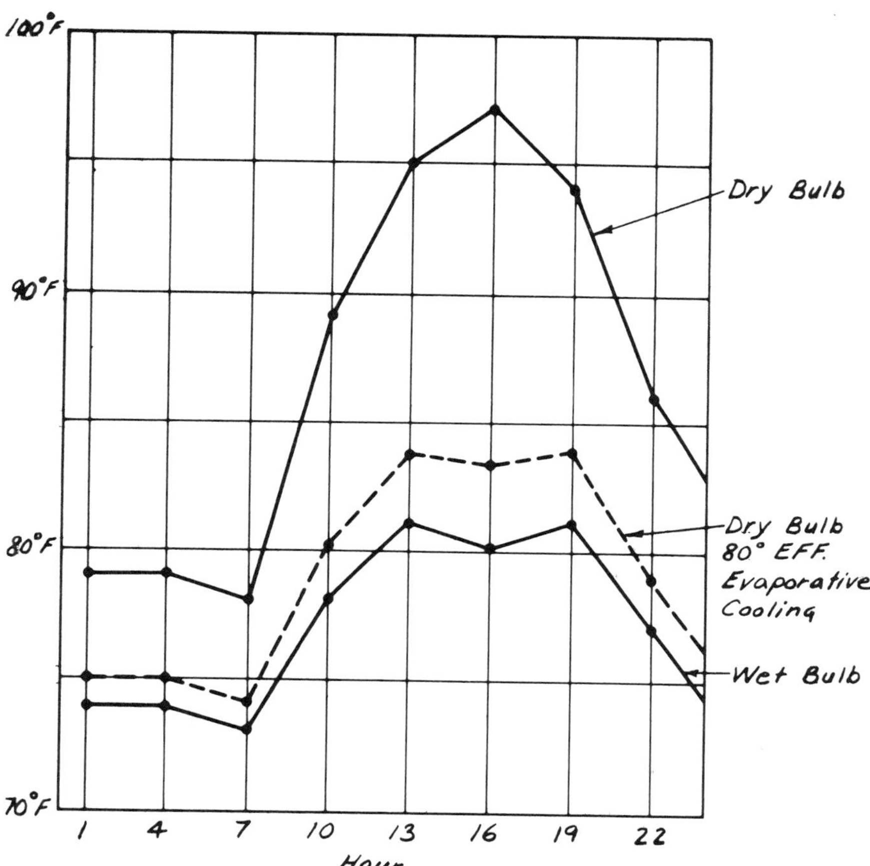

Fig. 15-5. Reduction in dry bulb temperatures with evaporative cooling.

Index

A

aerodynamic drag on contaminants, 56
aerosol, 17
air cleaning plants, 128-130
  cleaning efficiency, 129
  location of discharge, 130
air, compressibility of, 1
Air Moving and Conditioning Association, Inc., nomenclature, 213
air supply
  in area ventilation, 242-243
  makeup air, 244-245
  in spot ventilation, 240, 242
air volume determinations, 55, 57
air volume entering hoods, 74
  nomogram for calculating, 75
anemometers, 249-250
ASA Code Z-9.1, 71
atmospheric pressure, sea level, 1

B

Bernoulli's theorem, 5-6, 80-81, 103
blast gates, in piping design, 112, 226
booths (*see* hoods, booths or enclosures)
Borda's mouthpiece, 77

C

capture velocity (*see* velocity, capture)
clean room, 36
coefficient of discharge, of metering orifice, 82
coefficient of entry, 75-76, 79, 84
  of hoods, 83, 86-87
  physical significance of, 75
  synthetic, 83, 86
collectors
  for air-pollution control, 127-128
    BAT standards, 128
    opacity standards, 128
    process weight standards, 127
  chemical additives for improved efficiency, 164, 166
  electrostatic precipitators, 134, 136-137, 174-176
    plate type, 175-176
      collection efficiency of, 176
    tube type, 176
  fabric, 134, 135, 136-137
    advantages, 166
    disadvantages, 166
    dust-cake removal, 169-174
      mechanical shaker, 170-171
      pulse jet, 170-171
      reverse flow, 171
      reverse jet, 174
    exhaust volume through, 168-169
    fabric selection for, 169
    maintenance of, 174
    operational principles, 166-167
    pressure-drop relationships in, 167-169
  location of discharge, 130
  particulate removal
    air filters, 178-179
      dust-handling capacity, 178-179
      efficiency, 179
    characteristics of, 135, 138
    wet, 158-166
      advantages of, 158-159
      designs
        orifice, 160-161
        tower, 160
        venturi, 161-164
      disadvantages of, 159
      requirements for efficient operation, 159
  salvage, of product, 128
  separation, mechanics of, 131-134
  unit, recirculating, 176-178
conservation of fuel in exhaust systems, 266, 269-271, 273
  interlock exhaust system, 271, 272, 273
  local exhaust system, 269
  recirculation from exhaust systems, 269-270
    advantages, 270
    cautions, 270
    favorable conditions for, 270-271
  reduction in infiltration of outside air, 271
construction specifications for local exhaust systems, 233-235
contaminants, 17-18
  dust, 17, 54, 131
    dispersion, 18
    drift, 18
  fume, 17
  gas, 18
  mist, 17
  smoke, 17, 47
  vapor, 17-18
conveying systems
  all-pressure, 189
  belt driven fans, use in, 192-193
  double fans, use in, 192

pneumatic, 182
air volume per pound conveyed solids, 183-185
conveying velocity, 182-183
table, 184
economical pipe size in, 193
low-pressure types, 186
mechanical efficiency, 182
relay systems, 193-194
special considerations, 194-195
suction vs. pressure systems, 185-186
tandem fans, use in, 189-192
curtain walls, 238
cyclones (*see* separators, cyclone)

D

degree day, 266
values, 268
density changes, 2, 14
dimensional analysis, 7-8
downdraft hoods (*see* hoods, downdraft)
dust, 131
settling rates of, 131
size properties of, 132
terminal velocity of, 131

E

ejector systems, 210-211
elbows
angle of turn, 99
approach velocity, 100
aspect ratio, 98-99
compound, 100
curve ratio, 97, 98
double, losses in, 101
hardness of bend, 97
losses in, 97-98
radius ratio, 97, 98
venturi, 100-103
enclosures (*see* hoods, booths or enclosures)
enlargements, 103
losses in abrupt enlargements, 104
equivalent length of pipe (chart), 96
exhaust system design
characteristic curve, 123, 125
checking purchased system design, 126
fire and explosion hazard reduction, 125-126
makeup air, 126
for a pattern shop, 112, 114, 115-119
for a spray-dryer system, 112-114, 120-123. 124
tor a woodworking system, 115-116
exhaust volumes
field determinations of, 58-61
usual values for, 62-65, 66-69
grinding/polishing type operations, 69, 71
woodworking, 61, 69

F

face velocity (*see* velocity, face)
fans, axial-flow
characteristics, 217-219
curves, 219
direction of flow, 216
performance curves, 220
propeller, 213-214
blade-tip speed, 213
representative installations, 216-217
sound level, 226
tubeaxial, 213, 214-215
vaneaxial, 213, 215-216
vs. centrifugal fans, 221
fans, centrifugal exhaust
inlet and outlet connections, 198
performance curves, 200-201
power consumption, 198-199
effects on air density, 199-200
rotation direction effects, 203
speed effects, 201-203
curves, 202
size effects, 203
fan drives, 207-208
fan noise and vibration, 208-210
pitch, 208, 209
fan types, 203
backward-blade fan, 206, 209
performance curves, 206
dust-separating, 211-212
for gaseous materials, 205-207
forward-blade fan, 209
material handling fans, 203-204
paddle wheel, 59, 203, 204
radial blade, 203, 209
vaneaxial, 58
wheel, 204-205
long-shavings, 204
wool, 204
floor sweeps, in piping design, 112
flow calculations, hoods, 87-88
and economical hood design, 88
flow direction finder, 256
flow lines, 76-77
fluid flow, nature of, 6-7
laminar, 6, 10
mixtures, 14
streamline, 6
turbulent, 9
in exhaust piping, 9
viscous, 6
friction factor, 8, 9, 95
for turbulent flow, 10

friction loss
in abrupt enlargements, 104
in breechings, 107
in elbows, 97-98
in expansions/contractions (table), 105
in hose, 95-96
chart, 97
of mixtures, 94
chart, 95
in rectangular pipes, 91, 94
in round pipes, 91
chart, 92-93
in tapers, 104-105
in tees, 105
vacuum booster, 107-108
in transformers, 108
in weather protection, 108-109
fuel conservation (*see* conservation, fuel)
furnace, electric arc, 60, 61

G

gaseous emission control, 180-181
absorption, 180
adsorption, 180
dilution, 180
incineration, 181
gravity chambers (*see* separators, gravity chambers)

H

heat loss, with exhaust air, 266
sample calculation, 267
heat recovery, 273-275
evaporative cooling, 274, 275
heat exchangers, 274
makeup air supply, 273-274
reversed roof fans, 273
from roof truss accumulations, 273, 274
vertical space heaters, 273
hoods
air flow distribution in, 38-40
for bench operations, 45-47
booths or enclosures, 15, 16, 35-40, 57
clean room, 36
complete, 36
downdraft, 36, 56
indraft velocity, 56
overhead, 36, 37
and side hood, 37, 53
tunnel-type, 36-37
for bulk loading, 53, 54
coarse particle capture, 29-30
design rules, 16
double, 52
double lateral, 52, 54
downdraft, 15
face
characteristics, 26
flanged, 26-27
influence of
adjacent planes, 127
rear structures, 26
local, 15-16, 20-35, 58, 59
for hand tools, 28-29
horizontal baffles, 51, 52
for material handling, 40-45
for melting furnaces, 47-51
crucible, 49-51
electric arc, 47-49
overhead, 15, 36, 56
portable, 28
for planers, 33-35
rear, 54
for sanders, 35
for saws, 31-32
for shapers, 32-33
for surface treatment operations, 51-54
side, 15, 56
for woodworking machinery, 30-31
hydraulic radius, 91

I

impact pressure (*see* pressure, impact)
impact tube, 4, 248, 249
increasing the distance between worker and process, 263, 265
mechanical manipulators, 263
remote control stations, 263
TV cameras, 263, 265
isolation
of process, 260
of worker, 260
of workspace, 260-263
air showers, 262, 263
air supplied respiration, 262-263
open ports, 262
tight enclosures, 260-261

L

local air movements, 19-20
local hoods (*see* hoods, local)
loss at hood entry, 79

M

magnehelic gages, 247, 248
makeup air, 269
manometer 2, 3, 59, 247-248
measuring tips, 249
mechanical feeders, 183, 187
metal thickness recommendations for var-

ious classes of service, 224
movie-scaling technique for plume flow rates, 238

O

open surface tanks, 71-73
orifice, 76-77, 79
  forms of, 78
overhead hoods (*see* hoods, overhead)

P

paddle wheel centrifugal fan (*see* fan, paddle wheel centrifugal)
pipe
  friction, 9-10
    in laminar state, 10
    in turbulent state, 10
    velocity head rule in, 94-95
  rectangular, friction loss in, 91, 94
  round, friction loss in, 91
    chart, 92-93
piping design
  balancing the system, 119-120
  density changes, influence of, 120
  density factors for changes in temperature and elevation (table), 121
  necessity of
    data sheets, 112
    systematic calculations, 111–112
  pneumatic, 110
  procedures for, 110–111
pitot tube, 4, 12, 249
Poiseuille's law, 10
pressure
  atmospheric, 1
  in exhaust systems, 196–197
  fan rating, 197–198
  impact, 2, 3
  measurement of, 3–4
    impact tube, 4
    pitot tube, 4
  static, 2, 196
    in fan casing, 209
    measuring holes in pipe walls, 254–255
  at suction openings, 80–81
  units, 2
  velocity, 2, 4–5
propeller fan (*see* fan, axial-flow, propeller)

R

Reynolds'
  color band experiment, 6–7
  dimensional analysis, 7–8
  number, 8–9
    critical, 9
  in industrial ventilation systems, 9
  nomogram, 11

S

secondary air, 31–32
separation coefficient (*see* separators, cyclones, separation coefficient)
separators
  axial flow, 154–155, 157
  collection mechanisms of
    centrifugal force, 132
    diffusion, 133–134
    direct interception, 133
    electrostatic, 134
    gravitational force, 132
    inertial impaction, 133
    utilization of, 134
  cyclones, 142–158
    air outlets, 151–152
    angular travel in, 144, 146
    factors affecting separation, 142, 144
    high efficiency, 148, 153, 155
    intermediate diameter, 149, 152, 153
    large diameter, 145–146
    low loss, 148, 149, 151
    pressure drop through, 147–148, 153
    separation coefficient, 144
      chart, 145
    small diameter, 149–151, 155, 156
      efficiency of, 156
    vertical flow in, 142
  dust bins, 154
  factors affecting separation, 152
    separation coefficient, 144
  gravity chambers, 139–141
    hood traps, 139–141
    miscellaneous traps, 139
  inertial separators, 157–158
side hoods (*see* hoods, side)
spray booths, 73
standard air, 1, 5, 14
static pressure (*see* pressure, static)
structural details of
  ball and telescope or slip joints, 226, 227
  backpressure dampers, 228–229
  blast gates, 226
  cleanouts, 227–228
  elbows, 224
  equalizers, 225–226
  pipe supports, 229–230
  piping
    floor level, 231–232
    overhead, 231–232
    underfloor, 231–232
  system
    arrangement, 232
    size, 231

switches
single blade, 229
double blade, 229
tapers, 223
tees, 225
suction openings, 19
contour
line, 19
surface, 19
typical configurations, 24
effectiveness, 20–24

T

traverses of pitot and impact tube, 251–253
preferred location for pitot tube, 253–254
tubeaxial fan (*see* fan, axial-flow, tubeaxial)

U

unloading and feeding devices, 186–188
mechanical feeder use in, 187–188
venturi tube use in, 187
"U"-tube (*see* manometer)

V

vaneaxial fan (*see* fan, axial-flow, vaneaxial; fan types, vaneaxial)
velocity
capture, 15, 56
centerline, 24
nomogram for calculation, 25
contours, 56
conveying, table of, 90
critical, 7
higher, 7
lower, 7
distribution, in pipes, 12–14
hood face, 55
indraft for hoods or enclosures, 57
and relation of hood face, 24–25
velocity pressure (*see* pressure, velocity)
Velometer, 250
vena contracta, 76, 77, 81
venturi tube theory, 188–189
pressure relationships in, 188
ventilation
area, 236–238
general, 236
ventilation performance monitoring
benefits of, 246
field measurements, 247–250
location of test points, 250–251
schedule, 246–247
ventilation system
design assumption check, 256, 258
locating and diagnosing trouble, 250–259
ventilation techniques, combination, 265
viscosity, influence on laminar flow, 10, 11
volume flow rate, estimation of, 255–256